To
A. H. M.

PRAEGER ADVANCED GEOGRAPHIES

EDITED BY S. H. BEAVER

CENTRAL EUROPE

CENTRAL EUROPE

A Regional and Human Geography

BY

ALICE F. A. MUTTON

Second Edition

FREDERICK A. PRAEGER, *Publishers*

New York · Washington

BOOKS THAT MATTER

Published in the United States of America in 1968
by Frederick A. Praeger, Inc., Publishers
111 Fourth Avenue, New York, N.Y. 10003

*This is a revised and enlarged edition of the book first published
in the United States in 1961 by John Wiley and Sons, Inc.*

© 1961, 1968 in London, England, by Alice F. A. Mutton

Library of Congress Catalog Card Number: 68-15652

Printed in Great Britain

PREFACE TO THE SECOND EDITION

THE CHANGES which have taken place in the economy of Central Europe and the political cleavage between the two Germanies which has become further emphasized during the past five years, especially since the erection of the Berlin Wall in 1961, have made necessary an extensive revision of the original text. Moreover, rapid progress in the rebuilding of war-shattered cities and also the replanning and expansion of urban centres and of industry, especially in West Germany and the Netherlands, as well as the changing emphasis on sources of motive power, have called for new material. Statistics have been brought up to date, some maps modified or replaced and recent references have been added.

ALICE F. A. MUTTON

London, 1967

PREFACE TO THE FIRST EDITION

THE NEED for an advanced textbook in English on Central Europe has been apparent to the author for many years, not merely for those students who are taking honours and general degree courses in geography at the University but also those whose interest in the complex interrelationship between physical and human geography in this ' problem ' region of Europe has been aroused, either by travel or by contact with modern social and political developments on which the geographer cannot always presume to throw much light. It has often been asserted that the essential rôle of the geographer is to describe the facts of the environment with which he is concerned and to note man's reaction to it in its various facets. This book is an attempt to show this relationship, taking into account the broad elements of the physical background and human economy before proceeding to a regional analysis of the great component elements of Central Europe: the Alpine lands, the Czechoslovak lands, Western and Eastern Germany, and finally the Benelux countries, namely the Netherlands, Belgium and Luxembourg. A justification of what must be an arbitrary inclusion of nation states will be attempted elsewhere but it will be noted that the area regarded by the author as ' Central Europe ' is rather more restricted than that of the continental geographers, notably those of the French and German schools.

Before the Second World War, the classical work of reference on Central Europe was that of the late E. de Martonne, whose two volumes entitled *Europe Centrale* appeared in the Géographie Universelle series in 1931. That monumental treatise, with its fine technique of description, comparison and analysis, illustrated lavishly by a number of splendid maps, diagrams and photographs, has been the book to which all concerned with the geography of this part of Europe have turned for reference for the past quarter of a century. More recently, P. George and J. Tricart have published a two-volume work entitled *L'Europe Centrale* (Orbis, 1954) and it may be regarded, in spite of serious blemishes in the section on human geography, as a valuable supplement to the masterpiece of E. de Martonne. Apart from the classic of J. Partsch on 'Central Europe', of which a translation appeared in English in 1905 before the German hegemony of Central Europe had been contested in two world conflicts, no German geographer has attempted a text equivalent to the French school, in spite of the German obsession with *Mitteleuropa* during the last half century. A number of regional geographies have appeared on Germany, especially in the *Landeskunde* series, notably that of G. Braun, whose *Deutschland* appeared in 1936, and some of these transcended the national frontiers without apology, for example that of N. Krebs, entitled *Südwest Deutschland* (1931) and again *Österreich* (1928). The late R. Gradmann also wrote two useful volumes on *Süddeutschland* (1931), while B. Brandt has described *Der Nordosten* (1931). A concise and comprehensive study of Germany had been published a few years earlier, entitled *Deutschland*, a separate volume in the great reference work of the E. von Seydlitz *Geographie, Europa*, published in 1925. In English, only R. E. Dickinson's 'Germany', in Methuen's Advanced Regional Geography series, appearing in 1953, attempts to cover in detail Germany's rôle in Central Europe. In America, G. Hoffman has edited a series of essays by various authors, mainly of Central European origin, entitled 'Europe' (1953). More recently, a trans-Atlantic compendium, *Man's Rôle in Changing the Face of the Earth*, by various authors from both the Old World and the New, contains useful chapters which relate to Central Europe, especially by H. C. Darby and G. Pfeifer. Another reference work, edited by W. G. East and A. E. Moodie, bearing the title *The Changing World*, also published in 1956, has some chapters dealing with the political geography of Europe.

The suggestion that the author should undertake to write this book was made by the late Margaret R. Mann (née Shackleton), whose textbook on *Europe* in The University Geographical Series

(Longmans) has been a standard work for students for over twenty-five years. Travel and research were undertaken by the author in the 1930's in Germany and also in Czechoslovakia and Alpine Europe, partly under the auspices of the Le Play Society but more often independently. During the post-war years, extensive field work has been carried out in all the countries included in this book, with the exception of those beyond the 'Iron Curtain', so that the author is very mindful of the numerous helpful contacts made and of the several friends, especially Swiss and German, who have in various ways helped to make the completion of this book a reality. It is, of course, only possible to name a few of those academic geographers who have helped to shape the viewpoint of the author. The earliest influences were those of two of the late Prof. A. J. Herbertson's former Oxford students, Miss D. D. Adam, without whose stimulating teaching in her youth the author would probably never have 'taken up' geography. The other is the late Miss B. E. M. Hosgood, for many years Head of the Geography Department, Bedford College. Another debt of gratitude is owed to the late J. J. Fairgrieve, whose interest in the field work of the author, especially when associated with groups of students, was always maintained. The first years at Queen Mary College were those of 'pioneering' under the late H. G. Smith, Head of the Geology and Geography Departments of Queen Mary College. When a separate Geography Department was created in 1947, Dr. (now Professor) Crowe came as the first Head. No-one who has worked with him can ever adequately express their gratitude for the high standard of criticism set in all matters of research. In the final stages, Professor Smailes, the present Head of the Department, has given the author every encouragement to complete the task. My very real thanks are due to Miss Eileen Harvey, Senior Technician in the Geography Department, Queen Mary College, and also to Mr. A. Carson Clark, Senior Technician in the Geography Department, University of Southampton, for their endless care and skill in preparing the maps and diagrams from divers sources. I am also grateful to Miss Heidi Killias for the sketches of landscapes and houses, and to Miss Cissie Blythe, for her services in typing much of the manuscript. Professor Beaver has been remarkably patient, as the General Editor of the series, in awaiting the completion of the work and also in giving me invaluable help and criticism in the final stages. For any errors in the text, the author is alone responsible.

Whatever may be the particular interest of the reader, for the writer, the challenge of Central Europe has been found in recent years not so much in the Germanic lands, with their complex post-war problems of reintegration and reorganization, spectacular though the recovery has been; it is rather in the Alps, with their deeply humanized geography, where especially the Swiss have triumphed so remarkably over their environment, that the greatest stimulus is to be found; for, as Siegfried expresses it, ' The Alps cast their shadow over Europe '. One might add that they also cast the radiance of their bright light and eternal snow. Here is an introduction to a most complex and challenging part of the Old World. Research problems present themselves on every hand, so that this book only offers a groundwork and an introduction to the tasks that lie ahead.

ALICE F. A. MUTTON

Davos,
Graubünden,
1961

CONTENTS

PART I

GENERAL SURVEY

PART II

REGIONAL AND HUMAN GEOGRAPHY

Section I: The Alpine Lands

Section II: The Czechoslovak Lands

Section III: The Germanic Lands

PLATES

xiii

MAPS AND DIAGRAMS

PART I

GENERAL SURVEY

CHAPTER I

INTRODUCTION : THE CONCEPT OF CENTRAL EUROPE

ATTEMPTS to define Central Europe as a major geographical region seem to defy objectivity. While the physical environment provides a

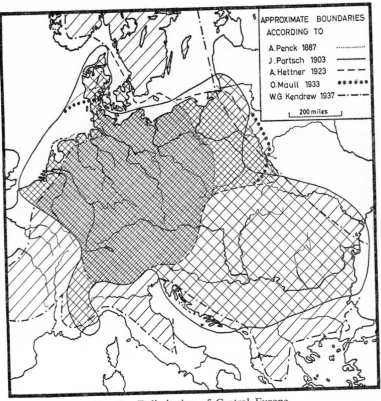

APPROXIMATE BOUNDARIES
ACCORDING TO

A. Penck 1887	....
J. Partsch 1903	————
A. Hettner 1923	— — —
O. Maull 1933	••••••
W.G. Kendrew 1937	—·—·—

200 miles

FIG. 1. Delimitation of Central Europe.

complex but constant set of pictures capable of analysis, the human scene has changed frequently, in fact kaleidoscopically, in modern times. It is no wonder then, that the concept of *Mitteleuropa* appears as the assessment of a particular writer, be he geographer, historian or politician, and recent attempts to find a common element have proved singularly unrewarding.[1] The term 'Central Europe' has been used in the present context to denote a rather more restricted area of Europe than that used in de Martonne's two great volumes, *Europe Centrale* (1931), for there is no coverage of the Danubian lands beyond Austria, nor is post-war Poland included. On the other hand, a description of the Benelux countries seems essential to complete the description of the Rhine basin, and some justification may be found in the classic line drawn by Sir Halford Mackinder when he demarcated the 'Latin Peninsula' of Europe along a line from Ostend, on the Belgian coast, to Trieste at the head of the Adriatic.[2] Although, on physical grounds, the Jutland peninsula and the Danish archipelago might be regarded as an extension of the Germano-Polish lowland between the North Sea and the Baltic, the fact that Denmark belongs to the cultural region of Scandinavia leaves its exclusion from this book in no doubt.[3] Attempts to include northern Italy within Central Europe, even on a basis of climate (Kendrew), seem to the writer far-fetched, and the lands south of the Alpine divide are relegated to the realm of the Mediterranean. On political grounds, the inclusion of Czechoslovakia may appear inconsistent, as indeed it would be if post-war 'Central Europe' is to be restricted to the 'free' states immediately west of the 'Iron Curtain'. The justification for the section dealing with the prolongation of Slavonic Europe westwards into the geometrical centre of the continent lies in the physical affinity between Bohemia-Moravia and the Hercynian uplands and basins of Germany, while the northern Carpathians of Slovakia have their counterpart in the Alpine system. The fact that the Czech lands were part of the Austrian Empire until 1919 is a further reason for their inclusion, for their economic development in the late 19th and early 20th century must be seen in relation to the Habsburg Empire, for Bohemia and Moravia were the most industrialized provinces of that Empire and their agriculture compared in progressiveness with that of the Vienna basin and Upper Austria. Poland, on the other hand, wiped off the map as an independent nation state after the partitions of 1772, 1793 and 1795, emerged

[1] K. Sinnhuber: *Central Europe—Mitteleuropa—Europe Centrale, An Analysis of a Geographical Term*, Trans. Inst. Br. Geographers, Vol. XX, 1954, pp. 15–39.
[2] Sir H. Mackinder: *Democratic Ideals and Reality*, 1919.
[3] See A. C. O'Dell: *The Scandinavian World*, 1956, in the same series as this book, and also C. B. Fawcett: 'The Nordic Region', *Scottish Geographical Magazine*, Vol. 48, 1932, pp. 78–83, and also W. R. Mead: *An Economic Geography of the Scandinavian States and Finland*, 1958, and A. Sømme (ed.): *The Geography of Norden*, 1960.

anew in 1919, when Czechoslovakia was created a succession State, but her rate of economic progress in the twenty years between the wars was slight, especially in the Polish countryside, and the violent changes and land reforms since 1945 have seen in Poland, as in the other satellite states of eastern Europe, a new economy oriented towards the Soviet Union. Thus, although Poland has made a major advance westwards to the Oder-Neisse line, thus acquiring the Baltic port of Stettin (Szczescin), in addition to Danzig, she cannot be regarded in any sense a Central European state, but, like her tragic counterpart Hungary, she remains a member of the Soviet Communist *bloc* and part of East-Central Europe.

It has recently been suggested that Central Europe is a ' middle term ', a region of transition, in a physical sense between the diversity of western Europe, the sharp local contrasts to be found in the Mediterranean lands, and the vast uniformity of eastern Europe.[1] Central Europe itself consists of a mosaic of regions but these may be classified into types, such as the regions of Alpine folding, the Alpine foreland, the Hercynian uplands and basins, the Jurassic scarplands of southern Germany and the delta lands of the Rhine-Maas. Only in the north does the Germano-Polish lowland recall the greater expanse of the Russian platform. The physical variety of Central Europe is also reflected in its fragmented history for, in spite of the centralizing tendency of the Habsburgs, *Mitteleuropa* remained a mosaic of duchies and principalities until the first steps towards economic unification were taken by the initiation of the *Zollverein* in 1819, to be followed by the emergence of Prussia as the dominant military and industrial power of Central Europe after the defeat of the Austrians at Sadowa in 1866. The regional contrasts between Bavaria, the Rhineland, and Prussia are today reflected in separatist tendencies. The northern lowland, so long a zone of conflict between the Teutons and the northern Slavs, has witnessed the re-advance of the Poles westwards to the Oder-Neisse line, at the expense of a defeated Germany and of the German minorities who formerly lived in the ' lost lands of the east ' and who have now been added to the thousands of ' Displaced Persons ' in West Germany. This post-war movement has reversed the advance of the Slavonic tribes to the line of the Elbe-Saale at the time of Charlemagne, when the *limes Sorabicus* was created, to be followed by the gradual reconquest of these infertile northern plains by the Teutonic Knights and the subsequent planting of German settlers in ' colonial ' towns and villages in the Slavonic lands to the east of the Elbe, notably in Brandenburg, Pomerania and East

[1] P. George and J. Tricart: *L'Europe Centrale*, Vol. 1, 1954, p. 1.

Prussia.   Siegfried describes this spread of Germanic 'civilization' over an originally heathen Slav substratum as being 'like piles in a marshland'.   In Austria, the *Ostmark* of Charlemagne, there is no such vague limit to the culture of western Christendom, for 'east of Vienna, the east begins',[1] or as Metternich expressed it: 'the Balkans begin at the eastern city gate of Vienna'.

Whereas, until recently, 'Central Europe was the axis of Europe; on the one side was Eastern Europe as a sort of march, and on the other was Western Europe, representing, together with Central Europe, the van of progress', today Central Europe tends to be 'a frontier rather than an axis'.   As Fischer has recently written: '*Mitteleuropa* has contracted to a line'.[2]   In so far as a united Germany was once the vital core of Europe, this heartland has indeed disappeared from the political scene.   The two cities of Germanic Europe which have played a major political rôle in the past, notably Vienna, as the heart of the Holy Roman Empire, and subsequently Berlin, as the symbol of militant Imperialist and Fascist Germany, have both been forced to play a divided part, since 1945, in the affairs of Europe.   Vienna is once more a free city but the persistent division of Berlin into a Western and an Eastern Sector symbolizes the fate of *Mitteleuropa*.   It is difficult to envisage Bonn, the federal capital of the German Federal Republic, ever playing a similar rôle to that of the traditional capital. An attractive city, on the banks of the Rhine, it lies excentrically and it has none of the political experience of Berlin.   However, the impressive new buildings of the *Bundeshaus* and of the embassies which have arisen to the south of the city mark the attempt of West Germany to begin again.   It is all too symbolical of this post-war democracy that the Federal Parliament building bears a large phoenix in mosaic on its entrance wall.

It seems that the definition of *Mitteleuropa* must be regarded as just as much physical as political.   De Martonne was clearly exhibiting Gallic prejudice when he wrote: 'Ainsi, l'Europe centrale n'est pas un mot'.   In the early 19th century, German writers such as Carl Ritter recognized *Mitteleuropa* as a natural region in which relief was the dominant feature.   In the first part of the present century, the expression came to be identified with the German Empire until 1919, and with the Third Reich of the 1930's.   Compared with the term *Deutsches Reich*, that of *Deutschland* is much less precise and the pre-war expression *Deutschtum*, used to designate

[1] A. Siegfried: *Switzerland*, 1950, p. 13.
[2] W. G. East and A. E. Moodie: *The Changing World—Studies in Political Geography*, 1956, Chap. II—'The Passing of Mitteleuropa' by E. Fischer, p. 62.

regions of German culture and speech, appears positively mystical[1]
J. Partsch, with his inclusion of the lower Danubian lands, Switzerland, Belgium and the Netherlands, went far in this direction in
1905. In 1923, however, Hettner disagreed with the inclusion of
the Danubian lands and with taking into account mainly cultural
criteria.

Historically, the term ' Central Europe ' is much more nebulous.
The early division of Europe was on a tribal basis, the Celto-Roman
west being distinguished from the lands of the Teutonic tribes of
Central Europe and those of the Slavs of the East. The Roman
limes marked a clear division from the lower Rhine to the Danube
between the romanized West and the pagan East. After the time of
Charlemagne, Austria stood out as the East March (*Österreich*) of
western Christendom. The antagonism between Austria and
Prussia in the 19th century for the hegemony of Central Europe was
not resolved until the economic unity enforced by the 1914–18 War,
which enabled Naumann to see Germany as the ' core ' of *Mitteleuropa* (1915), at a time when German certainly served as the *lingua
franca* of Central Europe. In the same year as Naumann's book,
Mitteleuropa, appeared, A. Penck wrote of *Zwischeneuropa*, including no less than the Low Countries, Italy, Germany, Denmark,
Sweden, Finland, Austria, Hungary, Poland and the Balkans. In
1917, H. Hassinger attempted to map Central Europe on the basis
of landscape features and he thus included the Low Countries,
Denmark, Germany, Switzerland, and the Austro-Hungarian
Empire. He labelled the lower Danubian lands as ' emerging
Central Europe ', as they clearly were at that time, but only in a
political and economic sense, for the foodstuffs of south-eastern
Europe were seen to be complementary to the industrial products of
the north-west. It is clear that ' Central Europe ' thus defined had
been the realm of German influence for centuries but nonetheless it
included a marked diversity of cultural and ethnographic elements.
Later these ideas, developed by German geographers during the
first world war, were revived and elaborated by geo-political writers
under Hitler's Germany, notably by E. Banse and Karl Haushofer
(1937), at the time of the annexation of Austria and Czechoslovakia.

The contraction and consolidation of the Germanic lands since
1945 has served to sharpen the definition of *Mitteleuropa*. It is also
borne out by the refugee problem of modern Germany, whereby
20 million Germans have been ' liquidated ' in the lost eastern
provinces, notably East Prussia, East Pomerania, the Neumark

---

[1] R. E. Dickinson: *Germany*, 1953, Chap. 13.

of Brandenburg and Upper Silesia, all of which are now Polish territory (apart from the Soviet acquisition of the northern half of East Prussia). In all some 13 million Germans have fled into the German Federal Republic and West Berlin and 400,000 into Austria.[1] In East Germany, as well as in the Sudeten lands of Bohemia, deserted farms and villages bear witness to the number of political refugees who have escaped to the West. It is estimated that three million acres in the ' lost ' provinces have reverted to wasteland and forests are reappearing where formerly there was cultivated land. In Czechoslovakia there are some 250 villages formerly occupied by German minorities, especially in the Sudetenland, which have been only partly re-settled by Slavonic peasants and gypsies. In all these eastern districts, under the present Communist régime, the former large estates of the *Junker* type have become the small-holdings of peasant cultivators or have been taken over as state farms, now increasingly mechanized.

REFERENCES

J. Partsch: *Central Europe* (trans.), 1905.

E. de Martonne: *Europe Centrale*, Géog. Univ. Vol. 4, Part I.

R. E. Dickinson: *The German Lebensraum*, Penguin Special, 1943.

H. R. Ormsby: ' The definition of Mitteleuropa and its relation to the conception of Deutschland in the writings of modern German geographers ', *Scot. Geog. Magazine*, Vol. 51, 1935.

Sir H. J. Mackinder: *Democratic Ideals and Reality*, 1919, republished as a Penguin Special in 1944.

E. Fischer: *The Passing of the European Age*, 1948. *Idem:* in W. G. East and A. E. Moodie: *The Changing World*, 1956, Chap. II, ' The passing of Mitteleuropa '.

K. A. Sinnhuber: *Central Europe—Mitteleuropa—Europe Centrale: An analysis of a geographical term*, Trans. Inst. Br. Geographers, Vol. XX, 1954.

[1] C. D. Harris and G. Wülker: ' The refugee problem of Germany ', *Econ. Geog.*, Vol. 29, 1953, pp. 10-25.

CHAPTER 2

THE ELEMENTS OF THE PHYSICAL ENVIRONMENT

PHYSICALLY, Central Europe presents a ' middle term ', as Tricart suggests, between the violent contrasts of the Mediterranean world south of the Alpine barrier, the vast expenses of plain extending into Soviet Russia, and the physical variety of maritime western Europe. Although transitionality is the keynote to the physical environment of Central Europe, as shown by its climate, soils and vegetation, these features, combined with those of relief and structure, remain constant elements, as a background to the changing political and economic scene. It is proposed to review the broad features of this environment so as to provide a basis for a subsequent study of the human and regional geography of the component parts of Central Europe, as defined in the previous chapter.

CLIMATE

Central Europe lies in cool temperate latitudes, the parallel 50° N. passing from southern Belgium across western Germany along the lower Main valley into Bohemia, thus bisecting the region latitudinally. Climatic features change gradually to north and to south of this parallel but the progress from cool temperate maritime conditions in the west to a semi-continental régime in the east is even more striking than the contrasts between north and south, especially in the winter months. Except in the north, relief provides sharp local differences, for example the summer heat of the upper Rhine plain around Freiburg contrasts with the cool, cloudy weather associated with the Feldberg in the southern Black Forest, or, to take an extreme instance, the heat and drought of the Valais in summer contrast notably with the eternal snows of Monte Rosa and the Matterhorn some miles to the south. It is only in such rare localities as in the Rhône valley near Sierre and on the loess-covered basalt slopes of the Kaiserstuhl in the Rhine rift valley that traces of a Mediterranean type of flora may be found.

Mean annual isotherms show a slow increase in warmth from north to south from the North Sea and Baltic coastlands to the Alps. In fact, there is only a difference of 4° F. between the Swiss

Foreland and the north Italian plain. In winter, the general trend of the isotherms is from north to south in response to the prevalence of the modifying effect ot tropical maritime air-masses. The crucial 32° F. January isotherm passes from Lübeck, at the western end of the Baltic, across western Germany to Karlsruhe in the upper Rhine plain, and then strikes southwards across the upper Danube valley to continue across eastern Switzerland *via* the lake of Constance to Zürich and thence south-eastwards across Austria into

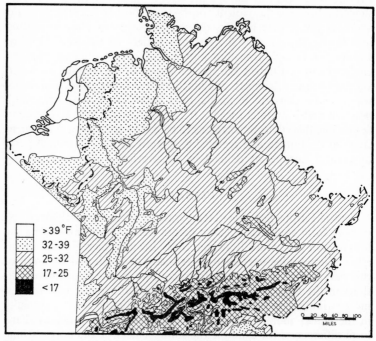

	>39°F
	32-39
	25-32
	17-25
	<17

FIG. 2. Central Europe: distribution of actual mean January temperature.

Yugoslavia *via* Carinthia. The effect of temperatures below freezing point in January on the closing of rivers and canals to navigation in eastern Germany is illustrated in Fig. 9. In summer, the general trend of the isotherms is from south-west to north-east; the mean July isotherm of 68° F. passing through Karlsruhe and Prague, while Bonn and Berlin both experience July temperatures averaging 65° F. The summers of Central Europe are generally warm but relief reduces temperatures at the rate of 270 ft. of ascent.

A map of mean annual precipitation reflects closely the pattern of relief.   The high mountain barriers, notably the Alps and the Carpathians, receive over 40 in. annually, except in the enclosed valleys and basins (upper Rhône valley and Engadine, under 25 in.). In contrast the lowlands usually receive under 25 in., as in the middle Danube valley and the upper Rhine plain.   Whereas the Primary massifs receive between 30 and 40 in. per annum, the sheltered basins record as little as 20 in. (*Polabí*, northern Bohemia; the Main valley around Würzburg; the Moravian lowland).   In general, the total precipitation increases from the North Sea–Baltic coastlands towards

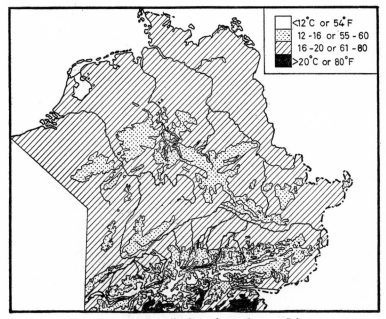

FIG. 3.   Central Europe: distribution of actual mean July temperature.

the Alps and from eastern Germany towards the Rhine highlands. Humidity is high in the west and south, where Atlantic influences prevail, and summers are often cloudy, especially in the mountainous regions.   The 'continental' character of the seasonal rainfall distribution is illustrated by the increasing proportion of summer rain from west to east, Karlsruhe recording 33 per cent of the total precipitation as summer rain but Prague 39 per cent.   There is also an increase in the cold season precipitation on slopes exposed to south-westerly air streams, whereas basins to the leeward record a much lower percentage (Prague, 13 per cent).

In Central Europe, the conflict between tropical maritime and polar continental air masses is at its height, especially in winter. The fact that stations record rain at all seasons points to the remarkable penetration of Atlantic influences into the heart of Europe. When polar continental air prevails, spells of prolonged cold and snowfall occur in winter. In spring, winds from the Scandinavian high-pressure area may give rise to a rapid reduction in temperature

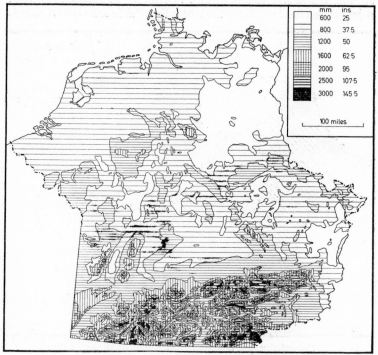

mm	ins
600	25
800	37·5
1200	50
1600	62·5
2000	95
2500	107·5
3000	145·5

100 miles

FIG. 4. Central Europe: distribution of mean annual precipitation.

and the breaking of vegetation into leaf is severely delayed. In contrast, the development of an intense depression north of the Alps in spring brings *Föhn* conditions in Alpine valleys, with speedy melting of snow and the danger of avalanches.

The same struggle for dominance in Central Europe is illustrated by atmospheric pressure conditions. The extension of low pressure into the region depends on the strength of the Tropical maritime, as well as Polar maritime air masses which dominate western and Mediterranean Europe in the winter. In contrast, Polar continental air is associated with high-pressure conditions and a characteristic feature of the pressure distribution map is the general extension of high pressure along the Alpine-Carpathian barrier of south-central Europe. This barometric backbone, as Woeikof named it, divides northern Europe, with its frequent passage of depressions, from the Mediterranean region, with its winter depressions and secondaries. This ridge of high pressure accentuates the dryness of the sheltered valleys and enclosed basins of highland Central Europe and also the great heat of the summer. At this season of the year, regional differences are less pronounced, winds with a westerly component prevail everywhere and are generally lighter than in winter. The high pressure of eastern Europe breaks up and, under the influence of the Azores high-pressure centre, the main path of depressions moves northwards.

Central Europe experiences the maximum instability in the winter months, when intense depressions pass across north-western Europe and others across the Germano-Polish lowland and the northern Mediterranean. At the same time, Polar maritime air prevails over eastern Europe, from the Baltic to the Alps. When warm frontal conditions dominate northern Germany, temperatures are higher than those occurring in Bavaria, where anticyclonic weather prevails. Under such conditions, a winter day in Hamburg may be as mild as in Trieste, at the head of the Adriatic. On the contrary, if Polar continental air prevails, rivers freeze and calm air with clear skies and temperatures well below freezing point may persist for days. In the summer, conditions are broadly uniform over vast distances, for winds tend to be weak and variable, and storms, resulting from convectional overturning, cause sharp downpours of heavy local rain. In spring, depressions over the Mediterranean are intensified, the barometric divide is at its weakest, and depressions from the Mediterranean tend to link up with those over north-western Europe. Under these conditions, local winds may suddenly develop, such as the *mistral* in the Rhône valley, the *bora* at the head of the Adriatic and the *Föhn* in the Alps. The first two of these winds may cause sudden frosts and hail storms, severely damaging standing crops, orchards in blossom and vines breaking into leaf. The effect of the *Föhn* may also be locally catastrophic, though the end of the long winter in the Alpine valleys is welcomed.

It is possible to recognize, as does de Martonne,[1] several types of climate in Central Europe, based mainly on differences in position and relief. Where the surface is largely monotonous, except for soil and drainage variations, as in the Germano-Polish lowland, westerly

[1] E. de Martonne: *Europe Centrale*, Géog. Univ. Vol. 4, 1930, Part I, Chap. I.

air streams are able to penetrate beyond the valley of the Oder, in the absence of major relief barriers, so that ' continental ' influences only gradually replace those of the Atlantic.   Emden, on the Dollart, seldom experiences temperatures below freezing point and snow is rare, on account of the proximity of the North Sea.   In the east, temperatures are below freezing point and the winter is relatively long.   Spring comes suddenly and river ice begins to break up, the rapid release of water causing local floods.   In the west, rivers do not normally freeze, but spring is delayed and trees may not appear in leaf until mid-April.   Summers are mild, but temperatures seldom exceed 62° F., while the sky may be more clouded than in winter, when the rainfall is usually of short duration.   The autumn season is often prolonged, October being a warmer month than April, while damp weather may continue until December.   This condition of equability does out east of the line of the Elbe.

The uplands of Central Europe experience a wide variety of types of climate, on account of the diversity of local factors such as relief and aspect.   As de Martonne expresses it, ' relief explains climate '.   The uplands receive generally abundant precipitation, including a snow cover lasting for three months at 1,500 ft. and for five months at 2,500 ft., as in the Black Forest, the Middle Rhine Highlands, Bohemia and Thuringia.   In contrast with these highland regions, the interior depressions and basins, such as those of Thuringia and the plains of the Labe in northern Bohemia, are sheltered from the rain-bearing westerly air streams and their climate is relatively continental, with cold winters and warm summers, lower mean annual precipitation and a tendency to autumn drought.   The Rhine valley below Basle, shut in by the Hercynian massifs of western Germany, experiences nevertheless relatively mild winters, temperatures nowhere falling below a mean of 33° F. in January (Cleves 35° F., Cologne 35·3° F., Heidelberg 34° F.), while the relative humidity is usually low.   There may be heavy valley mists, especially when temperature inversion occurs under calm, anticyclonic conditions, and the bordering highlands may be at the same time bathed in sunshine.   Spring comes rapidly and April is as warm at Cologne as at Warsaw.   Summers are usually warm, the mean July temperature of Cologne being 65·7° F., but storms frequently interrupt fine summer weather and the Rhine valley receives more rain in summer than winter.   Nevertheless, the sun is hot enough to ripen the vine on terraced slopes, whether at the foot of the Black Forest, along the *Bergstrasse*, in the Rheingau, or along the terraced slopes of the gorge of the Rhine above Koblenz.   The Rhineland is noted for its mild and prolonged autumn, when the changing colours of the beech woods in the foothill zones are a striking feature. The mean temperature for October at Cologne is 51·5° F., a degree higher than that of the North Sea port of Emden.

The upper Danube valley has a more continental type of climate than that of the Rhine, although the effect of southerly air streams partly offsets those of 'continental' south-eastern Europe. Winters tend to be prolonged, with considerable snowfall, but spring comes with steppe-like rapidity. The summer heat at Vienna is often of a 'Mediterranean' order, a mean July temperature of 68° F. being recorded. Winter is the least rainy season, with only 19 per cent of the mean annual total, and the low winter temperatures reduce evaporation. Depressions originating over the Mediterranean bring abundant spring rain, favouring the rapid growth of plants. May and June are usually the rainiest months, when depressions pass away to the north-east. During the heat of summer, depressions are rare and most rainfall is of the convectional type. By the autumn, the parched appearance of the landscape resembles that of the steppes of south-eastern Europe. At this season, stream flow is very much reduced. As temperature falls, so the dry weather comes to an end. The first frosts may appear by late October but by mid-November severe frosts occur nightly and snow may fall.

Alpine Europe offers another element of marked variety of climate in Central Europe. The Foreland region, which extends from the lake of Geneva across central Switzerland into Upper Bavaria, narrowing between the Austrian Alps and Bohemia, experiences a modified Alpine type of climate. The average elevation of over 1,500 ft. is reflected in low winter temperatures. During the winter, high pressure dominates the Foreland or sub-Alpine zone, and much fog may persist as the result of temperature inversion, when Zürich and the Swiss piedmont towns may be shrouded in fog; while Davos, Arosa and Leysin, all noted Alpine health resorts, enjoy bright sunlight. On the other hand, if the sky is clear, temperatures may fall many degrees below freezing point. The mean January temperature for Augsburg, Munich and Zürich is 28·5° F., and snow usually lies for two months. During the abnormally cold winter of 1963, the lake of Zürich was frozen hard for six weeks. Spring comes late and is often rainy, while summers are relatively warm (64° F. being the usual mean for July), and thunderstorm rain is often experienced.

In the Alps, relief dominates the local climate everywhere, as it does in the Carpathians. Temperature decreases at the rate of 1° F. for every 270 ft. of ascent but more rapidly in summer and on southerly aspects, more slowly in winter and on northern slopes.

The deep, hemmed-in valleys and basins have a much more 'continental' régime than the peaks exposed to westerly air streams. An extreme example is that of the Klagenfurt basin in Carinthia, where the temperature is so low in winter that there is no noticeable decrease for 1,200 ft. of ascent. In view of the frequency of temperature inversion in Alpine valleys, much importance attaches to conditions on the slopes, especially above the usual inversion layer, for here settlements are situated so as to reap the benefit of maximum insolation. The contrast between slopes in the shade and those in the sun is recognized by the local use of the terms *ubac* or *envers*, *adret* or *endroit* in the French-speaking Alps, *Schattenseite* and *Sonnenseite* in the German-speaking regions. The significance of the insolation factor in the siting of village settlement in such valleys is referred to in the appropriate regional description of the Swiss and Austrian Alps (pp. 133 and 164); canton Valais, the Lower Engadine and the Hohe Tauern regions providing classic examples. In the Alps, precipitation increases everywhere with elevation but the windward slopes are twice as well watered as those to the leeward at the same height. Some of the high level valleys such as the Swiss Engadine, the Wörthersee basin in Carinthia, and the upper Rhône trench in canton Valais, appear as islands of dryness, and in the last region irrigation is needed to ensure the fruit harvest (apricots, peaches, etc.), as well as to maintain the valley pastures. The height of the permanent snow-line varies according to local factors, especially aspect and position, for, although the zone of permanent snow and ice lies generally at about 10,500 ft., it is 1,200 to 1,500 ft. higher on the High Alps than on the Pre-Alps. Each Alpine valley has its particular climatic features and, on clear, fine days, there is an alternation of valley and mountain winds, for example around the lake of Geneva and the lake of Zürich, where the local cold northerly wind is known as the *bise*. In valleys opening northwards, such as that of the Reuss at Altdorf, the *Föhn* becomes canalized and is especially frequent in spring. During the summer, a well-known feature of Alpine weather is the gradual ascent of a long line of cloud out of the valley and up the mountain slope as the day progresses, under the influence of rising air currents. By the evening the fall of temperature, especially after sunset, causes the cloud to disappear and the heavy air sinks again into the valley. It is, however, the *Föhn*, already mentioned, which has the most devastating consequences. When there is a strong barometric gradient from the Alps northwards into Central Europe, this warm, dry wind causes fog to disappear and snow to melt rapidly, while in autumn it may assist in ripening the vine. This wind may cause violent squalls, especially on the piedmont lakes.   Bludenz, on the lake of Constance, records many examples.   Where buildings are traditionally constructed largely of wood, with shingle roofs, especially in the Bernese and Tyrolean Alps, the dry air of the *Föhn* may cause fires to spread rapidly, as the galvanized iron roofs in the village of Scuols, in the Lower Engadine, bear witness.   The rapid melting of snow may give rise to a number of avalanches, especially in spring, and the *Föhn* may blow with sufficient velocity to lift off the roofs of chalets and hay barns.   The widespread use of boulders on roof tops is a frequent occurrence in Alpine valleys and is self-explanatory.

PLANT LIFE

Central Europe exemplifies a wide variety of vegetation zones in response to a large number of soil types, relief features and drainage, as much as to divers climatic features.   Apart from the Alpine zone of permanent snow and ice and the areas of ' steppe-heath ' found on the loess terrains, the vegetation of much of Central Europe appears once to have been forest, with the beech covering very wide stretches of well-drained lowland and the lower slopes of the uplands, from the Low Countries to Schleswig-Holstein and from the Jura to the Wienerwald.   The low total precipitation and temperatures below freezing point in winter cause this west European tree to die out in eastern Europe.   On the highlands and on the moraines of the north European lowland and of the Alpine Fore-land, coniferous woodland was once widespread: the ' horrida silva ' of Tacitus.   The Austrian pine flourishes in districts with a ' continental ' climate, where the relief is high and the summers warm and fairly dry as in the eastern Alps and the northern Carpathians. The sweet chestnut, which covers so much of the lower slopes of the French Alps, is limited to parts of the Swiss Valais and the foothills of the Jura and the Black Forest.   Another restricted type of vegetation is that of heather moorland, with gorse, dry oakwood and birch; it is found on the *Geest* of North-west Germany, as well as in the Kempenland of the Dutch-Belgian border and in the sandy country of Friesland.   This ' Atlantic ' plant association dies out beyond the Elbe lowland.

The plant cover of Central Europe by the time of Bronze Age settlement was largely a post-glacial development, few plants (notably the Alpine *Dryas octopetala*) surviving the Pleistocene glaciation.   There were two main lines of migration, namely the Danube valley, especially important in relation to the spread of

' steppe-heath' plants, and the Atlantic approach, favouring the spread of forest trees. Although some modification of this vegetation mantle was made in prehistoric times, as Gradmann has shown for the 'steppe-heath' regions,[1] the Romans made the first major attack on the lowland zones, especially in the Rhine and upper Danube valleys, west of the *limes Germaniæ*. The permanent clearance and settlement of the river valleys and lowlands of western Central Europe were, however, made by the various Germanic tribes, as they spread from the northern Lowland through the Rhine, Neckar and Main basins and into the Alpine Foreland. It was not, however, until the *Rodungszeit* of the later Middle Ages, that the forests of the uplands and highlands were penetrated and settlements of the 'forest clearing' type established.[2] In the Alps, the settlement of the Wälser in Graubünden and Vorarlberg are especially noteworthy. By the end of the Middle Ages, the Flemings had begun the systematic drainage and reclamation of the peat bogs, not only of 'Holland' but also of the German North Sea coastlands and of the district east of the Elbe known as the *Fläming*.

A number of types of forest may be identified in Central Europe, within the natural region of woodland which extends from the North Sea and Baltic coastlands to the Alpine-Carpathian zones. These forests occur in regions of high humidity, where the soils are heavily leached and lacking in lime. Whether the underlying soil is a true *podsol* or a brown forest soil depends on the type of forest cover. With coniferous forest, notably spruce and silver fir, light fails to penetrate the canopy and reach the soil, so that it remains damp and without undergrowth, but with broad-leaved trees, especially beech, light penetrates, especially in winter, though there is little undergrowth except for bilberry scrub to add to the accumulation of humus. In many of the Hercynian regions, there is a mingling of coniferous and deciduous trees, as in the Jura and outer Carpathians, so that an intermediate type of soil develops.

The most extensive lowland forests are developed on the plains of eastern Germany, especially on the light glacial sands of Brandenburg and pre-war Pomerania (now Polish Pomorze). These monotonous and sombre stretches of pine forest are varied only by the occurrence of lakes and peat bogs in the depressions between the morainic ridges. Towards the Baltic coast, however, the pine forests of the Havel-Spree region are replaced by extensive beech woods (Fig. 5). The riparian forests of the glacial *Urstromtäler*

---

[1] R. Gradmann: *Süddeutschland*, Vol. I, 1931, and earlier papers.
[2] H. C. Darby: ' The Clearing of the Woodland in Europe ', *Man's Rôle in Changing the Face of the Earth*, 1956, pp. 195–9.

also introduce another element, for on these damp soils, where the
water-table is always high, willows and alders flourish, as does the
damp oak, while reeds and other marsh plants abound. This type
of plant association is known as *Bruch* and is best preserved in the
Spreewald, south of Berlin, but much of it has been cleared in the
period of post-medieval 'colonial' settlement.

Mixed woodland, consisting of beech, oak, and various conifers,

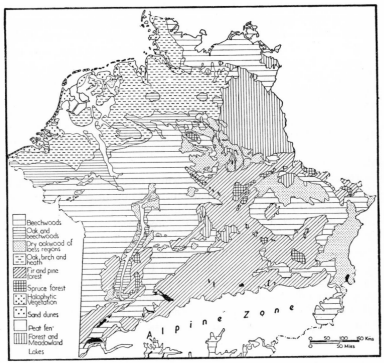

FIG. 5. Central Europe: natural vegetation.

extends across the north European lowland from Flanders to the
Elbe, while it is also widespread on the slopes of the Hercynian
uplands exposed to Atlantic influences. These trees need damp
soil, rich in humus, and winters where the temperature does not
remain long below freezing point. Eastern Schleswig-Holstein, the
Weser hill-country, the scarps of the Swabian Jura and part of the
Bohemian *Polabí* have this type of forest. In the lowlands, pure
stands of beech are rare and west of the Elbe the oak frequently
mingles with the beech, as on the lower slopes of the Ardenne and

in the Teutoburgerwald. The types of soil which are hostile to the growth of the beech are those derived from the Pliocene and Pleistocene sands, where the oak, birch, heath association is found, as in the Kempenland and on the *Geest* of the Lüneburger Heide. The other type is the peat fen, either the high fen (*Hochmoor* or *Hoogeveen*) of the Peel district of Belgium and the now reclaimed polders of the Netherlands and the peat fen of the marshlands of Oldenburg, or the low fen of parts of the *Geest*, where the raw humus favours the oak-birch-heath association. In the upper Rhine and Danube valleys, strips of alluvium support a wilderness of swamp-loving plants, especially the poplar, willow and alder, which abound in the no-man's land between France and Germany along the upper Rhine. The local name for this type of vegetation is the *Ried* and it also occurs in the upper Danube valley in the district known as the Donau*ried*.[1] Pure stands of beech survive in some of the Hercynian uplands of western Germany, notably in the Taunus, on the lower slopes of the Black Forest, in the north-west of the Thuringian Forest and in the southern Harz mountains, as well as in the Swiss Jura.

The sub-Alpine forests of the Hercynian regions have also invaded those of the Alps and the Carpathians, but not, of course, above a general level of 7,000 ft. In the Alpine valleys, the lower limit of tree growth is fixed by the extent of forest clearance dating mainly from the medieval *Rodungszeit*.[2] The upper limit is that of the *Alpen* or spring and autumn pastures used for cattle grazing. The amount of forest that has survived in the Alps is very unevenly distributed, the dry and sunny upper Rhône valley in canton Valais supporting far less timber than the sombre Vorderrhein between Chur and Disentis. The preservation of the forest in many Alpine valleys depends on aspect, for often the *adret* or *Sonnenseite* is cleared for pasture and settlement while the *ubac* or *Schattenseite* remains thickly wooded, an example being provided by the Schächental east of Altdorf, and the Pays d'Enhaut above Gruyère.

The zoning of vegetation according to elevation is very pronounced both in the Alps and in the High Tatra (Fig. 72). The upper limit of the forest zone varies according to the total precipitation and the duration of the snow cover; the tree-line in the Pre-Alps and in the High Alps differing by 2,500 ft. (de Martonne). The Central Alps have less total precipitation and snowfall and are less windy at the

---

[1] Troll, K.: 'Die natürlichen Landschaften des rechtsrheinischen Bayerns, Geog. Anzeiger, 1926.

[2] *Rodungszeit* is the German term applied to the late medieval period of forest clearance.

same height than the Pre-Alps. The tree-line therefore rises to 5,000 ft. on the Säntis but to over 7,000 ft. in the Ötztal and to 7,500 ft. on Monte Rosa. At the lowest levels. the forest is varied, beech intermingling with fir and larch, but at greater heights pines and firs, especially spruce, reign supreme, as on the summits of the Hercynian massifs. Above the tree-line are the alpine pastures, with their wealth of spring and summer flowers which may appear before the snow melts; notably the crocus and soldanella. In some parts of the Alps, the dwarf rhododendron or Alpine ' rose ' forms an intermediate zone between the forest and the *mayen*, and, in some regions of primeval vegetation as in the High Tatra, a transition zone of stunted firs (*Krummholz*) occurs, typified by the *Pinus pumilio* of the northern Carpathians. In the Swiss Alps, the ' natural vegetation ' is best preserved in the Swiss National Park, which lies in the remote frontier region of the Lower Engadine. Here certain flora are protected, notably the silver thistle. In places, bare slopes may appear in the midst of the forest, marking the courses of avalanches or rock slides.

In contrast with the primeval forest associated with the parts of Central Europe that have repelled settlement, there are the relatively open belts of country associated with the loess soils (Figs. 5 and 8). Much controversy has arisen since R. Gradmann first propounded his *Steppen-heide* theory in relation to Neolithic settlement.[1] Recent research suggests that these regions probably supported light oak-wood in earliest times and this was easily cleared compared with the mixed and spruce forest of the Hercynian and Alpine regions.[2] These tracts of dry oakwood, as indicated on the vegetation map in the *Atlas von Mitteleuropa*, include the high terraces of the Rhine rift and the upper Neckar valleys, the Wetterau and Rheingau, the *Börde* zone of sub-Hercynian Germany, the Leipzig embayment, and the lowlands of northern Bohemia (the *Polabí*) and of Moravia and the Vienna basin. Isolated patches also occur in the upper Danube valley, at the head of lake Constance, and in the Sundgau, west of Basle. In the Rhine and Neckar valleys, these loess terrains experienced four centuries of Romanization, including the introduction of the vine, before the arrival of the Germanic tribes. Place-name evidence suggests that these easily cultivated, loamy soil tracts were rapidly settled by the Franks and the Alemanni, before there was any major onslaught on the heavily forested lands.[3]

[1] R. Gradmann: *Süddeutschland*, Vol. I, 1931, and other writings.
[2] A. Garnett: ' The Loess Regions of Central Europe in Prehistoric Times ', *Geog. Journal*, Vol. 106, 1945, pp. 132–43.
[3] A. F. A. Mutton: ' Place Names and the History of Settlement in South-West Germany ', *Geography*, Vol. 23, 1938, pp. 113–19.

RELIEF

Although Partsch saw in Central Europe ' the triad of Alps, hills and plain ' as ' the governing chord of the symphony of the Central European landscape ', detailed examination of the surface features shows them to be the most varied of all Europe. The Alpine element includes the well-known pyramidal forms of the Matterhorn and of the Salzburg Alps, the fantastically weathered peaks of the

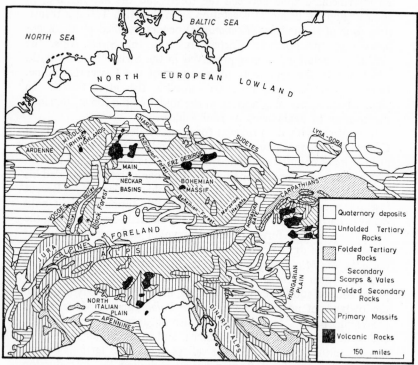

FIG. 6.   Central Europe: structural features.

Dolomites, the contorted forms of the Diablerets and the great massifs of Monte Rosa and the St. Gotthard.   In the Carpathians, the crystalline peaks of the High Tatra, such as the Rysy, contrast with the high bevelled erosion surfaces of the *Flysch* ranges of the Beskyds.   In Hercynian Europe, the asymmetrical faulted blocks of the Black Forest and Vosges contrast with the monotonous block

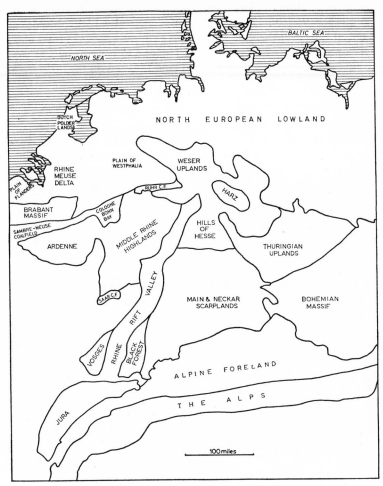

FIG. 7.   Central Europe: physiographic features.

plateau of the Middle Rhine Highlands, varied only by the volcanic features of the Voreifel and the Siebengebirge.   The scarplands and other uplands of Central Europe are just as diversified, for the fretted escarpment of the Swabian and Franconian Jura is no less a striking feature of the relief than the volcanic Volgelsberg and Hohe Rhön or the eroded sandstone landscape of 'Saxon Switzerland'. The most monotonous relief feature is to be found in the Germano-Polish lowland, which, like the Alpine Foreland, depends mainly

on the deposition of Pleistocene glacial and peri-glacial material for
its surface variety.   Nevertheless, the generally high altitude of
Central Europe, averaging 1,500 ft. over a quarter of the total area,
has a profound effect on climate, drainage and river régime, as well
as on the patterns of settlement and land use, and on the main trade
routes.

The Evolution of the Relief

Central Europe formed a region of sedimentation in front of the
Fenno-Scandian shield in early Palæozoic times, characterized by
alternating periods of sedimentation and orogenesis until the late
Tertiary era, followed by the climatic oscillations associated with the
Pleistocene glaciation.   Traces of Pre-Cambrian rocks may be found
in the Black Forest and Böhmerwald and there are signs of Caledonian folding in the Harz, the Ardenne, the Middle Rhine Highlands and the Sudetes.   Following the Cambrian period of sedimentation in the north of Central Europe, the Devonian saw the
deposition of limestones, marls and sandstones from the Ardenne to
the Sudetes.   Similarly, Carboniferous rocks, associated with the
coalfields of Aachen, the Ruhr and Saxony, as well as with those of
inner Bohemia, were laid down along the base of the Palæozoic
massifs, experiencing, together with these regions, extensive folding
in Carbo-Permian times.   The trend of these folds varies but it is
most typically from south-west to north-east in the Ore Mountains
(Krušne Hory) and the Vosges-Black Forest block but in the Middle
Rhine Highlands it swings from the ' Variscan ' direction through
west to north-west–south-east.   The oldest traces of ' Hercynian '
folding are in the Sudetes but the earth movements continued into
Permian times, when they were mainly vertical, and some vulcanism
also took place.   These Permian or ' Zechstein ' basins lie mainly
between the Hunsrück and the Vosges, the Odenwald and the northern Black Forest, and they also extend from the Harz to Bohemia.
During this arid period, salt and gypsum were deposited in the Werra
and Stassfurt regions, as well as potash and anhydrite.   At the
same time, salt domes were formed, especially at Sperenburg near
Berlin and near Hanover, where petroleum has been worked in
recent years.   These Permian beds have played a vital part in the
development of Germany's chemical industries.   Prospecting for
oil continues apace especially along the German–Dutch border and
off the North Sea coast.

The Triassic period was one of regular sedimentation in Bohemia,
the northern Black Forest and the Vosges, and in the central district
of the Middle Rhine Highlands.   The advance of the Triassic sea

covered the post-Hercynian peneplain which is today partly exhumed in parts of the Black Forest and the Taunus.   Bunter sandstone, *Muschelkalk* and Keuper sandstone and marls, with their associated beds of salt and gypsum as at Heilbronn in the Neckar valley, form the upland and basin country of central and western Germany

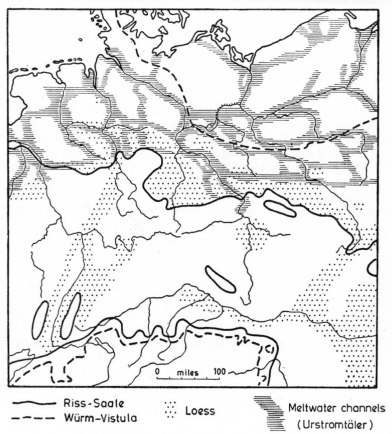

Riss-Saale
Würm-Vistula
Loess
Meltwater channels
(Urstromtäler)

FIG. 8.   Central Europe: glacial features and loess distribution.

between the Hercynian massifs, notably in the Kraichgau, dividing the Odenwald and Black Forest, and in the middle Neckar and Main valleys.

The Jurassic seas covered a wide area from the Jura Mountains and the outer Alps, across the scarplands of Swabia and Franconia northwards to Westphalia and the Weser Hills.   In this latter region 'Saxonian' folding took place. Subsequently, the Upper Cretaceous sea advanced over the northern rim of the *Mittelgebirge*, notably over the Ardenne, the Sauerland, the Weser Hills and Saxony, and the flat-topped appearance of parts of these uplands may be traced to this period of marine erosion. In the Alpine zone the sediments which were laid down in a great geosyncline were subsequently folded against the resistant massifs of the Hercynian 'windows', now exposed in the heart of the Alps, as well as against those lying beyond the Alpine arc in Central Europe. The intense folding of the Carpathians took place in Eocene and Miocene times and this system of folds has been much eroded, so that crystalline basement rocks appear in the High Tatra. Here high undulating surfaces and deep gorges suggest the predominance of vertical movements and a general transition from the Alps to the Hercynian zone.[1] In the Alps, the Miocene Helvetic folds, together with the Austrides, represent the major period of *nappe* structure development, while the evolution of the Dinaric folds, accompanied by local vulcanism along the south-eastern margin of the Alpine arc, completed the sequence.

The Pleistocene period saw the advance of the Riss-Saale ice sheets both into the northern Netherlands and also across the Germano-Polish lowland to the foot of the Hercynian uplands. In the Alpine zone, the ice moved forward to the base of the Jura, across the present Rhine valley at Schaffhausen to the line of the upper Danube. The northern Carpathians were the scene of local glaciation in the High Tatra, as were the Black Forest, Vosges, Böhmerwald, Sudetes and Harz Mountains. Today the drift-covered Alpine Foreland bears witness to the stages in the retreat of the ice, and, whereas permanent snow and ice have disappeared from the High Tatra, the great glaciers and snowfields of the Swiss Alps, notably in the Aar-St. Gotthard massifs, in the Bernese Oberland, the Bernina and the Pennine Alps, together with the Pasterze glacier of the Gross Glockner in the Hohe Tauern, mark the waning remnants of the Pleistocene ice. The interglacial and post-glacial periods have also seen the deposition of wind-borne loess along the edge of the continental ice sheets in northern Germany, in the Rhine, Neckar and upper Danube valleys, as well as in the *Polabí* of Bohemia and in the Moravian lowland.[2] The large-scale accumulation of peat along the southern North Sea coastlands, as well as in the Alpine Foreland, are Holocene features, the product of the humid climatic phase known as the sub-Atlantic, in contrast with the dry Boreal phase which preceded it.

[1] P. George and J. Tricart: *L'Europe Centrale*, Vol. 1, p. 14.
[2] H. J. Fleure: 'The Loess in European Life', *Geography*, Vol. 45, 1960.

The Alps

A distinction may be made between the relief forms which pre-date glaciation and those which result from it. Thus, resistant masses of granite, gneiss and schist form the central zones of high relief, flanked by the folded rocks of the sedimentary zones. The more resistant limestones form sheer rock faces, as in the escarpments of the Dolomites, the Salzkammergut and the Diablerets, while valleys are frequently eroded in the less resistant schists, slates and marls, for example the Rhine-Rhône, Inn, and Enns-Salzach trenches. The lower relief of the outer ranges is on account of relative ease of erosion, especially where the *Flysch* and *Molasse* are involved.

Whereas in the High Alps relief depends on structure, in the folded sedimentary zones the crests seldom correspond with the arch of an anticline or with the exposure of the hardest rocks, as the sectional diagram illustrates (Fig. 15). The great longitudinal trenches are also not always structural features, for the Rhône in canton Valais, the Enns and the Salzach cut across axes of folding and the Swiss section of the Inn below Zernez is eroded in the 'Lower Engadine window'. Some rivers have maintained their original course, cutting gorges and narrow defiles through highly resistant rocks, notably the Via Mala gorge on the Hinter Rhine, the Schöllenen gorge on the Reuss below Andermatt, and the Finstermünz gorge of the Inn cut on the Swiss-Austrian frontier. Whereas these master streams appear to be the relics of a past system, the tributaries follow the alignment of the Alpine folds, cutting into the softer rocks between resistant crests. A further result of erosion is the appearance of 'windows' of older rock beneath the higher *nappes*, not only in the Western Alps but also in the Austrian Alps, where the Pennine *nappes* appear as in the Hohe Tauern, surrounded by the younger Austride *nappes*. The conventional dividing line between the eastern and western Alps runs along the Rhine valley from the lake of Constance to Chur and thence across the Graubünden Alps to the lake of Como. In the western Alps, the front of the *nappes* is in the form of an arc, according to the resistance offered to the Pennine *nappes* by the external Hercynian massifs (Massif Central, Vosges-Black Forest, Bohemian Massif). The Helvetian *nappes* seem to have advanced more easily between the Massif Central and the Vosges-Black Forest, and the Jurassic folds are also splayed out and the limestones forming plateau blocks and faulted and tilted scarplands.

During the Pliocene rejuvenation of the Alps, tectonic movements extended over a wide area. Crests exceed 12,000 ft. but valleys are incised 6,000 ft. below. When seen from the valleys, the peaks appear as massive or broken blocks, wall-like or pyramidal but, when seen from the summit, they often appear as extensive plateau surfaces bitten into by *cirques* and into which the valleys have cut deep trenches. There are clear signs of peneplanation followed by uplift. Subsequent erosion has in places provided a source of *Molasse* transported to the Foreland. Bevelled surfaces, elements in the ' Rax landscape ', are especially evident in the Wienerwald and in Styria,[1] as well as in the Pre-Alps of Bavaria, the Vorarlberg and Switzerland. In the desolate limestone plateaux of the Salz-kammergut, rounded blocks of quartz and crystalline rock occur, known as *Augensteine*, brought by the Enns-Salzach from the High Alps during an earlier erosion cycle.

The Pleistocene glacial phases saw glaciers override cols, extend down the rejuvenated valleys and spread out over the Foreland. Here and there rocky eminences and isolated peaks stood as *nunataks* above the ice fields. Today the Concordiaplatz region of the Aletsch glacier is a surviving example of such Alpine glaciation. Although A. Penck was able to trace two glacial phases (Gunz and Mindel) in Württemberg and Bavaria which preceded the Riss and Würm phases, these latter two phases are most significant in relation to Alpine glaciation. Although the Riss ice was the most extensive, the Würm extended across the Swiss Foreland to the foot of the Jura and its retreat into the Alpine valleys was slow and broken by interglacial periods, a process closely related to the broken *talweg* of many of the Alpine valleys today. In fact, the longitudinal profile of an Alpine valley varies between a flat tread or *ombilic* and a narrow rock bar or *verrou*, the paternoster lakes of the Upper Engadine lying in such a tread above the rock bar below St. Moritz.[2] Many Alpine valleys have a surprisingly wide as well as long trench, in view of the steep longitudinal gradient. The elevation of the Swiss Upper Engadine (over 5,000 ft.) is difficult to appreciate in view of the mile-wide valley, for example at Samedan, and the upper Rhine and Rhône trenches offer other examples. Above this trench or *auge* rise steep slopes, often forested, before the shoulders or benches are reached, where lie the *mayen* or spring pastures and high level

[1] The term ' Rax landscape ' is used by Alpine geomorphologists to describe the 6,000-ft. Miocene erosion surface exemplified in the Rax region of the Styrian Alps near the Semmering pass. It is noticeably absent in the western Alps. (See P. George and J. Tricart, *op. cit.*, Vol. 1, pp. 107 and 110).

[2] C. A. Cotton: *Climatic Accidents*, 1942, p. 257.

permanent settlements. Above these terrace features, which mark the former level of the valley floor, rise the high massifs with their chiselled crests, *arête* ridges and *cirques* or *kare*. Many side valleys ' hang ' in relation to the main valley and streams may cascade over a waterfall, as in the Staubbach falls in the Lauterbrunnen valley, or disappear into a ravine cut in a rock step, as at the lower end of the Val d'Anniviers and of the Trient below Martigny.[1] Where cols occur, the relief is often confused and here *roches moutonnées* may occur and also basins filled with little lakes, surrounded by scree which is the product of frost weathering, as on the Grimsel and Flüela passes.

Where a glacier has ' recently ' left a valley, the ' U ' profile is usually clear and rock steps may be revealed, as at the site of the recently rapidly retreating Rhône glacier and Furka pass. Lower down the valley the glacial forms may not be so apparent, for example in the Vermala (Valais), where there is a series of benches on the slopes, cleared for pasture and cultivation but with forest on the steep slopes. These benches are known as *Ebenen* in the German-speaking Alps and as *replats* in the French, and they mark several phases in valley erosion, river and ice alternating. A series of *verrous* and hanging valleys may be seen to correspond to several *replats*. In the piedmont zone lie the great lakes, such as Constance, Geneva and Zürich, the flow of water from which is partly checked by moraines. At the head of these lakes extensive deltas often occur, as on the Rhône above Geneva or between the lakes of Thun and Brienz, where the Lütschine has built up the alluvial fan on which Interlaken stands. Some lakes occur in overdeepened valleys in true rock basins, like the Wörthersee in Carinthia, but the valleys are fundamentally river eroded and had almost reached grade prior to glaciation, as had the Inn. As the result of the drowning of part of a valley floor to form a ' finger ' lake, *verrous* have in places been submerged and appear as wooded islands, as in lake Maggiore, and moraines may similarly survive as islands, as in the Wörthersee and the lake of Lugano, where the railway from Lugano to Melide utilises such a feature. Post-glacial erosion, that is, normal river erosion, combined with frost weathering, etc., have considerably modified the glacial landscape of Alpine valleys. Apart from the formation of lake deltas, already mentioned, and further exemplified by the lake of Silvaplana in the Upper Engadine, great detrital fans have been built up, especially at the foot of deep ravines and where deforestation has taken place. Avalanches are a common occurrence and many slopes have to be protected by stone walls against

[1] J. Fuller: ' The Trient valley ', *Geography*, Vol. 40, 1955, pp. 28–39.

such catastrophes, for example on the slopes of the Weissfluh above Davos Dorf. In the Rhine valley above Chur, the great landslide at Flims has caused the Rhine to cut a new gorge, 1,200 ft. below its former course. The Alps today are characterized by torrential stream erosion and by heavy weathering by frost, so that slopes, especially above the tree-line, are seldom stable. Ice avalanches may also occur, such as the one in September, 1965, which destroyed the hydro-electric plant under construction at Saas Fee, in the Valais.

A description of the major physiographic regions of the Alps will be found in Chapter 4. It is sufficient to stress here the landscape contrasts between the crystalline, calcareous and metamorphic zones. In the crystalline Alps the peaks are generally higher than elsewhere and more massive, while the drainage is independent of the structure. Here the effects of mountain glaciation are most striking in relation to mountain and valley sculpturing and, in these regions of high relief, winters are severe, so that many of the peaks are permanently snow-capped. In the Calcareous Alps, the limestone ridges often alternate with slates, sandstones and marls, and there is a great variety of land forms closely related to structure. The effects of glaciation are generally less obvious. The most marked contrasts are between the waterless limestone ranges, with their broken crest lines, and the intensively farmed valleys and basins which lie below them. In the regions of metamorphic rock, as in the schist and slate zones, the relief is softer and the valleys wider. Here, on account of the lower relief and the less extreme climate, the slopes are frequently forested and the fairly accessible valleys are used for pasture with some cropping, with occasional small scale industry based on hydro-electric power, as in the Linthtal. The western Alps, with their wide sweep and their high peaks and glaciers, contrast with the eastern Alps, with their east-west ranges and general absence of present-day glaciers, on account of the lower average relief (except in the Gross Glockner). The western Alps appear much more eroded than the eastern Alps, though some isolated *nappe* fragments exist east of the Rhine, while the eastern Alps have more mature land forms. Whereas the western Alps are exposed to depressions from the Atlantic and from the Mediterranean, the eastern Alps have a more continental climate, with rainy summers and very cold winters, the seasonal temperature range in the Klagenfurt basin being extreme (see p. 16). Whereas the valleys of the western Alps have favoured the penetration of a west European flora, the eastern Alps are open to the migration of Danubian species *via* the Drave, Enns and Inn valleys. The western Alps have received in the main a Germanic type of rural settlement and culture, whereas the eastern Alps have seen the meeting of German and Slavonic elements.

The Carpathians

This range is a continuation of Alpine Europe across the Danube at Bratislava (*Ger.* Pressburg). The structure is similar and the folds swing through a great arc against the Bihor massif to the south. The general uplift was lower than that of the Alps, the High Tatra only just exceeding 10,000 ft. The main ranges lie below 6,000 ft. and more than half under 3,000 ft. In consequence, precipitation is lower than in the Alps and there are no glaciers, so that there is only snow-melt to swell the streams in late spring and summer. The Pleistocene glaciation was very restricted and the small glaciers did not descend beyond the mountains, though glacial lakes were formed, such as Morskie Oko on the Polish side of the High Tatra and Strebské Pleso in Slovakia. The heights are mostly flat-topped, especially where *Flysch* predominates, as in the Western Beskids. Escarpments are rare but Tertiary volcanics are of major importance, notably in the Matra massif and in the Hegyallia. There is a general lack of continuity of zones in contrast with the Alps, the *Flysch* formation being most widespread. There is no parallel to the limestone ranges of the Alps; the central crystalline zone consists of the isolated massifs of the High and Low Tatra, while the volcanic areas are mostly detached. The Carpathians are a centre of continental drainage dispersal, the Vistula headwaters rising on the southern slope of the High Tatra within a short distance of the Vah (Waag) tributary of the Danube. There are two cols in the northern Carpathians (Dukla at 1,647 ft. and Lupkow at 1,916 ft.); while the main route through the Western Beskids from Moravia to Cracow is *via* the Jablunka pass.

The climate of the Carpathians is 'continental', the winter isotherms running generally east to west instead of north to south as in Central Europe. The deep sunk valleys and basins experience frequent temperature inversions on cold and calm winter nights. There is a marked altitudinal zoning of vegetation, the alpine zone descending to 5,000 ft. in the High Tatra, followed by a sub-alpine zone, with *Pinus pumilio*, and then the coniferous forest zone. Many of the valleys have been cleared of forest for pasture and strip cultivation; timber being the usual building material in the villages. Crop cultivation extends to 1,800 ft. in Slovakia and in the valleys of the southern Slovak Carpathians the vine appears, as around Košice and Tokay. Settlements in these valleys of the northern

Carpathians are now entirely Slavonic, since the departure of the Hungarian landowners in 1919. Before the 1939–45 War, the population was divided between adherents to the Roman Catholic and to the Greek Orthodox Church.

Hercynian Europe

As far as Central Europe is concerned, the Hercynian massifs form a broken zone from southern Belgium across the Rhine valley into the *Mittelgebirge* and Bohemia. These regions of Carbo-Permian folding have undergone prolonged erosion and nowhere exceed 5,500 ft. The rocks range from schists and slates to gneiss and granite and the uplands have various alignments, from the Variscan type represented by the Black Forest, extending from north-east to south-west, through the Hercynian type represented by the Thuringian and Bohemian Forests, to the Armorican represented by the Middle Rhine Highlands. The folding of these regions in Carbo-Permian times also extended to the bordering Coal Measures, so that the coalfields lie in basin structures, disturbed by Tertiary faulting and thrusting, as in the Ruhr, Saar, Sambre-Meuse and Saxony coalfields.

The summits of the Hercynian ranges are typically rounded and locally glaciated, though there are also well-preserved erosion surfaces exemplified by the 4,000-ft. platform in Bohemia and the 1,200-ft. in the Ardenne, Taunus and Hunsrück. The effect of the Alpine orogenesis on these resistant massifs was to uplift them, with associated tilting and faulting, as in the Vosges-Black Forest block, and to rejuvenate drainage. Vulcanism, begun in late Tertiary times, extended into the Quaternary, and occurred in the Eifel, Siebengebirge, Vogelsberg, Hohe Rhön and north-western Bohemia. The Hercynian regions are broken into a kind of mosaic pattern, the somewhat monotonous forested uplands with their meagre population densities contrasting sharply with the fertile, thickly populated and in places industrialized zones which lie at their foot. These contrasts are very marked in the Taunus and Rheingau, the Sauerland and the Ruhr, the Hunsrück and the Saar. Some of the lowlands are richly cultivated, the *Polabí* of north-eastern Bohemia being noted for its sugar beet, wheat and hops.

The types of relief region associated with Hercynian Europe range from the slab-like uplifted and tilted plateaux of the Middle Rhine Highlands, where the heights are seldom over 3,000 ft., through the asymmetrical faulted massif of the Black Forest and the single spur of the Thuringian Forest, to the ' horst ' of the isolated Harz massif.

The included sedimentary basins are not so varied in surface forms as the Hercynian massifs, though the tilted secondary rocks dip under younger rocks, resulting in dissymmetrical relief with winding scarp faces, as in the Swabian Alb and the Franconian Jura.   In the Rhine Rift valley, the Tertiaries are partly buried beneath recent drift deposits.   The tectonic trenches are the most favoured regions of the Hercynian zone, for they are sheltered from the rain-bearing winds and have a dry, semi-continental climate, the warm summers offsetting the cold and frequently misty winters.   An extreme contrast is offered by the sandstone plateaux, as in the hill country of Hesse, where the valleys are deeply incised in the porous Bunter sandstone and the forest cover is almost complete.

The various elements of Hercynian Europe thus comprise six major areas.   The Bohemian massif is the most homogeneous of these major regions, except for the Tertiary vulcanism of the northwest and the fertile plains of the *Polabí*.   The Thuringian Forest and the Harz form isolated ' horsts ' distinct from the paired and faulted blocks bordering the Rhine rift valley.   The scarplands of Swabia and Franconia divide the Bohemian massif from the Black Forest and Odenwald, while the secondary rocks of the Weser Hills and the ' Porta Westfalica ' form a region of confused relief between Westphalia and Hanover.

The Lowland Regions

In contrast with so much of Central Europe which is predominantly a region of rather high, if broken, relief, there are two great lowland areas.   These are the Germano-Polish lowland in the north and the Alpine Foreland and upper Danube valley in the south.

The Germano-Polish Lowland.   The total east–west extent of this vast lowland sloping to the North Sea and the Baltic is over 800 miles, with a width of at least 250 miles.   Over all this region, the relief seldom rises above 900 ft. and then only in the region of the Würm-Vistula terminal moraines in Pomorze (Pomerania) and former East Prussia.   In this context only that part of the plain which extends from the Netherlands to the lower Oder valley is included.   Over all this area, Cretaceous rocks appear only significantly in Dutch Limburg, in Westphalia and in the Chalk cliffs of the Baltic island of Rügen.   Elsewhere the covering of Pleistocene and Recent drift material is virtually complete.   To the west, the Riss-Saale ice sheets advanced to a line across central Holland, across the Rhine above Duisburg-Ruhrort, and so along the base of the Hercynian uplands.   Much of the outwash material from this glaciation has been re-assorted by subsequent river action and the low hills of ' push moraines ' north of Utrecht and Arnhem and the Hondsrog ridge along the northern Dutch-German frontier are some of the few significant surviving relief features. To the south is a region of normal river drainage and of loess deposits, as in the *Börde*.

The Würm-Vistula ice sheets were, however, responsible for the Newer Drift features east of a line through the Lüneburg Heath across the Elbe into the Fläming and so to Nieder-Lausitz, on the Polish border. These are the sandy outwash regions or *Geest*, formerly under heath, though with modern spruce plantations, and they are regions of sparse population. Beyond these sterile expanses towards the Baltic Sea, the relief pattern is chaotic; damp plains developed on boulder clay contrasting with high morainic ridges, parallel to the Baltic coastline, with peaty depressions dividing them and with the frequent occurrence of irregular lakes, often surrounded by forest, as in the Mecklenburg lake plateau. Another major feature of the northern lowland is that of the *Urstromtäler*, the broad, shallow, ramifying valley trenches which extend in long lines, in some places trending east-west as in the Berlin region, and in others corresponding with the courses of the great rivers, like the lower Elbe and the Weser. In these regions, the melt-water from the Würm ice was trapped between the Baltic ice to the north and the pre-existing relief features to the south and south-west, including the remnants of the Riss-Saale moraines. Much of the peat fen which developed in these ill-drained trenches has been reclaimed, as have the coastal marshes and polders bordering the North Sea. The Baltic coast is frequently characterized by shingle spits backed by sand dunes. In contrast with the off-shore Frisian islands broken by the great tidal estuaries of the North Sea coast, the Baltic is noted for its delta formations, notably that of the Vistula, and for the development of *Haff* and *Nehrung* features which reach their finest development in what is now Russo-Polish territory, in the Frisches Haff and in the Kurisches Haff and Nehrung.

The Alpine Foreland and Upper Danube Valley. The wide sweep of country which extends from the lake of Geneva to Vienna is a major corridor between the Alps and Hercynian Europe, in the same way as the sub-Carpathian zone in Polish Galicia serves as a passage land between the Carpathians and the Lysogora. The Alpine Foreland is a continental divide, for the western region is drained by the Rhône to the Mediterranean, the centre by the Rhine to the North Sea, and the east by the tributaries of the Danube to the Black Sea. This great triangular feature is defined by the Alps to the south and by the Jurassic folds and scarplands of Switzerland,

Swabia and Franconia to the north, and also by the Bohemian massif. Only *Nagelfluh* and *Molasse* represent solid rocks and these Tertiary formations attain considerable heights, especially in Switzerland in the Napf plateau, and in the Hausruck of Austria. Otherwise the relief is the result of glacial deposition, for the Older Drift extends to the foot of the Jura and into Swabia. In contrast with the major terminal moraines of the Würm advance, there are the great fluvio-glacial gravel terraces especially impressive in Upper Bavaria, and wide stretches of peat bog, as in the notorious Dachau Moos. This Foreland region also includes some loess deposits, especially in the upper Danube valley, and their loamy soils, mainly under arable, contrast with the prevalent pastoral or mixed farming economy which characterizes this humid and ' continental ' climatic region. The Foreland includes a number of historic nodal cities, on account of its position in relation to trans-Alpine routes, and most of these are also major centres of industry, notably Geneva, Zürich, Augsburg and Munich. The intensive agriculture and high degree of industrial development found in Swiss Foreland is in striking contrast with the generally extensive agriculture and with the paucity of large industrial towns, other than the two mentioned above, in the upper Danube valley and those of its tributaries.

DRAINAGE FEATURES

As far as régime is concerned, the rivers of Central Europe exemplify transitional characteristics between the rivers of western Europe, with their regular flow, and those of the south-east, which are steppe-like. Whereas to the north rivers freeze for varying periods each winter, to the south, where Mediterranean influences are felt, streams tend to run low in summer. The broken relief of Central Europe favours considerable precipitation and the accumulation of snow on the heights. The large piedmont lakes of the Alpine-Jura zone and also those of the Baltic Heights serve to regulate stream flow, as do the frequently forested slopes of both Alpine and Hercynian Europe. De Martonne distinguishes four types of hydrographic region on a basis of river régime and they may thus be summarized:

The Northern Plains

Here surface drainage is abundant, soils are generally impermeable, the climate damp, and summers late and brief. Although lakes and peat bogs serve to regulate stream flow, when ice thaws in the spring, extensive flooding of river water meadows often occurs. It is estimated that the run-off is, however, only a quarter of the total precipitation, for there is an absence of steep slopes, a prevalence of sandy soils to absorb rainfall, and the Tertiary clays below the drift deposits serve to retain water which has percolated into the sub-soil. The main rivers of north Germany are never short of water nor do they flood excessively, though high evaporation may cause the level to fall in the summer months. Only short streams, such as those draining from the Harz to the Aller, are torrents; the great rivers, such as the Weser, Elbe and Aller, being calm and placid. Streams draining the peat fen, as in Oldenburg, may appear brown or black through peat discoloration. The rivers of the Berlin region, such as the Spree and the Havel, are also clear and calm, for their flow is checked by the chain of lakes into which they expand. The flow of the Havel is so slow that it carries off only a fifth of the total precipitation of the basin.[1]

The Hercynian Regions

Here there is prolonged winter snowfall, estimated at between 25 and 40 in. at heights of over 2,500 ft. This is largely conserved until the spring but then there is rapid run-off, facilitated by steep slopes and generally impervious rocks. In the upper Weser and Saale valleys, it is estimated that a third of the precipitation is carried off by the rivers. In these regions, surface flow is markedly affected by the proximity of Triassic and Jurassic limestones, sandstones, clays and marls to the Primary massifs. Springs abound, as at the foot of the Swabian Jura and in the limestone uplands of Westphalia. There is much variation in the amount of run-off from place to place and from season to season, summer being the general season of low water, broken by short floods, especially when storms occur on the heights. Autumn and spring are the seasons of maximum flow. In the Black Forest, middle Rhine Highlands, Thuringian Forest and Bohemian massif there is abundant surface run-off, where granites, gneisses and slates occur, and these regions are important contributors to the drainage of such great rivers as the Rhine, Weser, Danube, Elbe and Oder. The course of the upper Weser is regulated by the fact that much of its catchment area is formed by the highly porous Bunter sandstone. In Bohemia, the rain-shadow effect on the north-eastern lowland of the *Polabí* is reflected in the meagre volume of the Labe or upper Elbe, which is only navigable to Ústí (Aussig).

[1] E. de Martonne: *Europe Centrale*, Géog. Univ. Vol. 4, p. 66.

Alpine Regions

These regions of greatest elevation in Central Europe, like the northern Carpathians to a lesser extent, receive precipitation from all directions, though predominantly from the west and south-west. Snow accumulates for months on the peaks and much is released in late spring and summer when the flow of the Alpine torrents is greatly increased. The run-off is effectively checked by the great piedmont lakes, especially Geneva in relation to the Rhône and Constance in relation to the Rhine, the level of both lakes varying markedly according to season. However, although floods in Switzerland are generally limited, they may occur during summers of exceptional rainfall, such as 1954, and, in the past, before the Rhine was regulated between St. Gallen and Liechtenstein, the low-lying lands adjacent to the river were inundated periodically. In the winter, the flow is minimized on account of the freeze-up in the Alps, and in some valleys stream flow may be seriously reduced on account of the creation of high-level reservoirs to serve hydroelectric stations, as in the upper Dixence valley in canton Valais and in the region of the Grimsel pass (upper Aar drainage). Alpine streams have a glacial régime but an abundance of flow only paralleled elsewhere in Europe by the torrents which cascade into the fjords of western Norway. By July the rate of snow-melt dies down and, in view of high temperatures, evaporation is at its maximum.

The Upper Danube Valley

Rising on the eastern slopes of the Black Forest and crossing the Swabian Jura *en route* to Kelheim at the limit of navigation, and so to the narrow valley between the Bohemian massif and the Alpine Foreland of Austria, the Danube has a ' continental ' régime, with a summer maximum flow. Autumn is the season of minimum flow, when the summer rains have decreased. Icing is not uncommon in winter. The flow of the Danube above Vienna is largely conditioned by that of the Alpine tributaries, especially the Iller, Lech, Isar and Inn, for few major streams enter from the north. As far as Regensburg, the régime is similar to that of the upper Rhine; below Passau it is markedly affected by the Inn, but the Alpine régime continues in effect as far as Vienna.

THE NAVIGABLE WATERWAYS OF CENTRAL EUROPE

The part played by the great navigable waterways and related canal systems is dealt with in connection with the economic and industrial development of West Germany, Belgium and the

Netherlands (Fig. 94). The régime of two of the most important of these rivers, namely the Rhine and the Elbe, is of major significance in relation to their relative importance as navigable waterways.

The Rhine. Although a scheme is in progress to make the Rhine

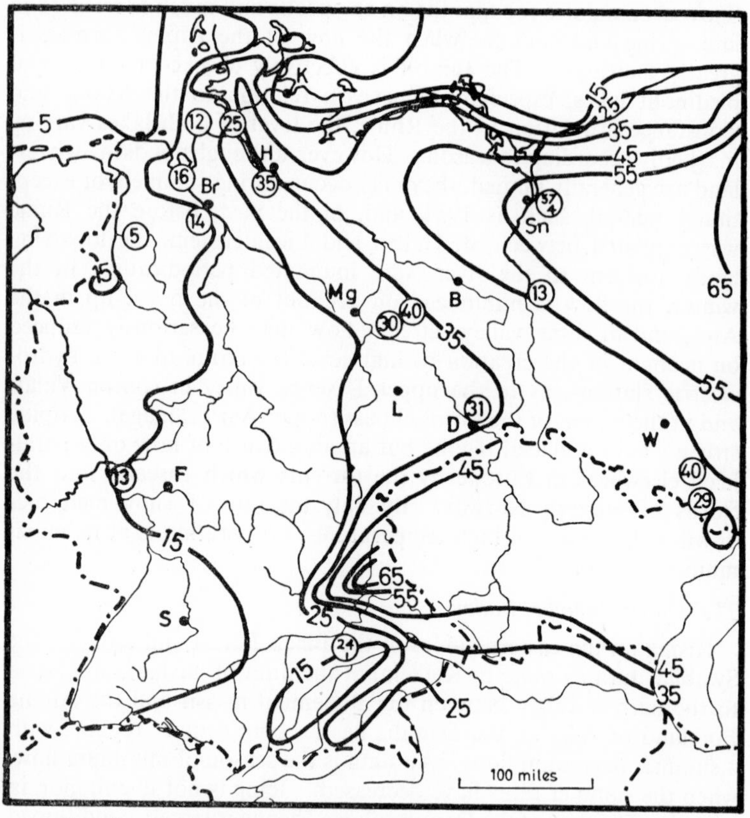

FIG. 9. Central Europe: number of days with ice on waterways.

navigable above Basle as far as the lake of Constance, the Swiss section of the Rhine is of interest from the point of view of navigation only in so far as this Alpine section of the river affects its course below Basle. In face, the Rhine remains an Alpine type river as far as Kehl-Strasbourg and the straightening of its course in the 19th century (Fig. 103) only served to increase its velocity. The Alpine Rhine has a generally regular flow, reinforced by the contributions of the Aar, Reuss and Limmat rivers. At Basle it has an average flow of 1,000 cubic metres per second, reaching a July maximum; the effect of lake Constance, as of the other piedmont lakes on the tributaries, being to retard the June flow, when snow-melt is at its height.   Between Alsace and Baden, the flow is affected by tributaries entering from the Vosges and the Black Forest, such as the Ill, the Wiese and the Kinzig, streams which have a regular ' Hercynian ' régime, reinforced by snow-melt in spring.   The pace of the river slows down at Mannheim-Ludwigshafen where the Rhine is reinforced by the Neckar from the Odenwald. This river has been made navigable up to Heilbronn by means of an elaborate series of locks and weirs.   At the entrance to the gorge at Bingen, the Rhine reaches its maximum in June, where Alpine snow-melt and spring floods are at their height.   Downstream, the Lahn, Sieg, Ruhr and Moselle bring much flood water in spring.   As the Rhine enters the flat country below Cologne the flow slows down and there is some loss by procolation into the river alluvium.   There is a winter maximum at Emmerich, related to a winter rainfall maximum.[1] The Rhine has one of the most balanced régimes in the world and the navigation of the river is only rarely impeded by ice (Fig. 9).

The Elbe.   Rising as the Czech Labe in Bohemia, the Elbe has a lower total volume than the Rhine and a less regular régime.   Its main catchment area is in the *Mittelgebirge* but it is also fed by the Saale from the Thuringian Forest and by minor streams from the Erz-Gebirge and the Harz Mountains.   The *Polabí* is a region of diminished precipitation and considerable summer heat.   The main contributors in Bohemia are the Vltava from the south and the Berounka and Ohře from the west.   The flow of the Elbe is at a maximum in February, when the flow of the Saale is torrential.   In contrast, the Havel coming in from the east is a stabilizing factor, for it flows through a maze of lakes, where the floods of the Spree spread out.   The river is at its minimum in summer, when evaporation is at its height.   Ice causes some trouble to navigation for short periods in most winters, but the position of the Elbe is intermediate in this respect between the Rhine and the Oder, as Fig. 9 illustrates.

REFERENCES

E. de Martonne: *Europe Centrale*, 1931, and P. George and J. Tricart: *L'Europe Centrale*, 1954, are the standard modern references.   An invaluable collection of atlas maps, unfortunately not completed, was being compiled before the last war by N. Krebs, entitled: *Atlas des deutschen Lebensraumes in Mitteleuropa*, 1937.   A useful morphological map is that of A. Waldbaur: *Landformen im Mittleren Europa*, 1 : 2,000,000, 1958.

[1] E. de Martonne: *Europe Centrale*, Géog. Univ. Vol. 4, 1931, p. 73, and A. Demangeon and L. Fébvre: *Le Rhin*, 1935. See also P. George and J. Tricart: *L'Europe Centrale*, Vol. 1, 1954, pp. 195–9.

CHAPTER 3

ASPECTS OF THE HUMAN ECONOMY

THE HUMAN geography of Central Europe today is the end product of centuries of adaptation to a highly complex and varied environment. Here are nearly 110 million people enjoying a reasonably high standard of living, with an ever-increasing population of urban dwellers. Whereas 56 per cent of the population of Germany lived in towns in 1900, the percentage had increased to 71 by 1952 in West Germany, and to 65 per cent in the East. The number of town-dwellers is slightly lower in Belgium (62 per cent) and in the Netherlands (55 per cent). In semi-industrialized Czechoslovakia the figure is 49 per cent and in Austria, where the great city of Vienna accounts for over a quarter of the total population, the percentage is 48. Only in Switzerland, with the highest overall standard of living of all European countries, the figure falls to 30 per cent, a reminder of the State's well-balanced economy and of the dispersed and frequently rural character of Swiss industry.

The population density distribution map (Fig. 10) illustrates in striking fashion the zones of Central Europe with the greatest concentration of settlement, both urban and rural. The lower Rhine-lands, especially the Netherlands, with a record of 828 people to the square mile, and Belgium, with 725, show one of the greatest massings of people in Europe and this is no modern development, as are the concentrations on the coalfields of the Ruhr, the Saar and Saxony, for the Flemish towns have their roots in the prosperous cities famed for their woollen cloth manufacture in the later Middle Ages. Similarly, the high density found along the Rhine valley, from the lake of Constance through the upper Rhine plain and gorge to Cologne, represents a thickening of the concentration characteristic of this fertile inner valley and passage land since Roman times. Other areas, with figures above the mean for Central Europe, include the *Börde* lands of Hanover and Brunswick, where rich soils derived from loess, combined with the rise of modern industry, have enhanced the traditional importance of these regions as centres of farming and trade. The Leipzig ' bay' region, as well as the minor Saxony coalfield developed in modern times, is also part of a belt of high population density spreading from Westphalia along

I. THE MATTERHORN

A triad of rock precipices, glaciers and scree slopes, set in a frame of late summer clouds.

(a) The High Calcareous Alps and the Diablerets *nappes*.

2. THE EFFECT OF ALPINE STRUCTURE ON SCENERY

(b) The Glarner Alps and the Churfirsten eroded monocline from the Säntis.

the foot of the *Mittelgebirge* into the embayment of Upper Silesia, Polish territory since 1945.

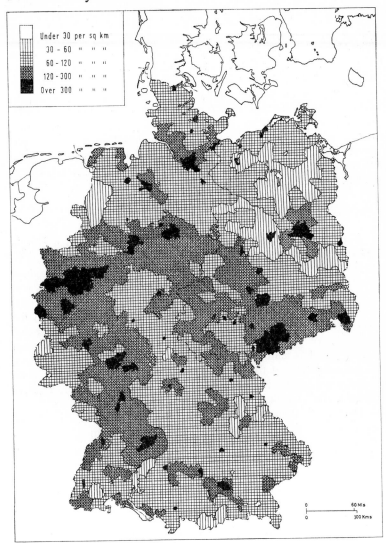

Under 30 per sq km
30 - 60 " " "
60 - 120 " " "
120 - 300 " " "
Over 300 " " "

Fig. 10. Germany, East and West: Density of Population, 1950.

In contrast, the areas which have a low population density include both lowland and highland regions. In the north German lowland, the sterile heath lands of the *Geest* are outstanding, with under 25

C.E.—C

to the square mile. The conurbation of West and East Berlin and the thickly populated lower Elbe and Weser valleys are exceptional to this general picture. In the Alpine lands, the density figure falls to under 12 per square mile, as might be expected, where the Alpine peaks rise above the permanently and temporarily inhabited zones. The Hercynian uplands, with their valley settlements and dispersed industries, as in the Black Forest and the Erz-Gebirge, support a strikingly high density, often over 260 persons to the square mile. Although rural depopulation has been a marked feature of most of Central Europe for the past century, the tendency has been partly checked by the establishment of industries drawing on rural labour, and, in Alpine Europe, dependent on hydro-electric power. The growth of the clock and watch industry of the Jura valleys is an outstanding example of rural location, as are the industries of the pre-war Czech-German Sudetenland.

RURAL SETTLEMENT

Although the urban pattern of Central Europe is to a certain extent a Roman legacy, especially in the Rhine and upper Danube valleys, rural settlement has evolved from the foundations laid by the Germanic and Slavonic tribes at the time of the *Völkerwanderung*. There is, of course, evidence of pre-Roman settlement, especially the Bronze Age pile dwellings on the shores of some of the Swiss lakes and at Meersburg on the lake of Constance; while it is clear that the Celts of Hercynian and Alpine Europe had a knowledge of cereal and flax cultivation as well as of stock rearing. In fact, Dopsch has argued for considerable continuity of settlement from pre-Roman to post-Roman times.[1] especially on the loess terrains of Swabia, the Danube valley and the Rhineland.

The great folk movements of the early Christian Era saw the spread of the Germanic tribes from the northern lowland into the Sambre-Meuse valley, into southern and western Germany and into the Swiss and Bavarian Foreland, by-passing the Hercynian forest barriers which offered a refuge to the Celts, as in the Ardenne and the Black Forest. In the Alps, there seems to have been a similar retreat into the mountain valleys. By A.D. 150 the Batavians had settled in the lower Rhine valley and the recent revelation of the remains of flat-bottomed boats on the floor of the former Zuider Zee, especially on the site of the East Flevoland polder, throws some light on this period. Much infiltration into the Roman Empire

[1] A. Dopsch: *Wirtschaftliche und Soziale Giundlagen der Europäischen Kulturentwicklung*, 2 vols., 1923.

behind the *limes Germaniæ* from the lower Rhine to the upper Danube appears to have taken place before the withdrawal of the Roman legions. With the major advance of the Alemanni, Suevi and Franks into the Rhine, Neckar, Main and Moselle valleys in the 4th and 5th centuries, the Latin language disappeared, but the cultivation of wheat, orchard fruits and the vine seems to have continued. At the same time, the Marcomanni established themselves in place of the Celts in the plain of northern Bohemia. By the 4th century, the Slavs had migrated from eastern Europe along the base of the *Mittelgebirge* to the line of the Elbe-Saale and some penetrated into the upper Main valley. Their movement was more extensive than that of the Germans and their halt along the Elbe marked a turning point in the history of Europe. By the end of the 8th century these large-scale movements were coming to an end and the broad pattern of rural settlement in Central Europe was crystallizing out.

Whereas in the west Germanic tribes inherited the Latin imperial traditions, especially in the Rhine basin and the Alpine Foreland, including superior powers of organization to those of the Slavonic world, beyond the Roman *limes* life was primitive and, especially in the Slav lands, politically rudimentary. By the 15th century, half of Central Europe had been occupied by the Slavs, who settled in the northern lowlands as far as the Elbe and who penetrated up the Save-Drave valleys into northern Carinthia and as far west as the Inn and Adige valleys. Place-name evidence bears witness to this penetration, especially in Carinthia, where such names as Dobratsch and Jauken are of Slavonic origin, in the same way as place names ending in *-ig* in north Germany (Leip*zig*, Dan*zig*, etc.) are typically Slavonic. In the Rhineland, the early Germanic place-name endings are *-heim, -ing, -ingen* and *-wyhl* or *-weier*; these forms occurring abundantly on the plain of Alsace; in Baden in the Kraichgau; in the middle Neckar valley, and in the Alpine Foreland.[1] In these regions, the population flourished and increased rapidly, so that there was an expansion into the fenlands of the lower Rhine valley and into the North German plain, as the early *esch* and *terpen* dry-point villages bear witness.

The later phases of rural settlement, belonging to the *Rodungszeit* associated mainly with the period from the 8th to the 10th century, saw the first major attack on the woodland, although a second phase lasted from the 12th to the end of the 14th century, when wars, pestilence (the Black Death) and the increasing freedom of the

---

[1] A. F. A. Mutton: ' Place Names and the History of Settlement of South-West Germany ', *Geography*, Vol. 23, 1938, pp. 113–19.

peasants led to the desertion of some of these forest clearing settlements, so that they became known as *Wüstungen*[1] or ' deserted villages '. Some of these *Waldhufendörfer* were in existence by the 10th century in the Black Forest and Middle Rhine Highlands, where monastic houses, such as those of St. Blasien, St. Peter and St. Märgen in the *Schwarzwald*, at Fulda east of the Vogelsberg,

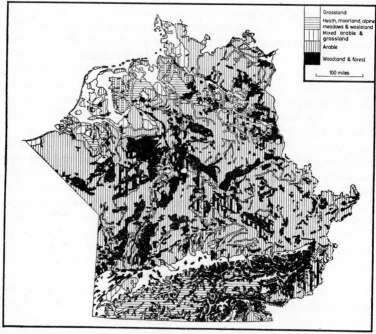

Fig. 11.　Central Europe: land use.

and at Maria-Laach in the Voreifel, as well as at Einsiedeln in canton Schwyz, were responsible for converting much of the forest land to sheep and cattle pasture and arable land. Sometimes there was slow penetration of the Hercynian uplands by German foresters and miners who came at the invitation of Slav princes, as in the Harz and Erz-Gebirge. Other late medieval settlements were made at the expense of marshland and fen, especially by the Flemings who settled in Westphalia and in the *Fläming* in the 12th century. At the same time the Friesians carried out reclamation of the peat fen of the Low Countries and of the North Sea coastlands; while new

[1] G. Pfeifer: ' The Quality of Peasant Living in Central Europe ', contribution to *Man's Rôle in Changing the Face of the Earth*, 1956.

villages, with names ending in -*rodt*, appeared in Hainaut and Brabant. On the heathlands or *Geest* some settlements were also made, after the heath had been destroyed by burning, and these were known as *Esche*.

Since the pioneering work of Meitzen, entitled *Siedelungen und Agrarwesen*, was published at the end of the last century, much work has been done in Germany and elsewhere on the relationship between rural settlement types and field systems. In fact, it has been realized that, apart from the origin of the settlement, its present form may often be related to the type of medieval field economy in that particular district, though the dispersal of farms following extensive 19th century enclosures is frequently responsible, especially in the loess lands. In the poorest regions, that is, the heath, the one-field system developed, with rye as the grain crop. Surrounding the *Esche* or arable land was the rough grazing and moorland, occasionally used for cultivation. This is the equivalent of the in-field and out-field of northern Britain. Such settlements were made on the *Lüneburger Heide* of north Germany and on the heath lands of Overyssel and Gelderland in the north-eastern Netherlands.

On the tractable loam soil regions of central Europe, the usual type of settlement was typically agglomerated, whether in Hesbaye, Limburg, the Rhineland or the Swiss Foreland. This compact type of village was surrounded by open fields, the *Gewannflur*, the essential feature of both the three-field and the two-field system. These arable lands were later divided amongst the peasants, so that each cultivated a series of strips which were parcelled out all over the field and were usually equivalent to a *Morgen* in length, that is, a day's work to plough with a team of oxen. As later settlements were established, these took the form of small hamlets or *Drubbel*, or single farmsteads or *Einzelhöfe*, which survive today in the great chalet structures of the Alps and the Black Forest. This strip pattern, which reaches extremes in areas of dense rural population, as in the Catholic Rhine rift valley, is slowly being superceded by larger fields, more amenable to the tractor and mechanized farming in general.

The forest-clearing settlements of the later Middle Ages assume various forms, as in the northern Black Forest, though they are usually regarded as typically linear, especially where they represented German inroads on Slavonic lands, as in Saxony. Each peasant strip or *Huf* extended from the valley floor to the crest of the ridge; thus combining a single farmstead settlement with a village community organization (Pfeifer). These *Waldhufendörfer* were often

(a) Swiss chalet (Alemannic type, Berne)

(b) Black Forest farmhouse

Fig. 12. Central Europe: four ty

(c) Swiss Engadine house

(d) Slovak Carpathian house

highland rural dwelling.

too remote and unsuitable for the cultivation of grain, the grassland alone being rotated with ploughed land in a *Feldgraswirtschaft*. This emphasis on livestock farming, supplemented by work in the forests or at handicrafts (textiles, glass-making, wood-carving), together with some mining and quarrying, has continued into modern times, though in favourable valleys such as those of the Jura, the Black Forest and the Thuringian Forest, labour has been drawn increasingly into factories. This open-field type of cultivation may still be seen in remote parts of the Middle Rhine Highlands, where sheet villages such as Oberrod and Waldorf in the Taunus are surrounded by fields under strip cultivation (Plate 20(c).[1]

Another type of rural settlement is to be found on the Dutch polders and in the marshlands of the North Sea coasts. The simple draining and dyking of the peat fen was undertaken by the Flemings in the 12th century and these experts were invited to reclaim the Weser marshes behind Bremen in 1106. Marsh villages resemble the forest-clearing type in that they were built in straight lines but along the crest of a dyke. These *Marschhufendörfer* were often able to supplement their earnings from the marsh pastures by trading in wool and fish. These villages contrast with the earlier *terpen* or *wierden* made on artificial refuge mounds above risk of flooding and found especially in Zeeland, Friesland and Groningen. Many of these villages now have a ' ring' character, for, with the progressive drainage of the marshes, farms have been built at the base of the original mound[2], for example Hoogbeintum in Friesland and Marsum in north-east Groningen.

There are two final aspects of the growth of rural settlement which serve to illustrate the general pattern today. These belong to what has been termed the ' colonial' phase. In Alpine Europe it was associated with the spread of the Germanic type of settlement from the Alpine Foreland into the valleys of the Alps and Jura, and sometimes centred round monastic foundations such as those at Füssen in Bavaria, at Disentis in the Vorderrhein valley, at Einsiedeln in Schwyz and at Moutier (Münster) in the Jura. From Bavaria, settlements advanced into the Tyrol, Carinthia and Styria, and today the contrast persists between the orderly Teutonic villages with their strip cultivation and the untidy Slovene settlements, with their crude thatched roofs to the farmhouses and barns.

East of the Elbe, an advance was made after the 10th century, mainly by surplus population from the Rhineland and directed by

[1] H. Uhlig: ' Old Hamlets with Infield and Outfield Systems in Western and Central Europe', *Geografiska Annaler*, Vol. 43, 1961.
[2] *Atlas van Nederland*, 1963.

the Prussian nobility as well as by Cistercian monks who established a number of colonies east of the Rhine in the 12th century.[1] These planned settlements derived their form from traditional types in the west but were adapted to conditions in the east. The *Huf* remained the unit of cultivation but was also a measurable quantity of prosperity. Farm buildings or *Höfe* were built along the sides of a rectangle, a circle (*Rundling*), an almond-shaped space (*Angerdorf*) or along a road through a forest (*Waldhufendorf*). Some villages were laid out on a grid plan and were subsequently fortified, Neu-Brandenburg being an example. Around the settlement, the *Flur* were laid out on the three-field system and the *Hufen* divided into long strips. These long narrow rectangles of cultivation survived until modern times around such settlements as Papenburg in the reclaimed marshlands of the north. The results of post-war changes in the German Democratic Republic have cut right across these long-established traditions. In particular, the *Junker* estates of former East Prussia and Pomerania, dating from the ' reforms ' of the 18th century, have disappeared, and they have now passed to peasant ownership, under a ' planned ' economy. In consequence, the reduction in the size of holdings in the East has now made them more comparable with the West than prior to 1945.

LAND REFORM IN GERMANY AFTER 1945

Size of Holding in Hectares	E. Germany		W. Germany	
	(%) 1939	(%) 1946	(%) 1949	(%) 1960
0–5	9·1	9·7	20·5⎫	54·9
5–20.	31·7	53·4	43·6⎭	
20–50.	22·5	24·0	23·4	37·0
50–100	8·4	7·7	6·3	7·9
100 and over . . .	28·3	5·2	5·8	·2

In eastern Germany, the system of land inheritance differed from that in the Rhineland, for undivided inheritance predominated (*Anerbenrecht*), so that the estates were preserved as a whole, whereas in the Rhineland the system of dividing the estate between each son of the family, a system known as *Realerbteilung*, has resulted in excessive sub-division of the arable land and the cultivation of tiny uneconomic strips. This problem has been examined by

[1] H. Trevor Roper: *The Rise of Christian Europe*, 1965, p. 122 and Fig. 81.

Juillard[1] for Alsace, and the same conditions apply on the eastern side of the Rhine in Baden and in Rhenish Hesse.[2]. In many of the rich loess regions known as the *Gäulandschaften*, smallholdings are also typical, many being under five hectares in extent. However, in the *Börde* lands of the north, much urban and industrial capital has been invested in real estate during the last century and these absentee landlords have developed large-scale production of sugar beet and wheat in Hanover and Brunswick, and of wheat and potatoes, a former major source of foodstuffs for the industrial Ruhr, in former Pomerania (now Polish Pomorze) and East Prussia. In spite of the great increase on Germany's population (from 25 million in 1815 to 66 million in 1935 and again to 75 million in 1963), it has been estimated that 80 per cent of the population is self-sufficient in foodstuffs.

URBAN DEVELOPMENT

The continuity of peasant life in rural Central Europe is paralleled by the persistence of town life throughout the centuries, often having its roots in the Roman conquest and occupation of the Rhine and upper Danube basins. It would appear that the Roman settlement sites from Nijmegen in the Rhine delta lands to Basle and Chur in the upper Rhine valley were continuously occupied during the period of the *Völkerwanderung*. These Roman towns developed along the great roads linking the Rhineland with northern Italy, over the Julier, Splügen and Brenner passes. Chur (Roman *Curia*) lay where the Rhine turns northwards towards the lake of Constance and where the Alpine routes converged on the Splügen pass from Verona and Bergamo. Innsbruck, with a Roman settlement at Vildedina (medieval Wilten) had a similar rôle in relation to the Brenner pass. In the Swiss *Mittelland* of today, towns such as Windisch (*Vindonissa*), Baden, Augst (*Augusta Raurici*) and Basle itself (*Basilea*) all lay on Roman roads linking Chur and Constance with the Rhine valley. At Augst and Windisch, as well as at Avenches near Lausanne, the remains of Roman theatres are still well preserved. In the upper Rhine plain, Roman roads were built parallel with the Rhine along the well-drained terraces, on the left bank through Strasbourg (*Argentoratum*), Speyer, Worms and Bingen to Koblenz (*Confluentes*) and so to the towns of the lower Rhine valley, viz. Cologne (*Colonia Agrippina*), Neuss, Xanten and Nijmegen. On the right bank, the road followed the high gravel

[1] E. Juillard: *La Vie Rurale dans la Plaine de Basse Alsace*, 1953.

[2] G. Pfeifer: ' The Quality of Peasant Living in Central Europe ', *Man's Rôle in Changing the Face of the Earth*, map on p. 257.

terrace at the foot of the Hercynian uplands through Baden-Baden (*Aquæ Sulis*), Heidelberg and Darmstadt to Mainz (*Moguntiacum*), where a major road struck off through Bingen and over the Hunsrück to Trier (*Augusta Treverorum*), an imperial town, where the great sandstone Porta Nigra, the amphitheatre and ruins of the emperor's baths remain today. Trier was a Roman bridge town across the

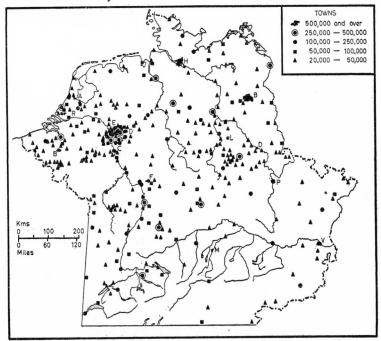

FIG. 13. Central Europe: distribution of urban population.

Moselle, in the same way as Cologne was the crossing point of the Rhine below the point where the *limes Germaniæ* took off at Andernach. On the Danube another important strategic site was at Regensburg, where the Regen joins the main river. Downstream, a Roman fort was established at Passau (*Batava*), at the confluence of the Inn and the Danube, and other trading centres developed at Augsburg, Ulm, Donauwörth and Kempten, related to the routes through the Alpine passes to northern Italy, especially the Brenner and the Reschen-Scheideck (*Rescia*). The lower routes over the Julian and the Carnic Alps were also used to tap the iron ore deposits of Styria and to link Vienna (*Vindobona*) *via* the Semmering pass with Aquileia, at the head of the Adriatic.

With the decay of the Roman *imperium*, there was little urban development until the period A.D. 1000 to 1400, for the Empire of Charlemagne was based on a feudal rural economy and there was little town development, except at Aachen where the romanesque cathedral was founded and where Charlemagne was crowned. This was a period of monastic foundations, as at St. Gallen, Füssen and Fürth, to quote random examples; with castle building, as at Wimpfen on the Neckar; and trading at bridge points and small walled towns such as Soest and Paderborn on the *Hellweg*. The first real towns of the Holy Roman Empire developed in the 10th century on the site of former defensive points, some of which, like Regensburg, were of Roman origin; while others, like Dortmund, Goslar, Würzburg and Bamberg, together with Magdeburg, were post-Carolingian. The 12th century was the period which saw the consolidation of urban rights and privileges in Germany; Cologne becoming a free city in 1106 and Goslar in 1107. The building of a great cathedral at Cologne attracted merchants and traders who settled within the precincts. The period of castle building came in the 13th and 14th centuries, when the ban on castle building was lifted.

The long-distance trade which developed in the later Middle Ages linked the Mediterranean towns with the Baltic and North Sea Hanseatic ports, the ' fair ' towns of Champagne and the ' wool ' towns of Flanders; while the trading cities of the Rhineland, Swabia and the Börde developed either along the guiding lines of river valleys or on the cleared, arable land at the foot of the *Mittelgebirge*. The main orientation of trade was at first broadly east-west, for example from Bruges and Ghent to Aachen; thence to Cologne, Soest and Paderborn along the *Hellweg* and so to Magdeburg on the Elbe, and thence to Frankfurt-on-Oder and Thorn. At the same time, the route through the Rhine valley, linking the Alpine passes with northern Europe, maintained its importance; as did that from Augsburg to Leipzig and Magdeburg. From Vienna other routes led *via* Prague to Dresden, Frankfurt-on-Oder and Stettin. Alternatively highways of trade led *via* the March or Moravian Gate to Cracow, Thorn and Danzig, and southwards *via* the Semmering to Venice.

Although most German towns were founded west of the Elbe by 1400, urban development east of the Elbe belongs to the period of ' colonial ' settlement in the domain of the Slavs. It is estimated that between 1200 and 1400 over 1,500 settlements were made, many on a ' planned ' basis, with a typical chequer-board lay-out. The ideal spacing of these towns was regarded as eight hours' travelling distance apart. Some were developed on earlier Slavonic sites, such as Lübeck in 1158 and Magdeburg; while others were entirely new foundations, such as Thorn and Königsberg. By the end of the Middle Ages, many of these towns had ceased to expand, but it is estimated that, by 1500, the Holy Roman Empire included 3,000 'towns', compared with 15 in the year 1000. While over five-sixths of these contained less than 500 inhabitants, Cologne and Lübeck each had over 30,000 and twelve other towns had over 10,000. There was a rapid increase in urban population up to 1350, then a more gradual increase until 1500, when probably over 15 per cent of the total population lived in towns. The increase continued until the early 17th century, when the Thirty Years War (1618–48) marked a great set-back. By this period, the cities of the Holy Roman Empire had grown to the limit of the medieval walls and these were subsequently pulled down, as in Vienna, Cologne, Basle, etc.

Modern urban expansion, associated with the growth of factory industry and the railway age, came rather late in Germany, in fact mainly after 1870. In consequence, although the population of industrial districts grew rapidly, as in the Ruhr, building was not quite so haphazard as in the industrial towns of Victorian England, and some mining towns, such as Essen, under the patronage of the Krupps family, included a garden city within their limits. The greatest rate of population growth in Germany was between 1870 and 1914, when few new towns were created, but industrial, commercial and residential districts were added to the medieval nucleus. Berlin was greatly enlarged and developed as the capital, first of Brandenburg-Prussia and then of a united Germany. New naval bases also arose, such as Kiel, and outports such as Cuxhaven and Bremerhaven. During the 1939–45 War, most of the industrial towns and also great historic and cultural cities such as Cologne and Dresden, as well as regional centres such as Stuttgart, with its baroque features, were largely obliterated. New streets and concrete blocks have now arisen on the bombed sites and modern 'functional' architecture has come to replace the buildings which were often a legacy from a rich past. Today, the great Gothic cathedral of Cologne dominates the resurrected town, but the medieval streets which led to the Rhine bridges, the Hanseatic quarter and the houses of the Staple (*Stapelhaus*) have gone for ever, as has much of the baroque architecture of Dresden and Stuttgart, to quote three instances.

REFERENCES

The general references are E. de Martonne: *Europe Centrale*, Géog. Univ. Vol. 4, 1930, and P. George and J. Tricart: *L'Europe Centrale*, 1954. Important studies of rural settlement include those of K. Schumacher: *Siedlungs- u. Kulturgeschichte der Rheinlande*, 1921–3, and G. Pfeifer: 'The Quality of Peasant Living in Central Europe', a contribution to *Man's Rôle in Changing the Face of the Earth*, ed. by W. Thomas, Jr., 1956. See also H. C. Darby: The Clearing of the Woodland in Europe', in the same volume. Hugh Trevor-Roper: *The Rise of Christian Europe*, 1965, provides a useful historical perspective. The historical geography of German towns is summarized in two papers by R. E. Dickinson: 'The Development and Distribution of the Medieval German Town', *Geography*, Vol. 27, 1942, as well as in his *The West European City*, 1951, and also in his *Germany*, 1953. There are excellent plans of the chief cities of Central Europe in E. von Seydlitsche's *Geographie*, 1925. *Europe from the Air*, by E. Egli and H. R. Müller, 1959, is a magnificent collection of air photographs.

PART II

REGIONAL AND HUMAN GEOGRAPHY

CHAPTER 4

THE ALPS: GENERAL PHYSICAL RELATIONSHIPS

THE ALPS are the most recent mountain system in Central Europe, as well as the highest (Mt. Blanc, 15,781 ft.). They have proved a classic region for the study of a multiplicity of problems related to both the physical and the human geography of mountainous regions in middle latitudes. Examination of the Alpine orogenesis has led to the concept of *nappe* structures, now well known in other regions of complex mountain building, both Tertiary and Primary, and glaciologists have found in the spectacular Alpine land forms, as well as on the Foreland, a wealth of evidence of mountain and valley glaciation, and also of the deposition work of valley ice.[1] The tectonic features of the Alps have long been known and Switzerland is especially well mapped, in the same way as the French Alps, by the modern Landeskarten, on a scale of 1 : 50,000 with partial coverage on a scale of 1 : 25,000. However, work on Alpine Pliocene and Pleistocene morphology is only just beginning and the effects of the Quaternary glaciation are still a matter for lively discussion, as is the interpretation of Alpine tectonics.[2]

THE PHYSICAL FEATURES OF THE ALPS

The reconstruction of the original structure and relief of the Alps is made almost impossible on account of the erosion of great thicknesses of sediment. Nevertheless, it is apparent that in the Alps the *nappe* structure is a dominant feature, in contrast with the Pyrenees and the Carpathians. These *nappe* folds are particularly

---

[1] W. M. Davis: ' Glacial Erosion in France, Switzerland and Norway ', *Geographical Essays*, 1900, pp. 636–8. E. J. Garwood: ' Features of Alpine Scenery due to Glacial Protection ', *Geographical Journal*, Vol. 36, 1910, pp. 310–39. A. Penck: ' Glacial Features in the Surface of the Alps ', *Journal of Geology*, Vol. 13, 1905, pp. 1–19. C. A. Cotton: *Climatic Accidents in Landscape Making*, Section II: Glaciated Landscapes, pp. 122–340.

[2] H. Gutersohn: ' *Die Schweiz* ', Vol. II, ' Die Alpen, ' 1961.

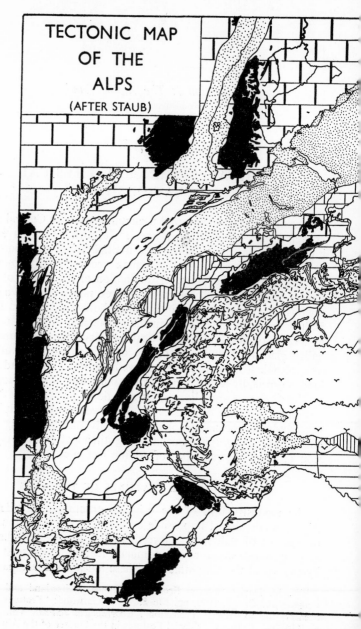

TECTONIC MAP
OF THE
ALPS
(AFTER STAUB)

Fig. 14. Tectonic

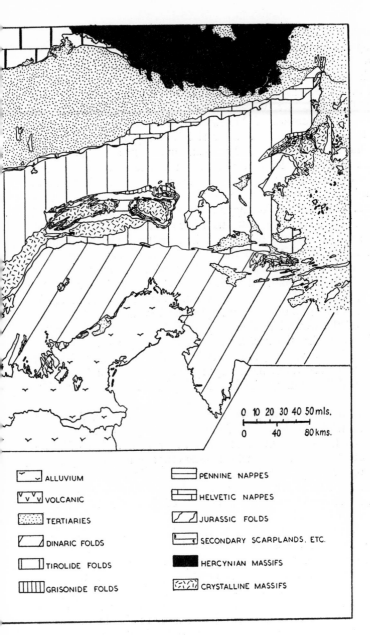

ALLUVIUM

VOLCANIC

TERTIARIES

DINARIC FOLDS

TIROLIDE FOLDS

GRISONIDE FOLDS

PENNINE NAPPES

HELVETIC NAPPES

JURASSIC FOLDS

SECONDARY SCARPLANDS. ETC.

HERCYNIAN MASSIFS

CRYSTALLINE MASSIFS

0 10 20 30 40 50 mls.

0 40 80 kms.

striking in the western Alps and they appear, for example, in cliff exposures in the Diablerets and also along the shores of the Urnersee branch of lake Lucerne at Flüelen, as well as in the Churfirsten north of the Walensee. The western French Calcareous Alps also exemplify this feature, where their alignment is controlled by the crystalline 'windows' of Mercantour, Pelvoux and Belledonne, lying to the east. The central or Helvetic *nappes* extend from the Dora Baltea valley and the Mt. Blanc massif to a line from lake Como to the upper Rhine at Chur. In this zone, the *nappes* frequently override the Hercynian massifs and the pre-Alpine zone of autochthonous folds, which is so important in France, is very much reduced. In front of the *nappe* zone is a narrow band of folded *molasse*, but behind this rise the *Flysch* and limestone Pre-Alps, which sweep across the piedmont lake zone from Geneva through Thun, Brienz, Lucerne and the Walensee to Liechtenstein. The *nappe* structure may be traced southwards as far as the foothills of the north Italian plain; the Hercynian 'windows' alone rising above this zone in Mt. Blanc, the Aar and the St. Gotthard massifs. On the southern margin of the Alpine arc lies the 'root' belt, the source of the central Alpine *nappes*, and here the highly metamorphosed rocks, the *schistes lustrés*, lie nearly vertically, as in the Dora Baltea valley (val d'Aosta) and the Örtler massif. East of lake Maggiore, the Dinaric Alps form a widening band of folded and faulted limestones, lake Garda lying in a major asymmetrical syncline.

East of the lake Como–Chur line, the eastern Alps or Austrides begin and these east–west folds form the greater part of the Austrian Alps. To the south, the Dolomites occur in a region of autochthonous folds and they include some eruptive regions, especially in the upper Adige valley. In Austria, the Dinaric folds cover a third of the Alpine arc and are succeeded northwards by the root belt of the Austrian *nappes*. About half of the eastern Alps belong to the Austrides and, to the north, lies a narrow belt of *Flysch*. The Hercynian massifs of the western Alps are absent from the surface, except for the Semmering 'window' in Styria, and the Austride *nappes* cover the older Helvetic folds, except where the Pennine *nappes* are revealed in the Lower Engadine and Hohe Tauern 'windows' (Fig. 14). The Swiss school of Alpine geologists, represented by Lugeon, Staub and Argand, regard the eastern Alps as a region where there has been the maximum piling up of *nappes*, whereas these folds have largely been eroded in the west, but this view is contested by Gignoux,[1] as well as more recently by P. Veyret.

[1] P. George and J. Tricart: *L'Europe Centrale*, Vol. 1, p. 97.

Alpine relief is remarkable for the contrasts presented between the deep, often glacially overdeepened valleys, which are frequently entrenched to a depth of over 3,000 ft., and the great uplifted massifs. The highest ranges and peaks are formed of crystalline rocks, notably Mt. Blanc (15,781 ft.), the Aar massif (Finsteraar-horn, 14,025 ft.) and Pelvoux (13,460 ft.). Other dominant peaks, but outside the zone of the Hercynian ' windows ', are also granitic or schistose, such as the Matterhorn (14,669 ft.) and Monte Rosa (15,298 ft.) in the Pennine Alps, the Piz Bernina (13,303 ft.) and the Gross Glockner (12,784 ft.). In contrast, the sedimentary rocks form ranges of somewhat lesser height, Triassic limestones pre-dominating in the east, but Jurassic and Cretaceous rocks in the west. These ranges include the Bernese Oberland peaks (Jungfrau, 13,634 ft.) and the Zugspitze (9,720 ft.). The main Alpine streams often show adjustment to structure, notably the upper Inn between the Karwendel and the Stubai and Tuxer Alps, the Brenner depres-sion between the last two ranges, and the Adige valley between the crystalline rocks of the Adamello group and the Triassic rocks of the Dolomites to the east. In the sedimentary zones, monoclinal relief is very typical and appears in the Grande Chartreuse, north-east of Grenoble, at Churfirsten overlooking the Walensee in Graubünden, and on the slopes of the Dachstein in Austria. This feature does not appear so conspicuously on the Italian slope. In the eastern Alps, the resistant dolomitic limestones often develop a tabular form, with steep slopes, as in the type region of the Dolomites and in the Salzkammergut. In eastern Switzerland, the precipitous slopes of Churfirsten descend to the shores of the Wal-ensee and they appear to correspond with a fault line escarpment, though it has also been suggested that the even sky line may represent a Miocene erosion surface (' Rax landscape '). In the pre-Alpine zone, the ranges are frequently asymmetrical and are divided by deep longitudinal trenches, such as that of the Pays d'Enhaut, dominated by the Gummfluh peak.

As Tricart points out,[1] the fundamental feature as far as Alpine relief is concerned is the way in which individual massifs are picked out by the deeply incised valleys. Thus, in the Savoy Alps, the sub-Alpine depression, followed in part by the Drac and the Isère in Grésivaudan, lies 3,000 ft. below the Calcareous Alps of the Grande Chartreuse, etc., and the High Alps. Similarly, the upper valleys of the Rhine, Rhône and Reuss form a major physical divide between the Swiss Calcareous Alps and the Pennine, St. Gotthard and Aar massifs. In Austria, the upper Inn, like the

<hr>

[1] P. George and J. Tricart: *L'Europe Centrale*, Vol. 1, p. 105.

Salzach and the Enns, follows great longitudinal trenches.   On the southern slope, valleys such as the Dora Baltea penetrate to the eastern foot of Mt. Blanc, the upper Ticino to the St. Gotthard, while the upper Adige cuts back to the drainage divide of the Brenner.   The massifs of the Alps are also isolated by valleys cut transversely to the main axis of the folds, notably that of the Rhône below Martigny, the Reuss below Andermatt, and the Aar below the Grimsel pass.   There is also some local convergence of drainage, as upon the branching lake of Lucerne and upon lake Maggiore. Some lakes lie in longitudinal trenches scoured by valley glaciers, such as Thun and Brienz, the Sarner-See between the Brünig pass and lake Lucerne, and the Walensee between the lake of Zürich and the upper Rhine.   Some valleys trend obliquely through the Alps, like the Swiss section of the Inn valley in the Upper Engadine, the Landquart valley in the Prätigau between Landquart on the upper Rhine and Klosters; while in Austria the upper valleys of the Lech and the Isar appear to be unrelated to rock structure.   The perpendicular axis is represented by lake Constance, lying in a zone of faulting, with local vulcanism and thermal springs (the Hegau), but such fault-guided features are rare in the Alps.   Many valleys appear to be related to differential rock structure, such as the Liassic trench of Grésivaudan, and also that of the Mürz, Enns and Salzach. Post-glacial drainage in the Alps is seldom superimposed, a rare example occurring in Salzburg, where the Salzach river leaves the broad trench of the Pinzgau below Zell-am-See and proceeds through a wild defile in the Pongau.[1]   Here the Salzach appears to have been diverted by glacial plugging north of the present lake at Zell-am-See.   Most Alpine valleys experienced Quaternary glaciation but river erosion has subsequently modified their form, especially where terracing is pronounced.

The Alps are a region of rapid surface erosion, as spectacular events marked by rock slides, avalanches, torrential floods and landslides frequently bear witness.   Today, flowing water including melting snow and ice, frost and torrential erosion are the chief agents of denudation, with glaciers playing a minor rôle.   The land forms resulting from the Quaternary glaciation are being continually modified.   Most valleys show the typical glacial ' staircase ' longitudinal profile and the side valleys ' hang ' in relation to the main valley, the stream leaving the lateral valley through a deep chasm. These post-glacial gorges frequently make the approach to the main valley from the side valley very tortuous and difficult, notable ex-

[1] A. Coleman: ' The Terraces and Antecedence of a Part of the River Salzach', *Trans. Inst. Br. Geographers*, Vol. 25, 1958, pp. 119–34.

amples occurring where the Trient stream joins the Rhône below Martigny, and where the Navigzanze enters the Rhône from the Val d'Anniviers, opposite Sierre. Above Thusis, on the Hinter Rhine, the Via Mala gorge has presented a fierce obstacle to progress between the Splügen pass and Chur since Roman times. It is a notable feature that the greatest difficulty in crossing the Alpine barrier lies in gaining access to the passes rather than in crossing them, a striking instance being that of the Schöllenen gorge of the Reuss below Andermatt (Devil's Bridge), at the approach to the St. Gotthard pass, and the Via Mala approach to the Splügen. The lower ends of the main valleys are usually regions of alluvial deposition; large detrital fans marking the break of slope as at Meiringen on the Aar and at Interlaken, where the Lütschine has built up an extensive delta dividing lakes Thun and Brienz. In the past, torrents have spread sheets of gravel over these flats, thus impeding drainage. Today, streams are usually regulated and confined between stone banks or dykes to prevent flooding. Much former marsh land has been drained and reclaimed for pasture and crop land, as in the Rhine valley between Liechtenstein and St. Gallen, and also in the Linthtal in Glarus, between the Klausen pass and the Walensee.

Within the Alps, many valleys show an alternation of cutting down and infilling, rock steps or *verrous* alternating with broad basins or *ombilics*. The Swiss Engadine illustrates this feature very well, though the ' treads ' are partly occupied by the paternoster lakes of Sils, Silvaplana and St. Moritz. The sides of the valleys show signs of rapid erosion, both where the rocks are coherent (limestone and granite), often forming precipices (Churfirsten, Dolomites), and where the material is less coherent (marls, schists, glacial drift). In these latter regions, landslides are common, as along the Achensee shores and at Flims, west of Chur, where an interglacial rock flow has blocked a valley over 4 miles long and 440 yards wide.[1]. In such valleys, the transverse profile becomes a sharp ' V ', as in the west-east defile of Unterschächental, east of Altdorf and below the Klausen pass. In places, the course of a stream may be blocked by boulders, and, as the river may be unable to move them, rock pavements form, as in the Vils gorge in the Allgäu Alps. Erosion is particularly active where bare rock has been exposed by avalanches or by rock slides and where steep grassy slopes have been overgrazed. Such gulleyed slopes are especially conspicuous in regions of seasonal drought, as on the Mediterranean slope of the Alps, notably in Haute Maurienne

[1] J. Früh: *Geographie der Schweiz*, Vol. 1, p. 203.

(upper Arc valley).   In the humid Alps, there is usually a continuous covering of forest or grass to check run-off, and the construction of irrigation ditches or *bisses* through alpine meadows is a frequent feature, these pastures often yielding a hay crop on incredibly steep slopes.[1]

Glacial features

The Alps are the richest in glaciers of all the mountain ranges in Europe, excluding Norway, but the existing ones are small compared with their Pleistocene predecessors.   Most lie above 8,000 ft., though tongues descend to lower levels, such as the Rhône, Grimsel and Chamonix glaciers.   The *névé* or *Firn* zone descends to 8,500 ft. on the northern side of the Swiss and Austrian Alps but is higher on the southern slopes and also in regions of lesser precipitation. The largest glaciers persist in the Ötztal and Hohe Tauern regions of Austria, where the Pasterze glacier descends from the Gross Glockner for a distance of nearly 20 miles; whereas the Aletsch glacier, in the Aar massif, attains a length of only 11 miles.   There has been a marked retreat of the Alpine glaciers during the present century, the shrinkage of the Rhône glacier revealing the rock step down which it descends above Gletsch.   Terminal and lateral moraines may extend some distance below the existing glacier, as below the Morteratsch glacier in the Bernina Alps.   The extent of the great Würm glaciers may be traced over much of the Alpine Foreland and also in the Klagenfurt basin in Carinthia, as well as in the Piedmont zone of the Italian lakes.   Some little glaciers remain in rock basins or *cirques*, as below the Jungfrau and the Zugspitze, but many of these partially enclosed *cirques* now contain only basin lakes, such as the Riffelsee below the Riffelhorn.   Some glaciers are left hanging above an overdeepened trench, like that at Les Bossons above Chamonix, and some survive in deep corridors opening northwards, where ablation is at a minimum, like the Triglav glacier in the Julian Alps.   In the final stage of melting, the glacier may be largely covered by rock débris and dirt moraine, as at Grindelwald.   There are a few ice fields in the Alps, such as La Plaine Morte in the Wildstrubel district and the Karleisfelder of the Dachstein.

Although increasing knowledge of pre-glacial erosion tends to minimize the part played by Alpine glaciers in the development of relief, yet everywhere there is evidence of the effect of the Pleistocene ice on Alpine land forms.   The main Alpine valleys are typically flat-floored, with steep slopes up to broad shoulders (the *auge*),

[1] E. H. Carrier: *Water and Grass*, 1932, pp. 220 and 269.

and a ' U ' cross profile. The Lauterbrunnen valley, extending from the northern foot of the Jungfrau to Interlaken, is a classic example, and so are the Val de Chamonix and the Zillertal, below Mayrhofen, in the Tyrol. Valleys showing a broken longitudinal profile, divided into a series of treads by rock bars or *verrous*, have already been mentioned. Apart from the Engadine example, the Kaprun valley below the Gross Glockner also shows these features and here the *verrou* at Limberg is the foundation of the recently completed barrage. Many main and side valleys end in *cirques* and these are dominated by rock ridges or *arêtes*. Although the typical frost-shattered peak is horn shaped like the Matterhorn and the Gross Glockner, there are many other forms, ranging from the massifs of Mt. Blanc and Monte Rosa to the tabular forms of the Dolomites and the Diablerets. The panorama of the Alps from the air reveals this majestic variety in unforgettable fashion.

ALPINE LAND FORMS

The summits of the Alps rise towards the main axis of the range more steeply than do the valleys, so that these become deeply incised, like the Aar above Meiringen. The intra-Alpine valleys, like the upper Rhine, Rhône, Inn and Adige, have very long slopes, often descending for more than 4,000 ft. The Pre-Alps are lower and the valleys less deeply cut. The western Alps appear to be more mature and more accidented than the eastern Alps, where the Miocene surface is much more in evidence (' Rax landscape '), notably in the Karwendel range north of Innsbruck, and in the Drau ranges of Carinthia, where accordance of summit levels is very marked. In Switzerland this feature is rare, the Churfirsten providing an exceptional example.

The crystalline massifs dominate the High Alps. They include both autochthonous and displaced rocks. These highly resistant rocks are sometimes eroded into needle-like peaks (Aiguilles Rouges), sometimes into rounded summits (Mt. Blanc), and sometimes into pyramidal peaks (Matterhorn). On account of their great diurnal temperature ranges as the result of high relief, these regions are the scene of rapid erosion favoured by mechanical weathering, especially by frost. Slopes are very steep, often exceeding 40°, and much scree and rock débris accumulate at the base, notably on the Flüela pass between Davos and Zernez, in the Lower Engadine. and on the north-facing slope of the Schächental east of Altdorf,

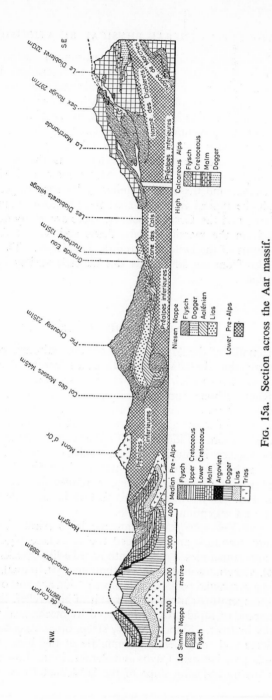

Fig. 15a. Section across the Aar massif.

At the greatest heights and on many of the cols, ice and *névé* preserve the glacial land forms and in these regions these features are best exemplified.   The very scale of the High Alps has hindered the disappearance of the ice, and freshness of land forms is not incompatible with violence of erosion.[1]   Whereas the granitic peaks weather readily into jagged ridges and needles, the gneiss gives rise to more massive forms, while the more easily eroded *schistes lustrés* readily break down into scree-covered slopes.   These may form good summer pastures above the forest zone but it is in this lower zone that landslides frequently take place, while avalanches originate above the tree-line in the zone of spring and summer snow-melt.

The limestone and dolomitic massifs are almost as extensive as the crystalline regions.   They form the high points of the great ranges which themselves are only second to the High Alps in elevation.   The High Calcareous Alps include the Bernese Oberland dominated by the Jungfrau, the Dolomites, and the northern ranges of the Tyrol and Salzburg, especially the Salzkammergut.   Except where marble occurs, as in the Dolomites and the Bernina Alps, the rocks are strongly stratified, the thick beds forming tabular masses, often with vertical cliffs, and the thin beds terraced slopes, especially where limestone alternates with beds of marl, as in the Dolomites.   These calcareous massifs are developed both on uniform and on varied rocks, the homogeneous outcrops developing land forms dependent on solubility and weathering along joints and fissures.   In strongly jointed regions, cliffs develop in shattered form, with boulders at the foot, but, in regions of strong solubility, karst features are apparent, including gorges, caverns and underground drainage.   Such a landscape may have developed in Pliocene times, after which the landscape was ' fossilized ' by the deposition of detritus to be later exhumed, especially in interglacial periods.   These regions are often devoid of vegetation and form high-level stony deserts, like the Totengebirge in the Salzkammergut, lying at 6,000 ft., and the Plaine Morte in the Wildstrubel.   In contrast, the heterogeneous massifs show an alternation of limestones and marls and they have been the scene of selective erosion since the Pleistocene.   These features characterize the Pre-Alps of Switzerland, where the crests of the ranges run parallel and are divided by deep valley trenches, like that of the Sarine (Pays d'Enhaut) and the Simmental.   Pyramidal peaks are often found here, sometimes where the beds are nearly turned on end, like the Gummfluh overlooking the village of Château d'Œx, but some also occur in the regions

[1] P. George and J. Tricart: *L'Europe Centrale*, Vol. 1, p. 123.

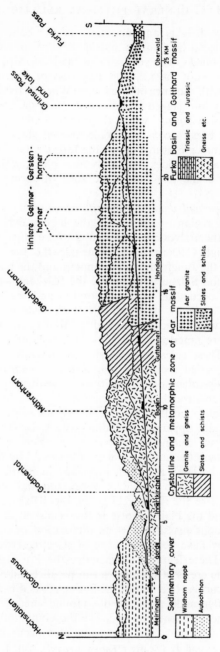

Fig. 15b. Section across the Col des Mosses.

of the great *nappes*, as in the Diablerets. The Säntis is an example of an asymmetrical peak where the relief is inverted, and in the Prätigau, between Landquart and Klostersplatz, monoclinal ridges dominate the valley.

The ' *Flysch* ' and ' *molasse* ' *ranges* are characterized by fairly subdued relief on the northern margin of the Alps, though the Rigi forms a sharp peak overlooking the lake of Lucerne. This zone of Tertiary conglomerates, sandstones and marls widens from west to east and extends from north of lake Geneva through the zone of piedmont lakes, including Lucerne, into Vorarlberg and so across the northern Austrian Alps to the Wienerwald behind Vienna. There are seldom high peaks in this zone but rather rounded eminences with convex summits, though these rarely rise above forest zone. Some of the *Flysch* beds are involved in the Helvetic *nappes* and alternate with beds of limestone and marl. Frequently broad basins develop between the limestone ridges at the head of the valley and the deep trench cut into the marls, as in the Sarine valley between the Wildhorn and the Gummfluh. Such regions favoured medieval clearance of the forest and pastoral settlement, as again in the Pays d'Enhaut. In Austria, these Pre-Alps are mainly forested, with larch and spruce on the higher slopes and beech on the gentler, lower levels.

The *basins and ranges of the south-eastern Alps* form a distinctive type of region. Here mountain ranges with a general elevation of 6,000 ft. divide broad, sunken basins and valley trenches developed on Eocene deposits but often mantled with Pliocene and Pleistocene material. These are regions of strong vertical movements, giving rise to rigid mountain blocks, like the Koralp of Carinthia, dividing the Klagenfurt-Villach basin from that of Graz. In Styria, the Gleiner and Fischbach Alps form similar block ranges and they dominate the Mur-Mürz-Semmering trench.

The *Alpine Foreland.* Between the Alps and the folded Jura, the Black Forest, the scarplands of Swabia and the Bohemian massif lies a geosyncline, where material eroded from the Alps has accumulated, though Tertiary rocks also enter locally into the build of the Foreland, especially in Switzerland and Upper Austria. Nevertheless, the region served as a ' fluvio-glacial piedmont ' (Tricart) in Pleistocene times and its surface features depend largely on the varying cover of glacial and fluvio-glacial drift deposits. The Foreland is almost pinched out between the southern end of the Jura and the lake of Geneva, but it sweeps across Central Switzerland and so into Upper Bavaria and Upper Austria, where it narrows again between the eastern Alps and the Bohemian massif.

The glacial and post-glacial features are seen at their maximum in Upper Bavaria, where Penck and Brückner first recognized the four Alpine glacial phases.   Here only the Würm moraines remain little modified, whereas those of the Riss phase are reduced to low hills,

Ridge developed on steeply dipping sedimentaries

Pyramidal peak – Bietschhorn from Lötschtalgraf

Block peak – Schwarzhorn, Valais

'Nappe' folding – Churfirsten, from Wallensee

Detrital fans

Drusberg, from Zürich

Fig. 16. Types of Alpine peak.

where not incorporated in those of the Würm advance.   Usually the two types of moraine are divided by some 9 to 12 miles, leaving little dissected plateaux between.   The Würm moraines frequently form an amphitheatre of hills, some 300 ft. high, and this may impound a lake, such as those of Chiem, Würm and Ammer.   These lakes are overlooked by the steep wall-like slope of the moraine (*Zungenbecken*), and this is often partly cut into terraces marking stages in the shrinkage of the lake.   The Foreland is also characterized by sheets of boulder clay, scattered with erratics, and north of lake Constance drumlin ridges abound, while eskers occur in the region of the Chiem See.   In front of the moraines, fluvioglacial gravels (*Deckenschotter*) spread out in wide sheets towards the upper Rhine and Danube.   These gravels have been cut into terraces by the long tributaries such as the Reuss, Lech and Iller, which cross the Foreland in broad trenches.   The highest terraces are those of Günz and Mindel date, but the Riss moraines form the *Mittelterrassen* and are frequently covered by loess deposits.   There are also stretches of sand and peat, the latter giving rise to bogs, such as those at Dachau and Erdinger.

The Foreland is also partly formed of *Molasse*, a soft calcareous sandstone of Oligocene-Miocene age, and also of *Nagelfluh*, an Oligocene conglomerate.   These rocks give rise to heights in the Swiss Foreland of between 2,500 and 4,000 ft., rising to 4,619 ft. in the Napf plateau between Lausanne and Aarau.   Towards the Alps, the *Nagelfluh* deposits form considerable hills, as between lakes Thun and Lucerne, and these ridges are deeply dissected.   *Nagelfluh* also forms steep hills around the margins of the piedmont lakes, such as Zürich, the shores of which are abrupt, as the names of some of the villages bear witness (Kilch*berg*, Herrli*berg*).   In Bavaria the *Molasse* and *Nagelfluh* form local east–west ridges, as in the Allgäu, but these features assume more significance in Upper Austria, where they underlie the Hausruck plateau, and here the Tertiaries are known locally as *Schlier*.

The Folded Jura.   The outermost Alpine folds are represented in the crescentic ridge of the Jura mountains on the frontier between France and Switzerland.   They are a type region for the study of simple and regular Miocene folding, where the valleys are eroded along synclines and the ridges are anticlinal folds.[1]   Local Pleistocene ice caused the development of *combes* in the higher anticlinal ridges and there is a striking contrast between these features and the generally even sky lines at about 6,000 ft.   The longitudinal valleys contrast sharply with the gorges or *cluses* cut transversely through the ridges by streams such as the Schüss above Biel.   The scenery changes towards Basle, where the relief is tabular or gently undulating.   Here the Jurassic limestones were faulted in Oligocene

[1] H. Gutersohn: *Geographie der Schweiz*, 3 vols., Vol. I: ' Jura ', 1958.

times, when the Rhine rift valley subsided, and minor rift valleys occur in the vicinity of Basle and the Sundgau, though many of these features are buried beneath *Molasse* and Pleistocene drift.

REFERENCES

The chief regional studies of the Alps are to be found in the two works of E. de Martonne: *Les Alpes*, 1926, and *Europe Centrale*, Géog. Univ., Vol. 1, 1931; in J. Früh's three volumes, *Geographie der Schweiz*, 1930–8; N. Krebs: *Die Ostalpen u. das Heutige Österreich*, 2 vols., 1928, and P. George and J. Tricart, *L'Europe Centrale*, 2 vols., 1954. Apart from the geological studies of the Alps by Heim, Sölch, Penck, Brückner and others, work on the evolution of the Alps has been summarized in L. W. Collet: *The Structure of the Alps*, 1927, and again in E. Bailey: *Tectonic Essays, mainly Alpine*, 1935. Parts of M. Gignoux: *Géologie Stratigraphique*, 4th ed., 1950, are also relevant, and a useful work in German is that of W. von Seidlitz: *Entstehen u. Vergehen der Alpen*, 1934. The geological and tectonic map of R. Staub is invaluable, as are the Swiss *Geotechnische Karte der Schweiz*, 4 sheets, 1930–7, in colour, scale 1: 200,000, with useful inset maps. The Swiss Dufour, Siegfried and the modern *Landeskarte* editions of the national topographic maps on a scale of 1 : 50,000 are outstanding examples of cartography. Switzerland is also covered by a series of geological and also vegetation maps on a scale of 1 : 200,000.

(a) Cloud filled trench of the Rhine between the Säntis and the Rhætian Alps.

3. TEMPERATURE INVERSION IN THE ALPS

(b) Early morning clouds in the Zillertal, above Mayrhofen, Tyrol.

(a) Ice flowers floating on the Dischmabach, near Davos.

4. THE WINTER FREEZE IN THE ALPS

(b) Snow-bound village of Sertig, near Davos.

CHAPTER 5

SWITZERLAND: GENERAL AND ECONOMIC SURVEY

SWITZERLAND HAS a special place in both the physical and human geography of Central Europe. Indeed Siegfried has described this vital little country as 'the heart' of Europe. Like Austria, the state has mainly an Alpine environment, though it has a larger share of the Alpine Foreland or *Mittelland*, where the majority of the population, both urban and rural, finds its means of existence. This 'plateau' region, which lies between the Alps and the Jura, is in fact a varied but relatively fertile area, especially where glacial drift deposits and occasionally loess overlie the solid rock, and the region is one of intensive farming, including polyculture as well as dairy and stock farming. Industrial sites are scattered over the region, partly in view of ready access to hydro-electric power, and the main Swiss towns are found within this region or along its margin in the piedmont lake zones of the Alps and the Jura; the frontier town of Basle, on the upper Rhine, being the major exception.

Lacking in well-defined frontiers, except for the upper Rhine, the lakes of Constance and Geneva, and the crest of the Pennine Alps, Switzerland lies on one of the major hydrographic divides in Europe. In the region of the St. Gotthard massif are the sources of the Rhône, the Reuss and the Vorder Rhine, while the Ticino drains southwards to the Mediterranean. The neutrality of Switzerland dates from 1848 and is reflected in its command of the great cross-roads of Europe, between the Rhineland and northern Italy, eastern France and the Danubian lands. Switzerland extends for a distance of 216 miles from the French frontier west of Geneva to the Austrian frontier on the upper Rhine above lake Constance, and has a maximum north–south extent of 137 miles, covering in all an area of 15,940 sq. miles. The national territory is divided into twenty-two cantons which today form the Helvetic Confederation, with the federal capital at Berne. Each canton enjoys a considerable measure of autonomy and four of the smallest cantons (Glarus, Appenzell (divided into Outer and Inner Rhoden) and Unterwalden) retain the *Landsgemeinde* which takes the form of an annual mustering of the male population (no woman is allowed to vote) to elect the Landammann (head of the canton) for the coming year.

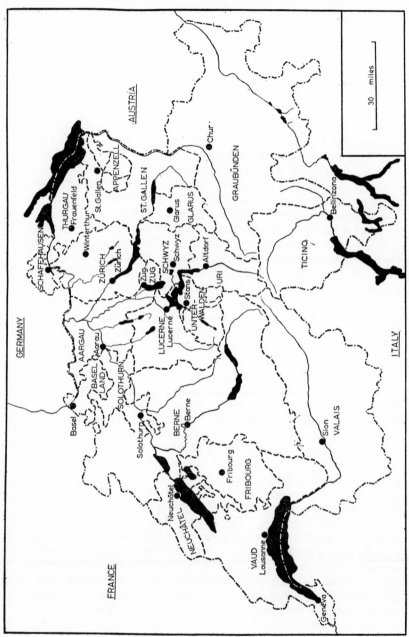

FIG. 17 The Swiss cantons and canton capitals

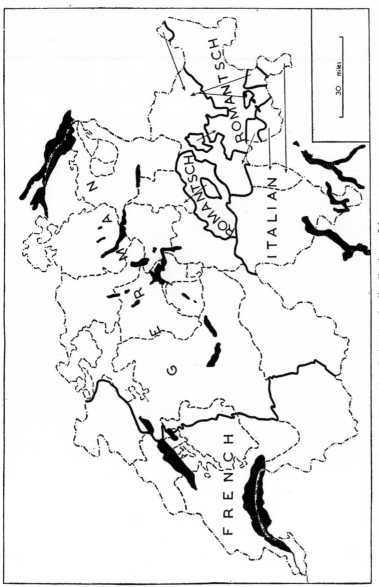

FIG. 18. Switzerland: distribution of languages.

The franchise has, however, recently been granted to women in four cantons, including Geneva and Baselland.

The population of Switzerland has nearly doubled during the last hundred years, the total population being only 2,507,170 in 1860 compared with 5,429,061 in 1960. In 1957, there were nine towns with a population of over 50,000, the largest being Zürich (438,800), followed by Basle (233,500), Geneva (175,500) and Berne (166,600). The industrial town of Winterthur totals 87,000 and the lake resort of Lucerne exceeds 67,400. Four official languages are recognized: German is spoken by 72 per cent of the population,

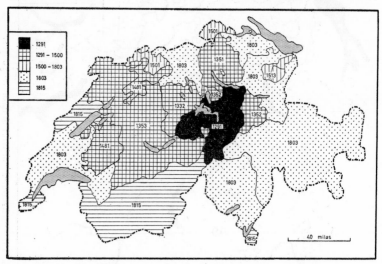

FIG. 19. Switzerland: growth of the Swiss Confederation.

French by 20 per cent and Italian by 6 per cent while Romantsch is the language of the Swiss Engadine, the valley of the Vorder Rhine and of south-eastern Graubünden (canton Grisons). The origin of the Swiss Federation dates from 1291, when the three Forest Cantons Uri, Schwyz and Unterwalden) united around the shores of the *Vierwaldstättersee* (Lucerne joining in 1332). Eight other cantons joined the League by 1353 and the number totalled thirteen in 1513. The remaining cantons came in ' by a process of aggregation ' (Siegfried), freedom from the Holy Roman Empire being achieved in 1648, at the Treaty of Westphalia. The last cantons to join the Federation were Graubünden (Grisons) and Ticino (Tessin) in 1803, Valais and Geneva in 1815 (Fig. 19). Under the leadership of

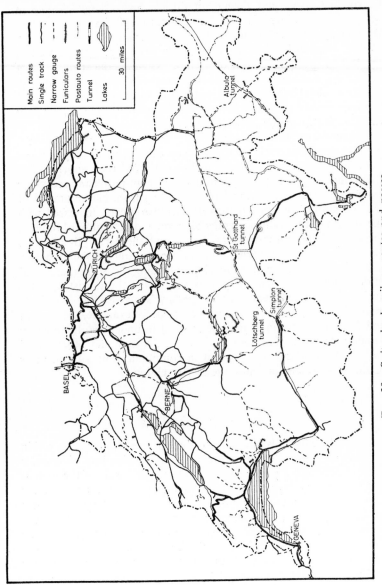

FIG. 20.   Switzerland: railway routes and passes.

Calvin in Geneva and Zwingli in Zürich, Switzerland adopted in general the doctrines of the Reformation, though the region around the lake of Lucerne remains today predominantly Roman Catholic, as does western Switzerland (Solothurn, Fribourg, etc.), as well as the Italian-speaking canton of Ticino. Geneva, the stronghold of Calvinism, adheres to the Swiss Reformed Church, as does the city of Chur, the 'county town' of canton Graubünden, where the Catholic bishop of Chur played a leading part in the struggle with the Habsburgs in the 17th century.

The modern rôle of Switzerland as a constitutionally neutral state, a bastion of democratic institutions and of freedom of religious and political thought and expression, has enhanced the importance of the country out of all proportion to its size, man-power and economic resources. Her international rôle, resulting from her command of the 'carrefour' of Central Europe, has also greatly increased with the growth of rail traffic using the Simplon and St. Gotthard tunnels, the most frequented modern routes through the Alps. In addition, an excellent system of mountain roads, second only to the mountain railways as feats of engineering skill, including the St. Bernard road tunnel opened in 1964, has greatly stimulated the tourist industry during the present century. Switzerland's accessibility has been revolutionized, too, in the jet age, now that, for example, the Geneva and Zürich air terminals may be reached in under two hours from London Airport. Through the B.E.A., Swissair and other world airlines, Switzerland is at present in communication with all parts of the world including now the Soviet Union.

PHYSICAL FEATURES

The surface features of Switzerland result from her position within the Alpine fold mountain system, of which the Jura mountains form structurally a part. Switzerland includes some of the highest and also the youngest mountains in Europe, as the result of the intense and complex folding of the sedimentary material laid down in the Tethys (or proto-Mediterranean sea) in Oligocene-Miocene times. As these sediments moved forward under intense pressure towards the resistant massifs of the Vosges and the Black Forest, they were folded into a series of *nappes*, and at the same time fractured and overthrust (Figs. 15 and 16). In consequence of the intense erosion of these complex features, the relief of the Swiss Alps is everywhere sharply accentuated, ridges are often knife-edged, the mountain summits are frequently eroded into pyramidal or

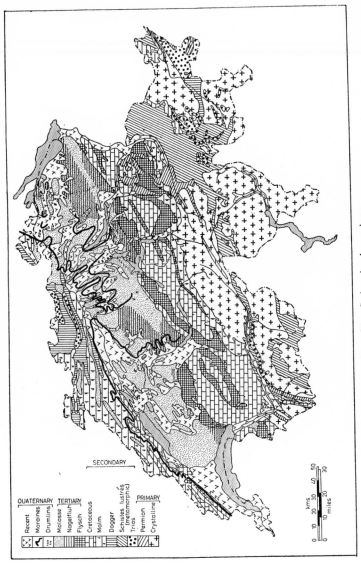

FIG. 21.   Switzerland: geology.

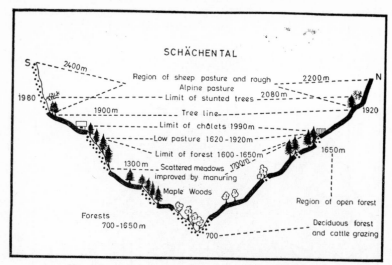

Fig. 22. Switzerland: section across the Schächental.

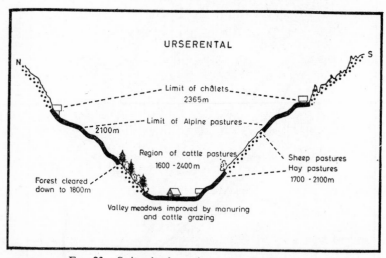

Fig. 23. Switzerland: section across the Urserental.

horn-like crests and the valleys are deeply cut. Pleistocene glaciation has further emphasized these features, so that the Swiss Alps have proved classic country for the study of the modification of mountain land forms by ice, as the work of W. M. Davis, Garwood, Suess, Argand and Kober testifies.

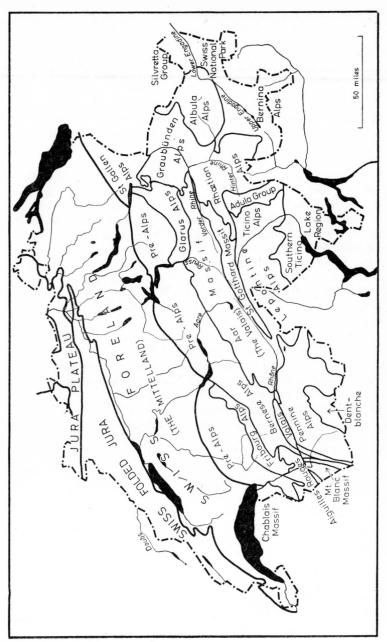

FIG. 24.   The physiographic regions of Switzerland and the Swiss Alps.

Switzerland lies entirely within the western Alps, the upper Rhine valley from the lake of Constance to Chur and the Septimer pass forming the eastern limit.[1] Within this major region are the Jura mountains, representing ' the outermost ripples of the Alpine storm ', together with the largely drift-filled Foreland or *Mittelland*. The Alps may themselves be subdivided. The outer ranges or pre-Alps extend from the lake of Geneva to lake Thun, and seldom exceed 6,000 ft. They are succeeded southwards by the High Calcareous Alps, of greater elevation, and thus including a number of ice-fields and glaciers. These ranges extend from the Dents du Midi east of Geneva, through the limestone masses of the Diablerets to the glistening snows of the Bernese Oberland (Jungfrau, 13,668 ft.) and so to Pilatus and the Säntis. To the south-west and extending across the French frontier rise the equally spectacular Hercynian massifs, including the Mt. Blanc and Aiguilles Rouges groups, while the St. Gotthard and Aar massifs dominate the central region of the Swiss Alps. The greatest elevations are, however, in the Pennine Alps, namely in the Monte Rosa massif (15,217 ft.) and the Mischabel group (14,941 ft.). The Lepontine and Albula Alps are part of the same system and it is succeeded by the ' root ' belt, a narrow zone on the Italian frontier, and in the south-east by the Swiss section of the Calcareous Dinaric Alps.

The most striking drainage feature of the Swiss Alps is the deep structural trench followed by the upper Rhône, a feature which is also picked out by the Reuss near its source and by the Vorder Rhine. The Inn, from its source below the Maloja pass to its departure from Switzerland *via* the Finstermünz gorge cut in the Lower Engadine ' window ', also follows a major tectonic furrow. The Rhône, flowing west-south-west through canton Valais, is divided from the upper Reuss by the Aar massif, while the St. Gotthard massif separates the trench of the Reuss at Andermatt from the Vorder Rhine above Disentis. Each of these rivers turns through a sharp angle through the Alpine barrier towards the Foreland; the Rhône describing a right-angle below Martigny towards the lake of Geneva; the Reuss plunging into the Schöllenen gorge north of Andermatt; and the Rhine turning northwards towards the lake of Constance below Chur. In spite of the physical impressiveness of this inter-Alpine trench, it is only since 1926 that it has been followed throughout by a railway, when the Furka-Oberalp line was completed. This railway operates only in the summer months between Brig and Andermatt. The international Lötschberg-Simplon route enters the Rhône valley and then follows it

[1] L. W. Collet: *Structure of the Alps*, p. 3.

between Visp and Brig; whereas the St. Gotthard line tunnels under the Reuss valley at Andermatt.   In canton Graubünden, the Rhætic railway, operated originally by a private company, connects Chur and Thusis with the Albula valley and the Engadine by means of a series of spiral tunnels constructed at a record height for a railway in Europe of 6,786 ft.   This costly railway continues southwards along the Bernina valley into Italy *via* Poschiavo, the line having to be protected by snow sheds near the summit of the Bernina pass (5,470 ft.).   Modern developments have been the operation of electric expresses such as the Cisalpin between Milan, Lausanne and Paris; the Gottardo, between Milano, Zürich and Basle; and the Rheingold between Geneva, Basle and Rotterdam.

The great mountain roads of Switzerland, constructed mainly since Napoleonic times, may also be related to the major drainage features and passes.   In the west, the St. Bernard pass links the Rhône valley and Martigny with the Italian Piedmont but this high level route, open only in the summer, now has the all-the-year-round road tunnel as an easier alternative.   From Brig a circuitous road ascends the Simplon pass to the Toce valley and northern Italy. The Haslital, drained by the Aar to lake Brienz, leads to the Grimsel pass, from which a sinuous road descends to Gletsch in the upper Rhône valley, thence *via* the Furka pass to the Maggia valley and lake Maggiore.   The Oberalp pass carries the road from Andermatt in the upper Reuss valley to Disentis in the Vorder Rhine valley. Both headstreams of the Rhine unite at Reichenau, above Chur, where the Rhine meanders in a great valley trench.   Roads of Roman origin follow the Hinter Rhine through the Via Mala gorge above Thusis to the Splügen and Septimer passes; while another road strikes off from Tiefencastel to the Julier pass and Upper Engadine, reaching lake Como over the Maloja pass.   Access to the upper Inn valley is also gained along the Albula road, linking Samedan and Pontresina with the Adda valley or Valtellina over the Bernina pass.   In the western Swiss Alps, the Sarine (Saane) valley, in the Pays d'Enhaut, is connected with the Rhône valley by a sinuous modern motor road over the Col des Mosses and also more directly over the Col de Pillon, between the resort of Gstaad and the Diablerets region.   Other ' internal ' passes include the Klausen, which divides the Unterschächental, east of Altdorf, from the Linthtal, west of the Walensee.   Again, the high-altitude resort of Davos in south-east Switzerland is connected in summer with the Lower Engadine via the Flüela pass (8,103 ft.).   Switzerland's direct connection with Austria is mainly over the Arlberg pass (under which the line from Buchs to Innsbruck tunnels).   All these

roads are closed by snow for varying periods during the prolonged
Alpine winter; the duration of the closure varying from year to
year according to the variation in the winter snowfall. Snow
ploughs extend the open season to the maximum but on the Flüela
and the Furka passes it is restricted to about twenty weeks of the
year.

The Foreland or *Mittelland* presents a striking drainage pattern,
most of the Alpine rivers converging eventually on the Rhine.
Thus the Sarine (Saane) and the Aare (Aar) drain the western
Alps, and these Alpine torrents are joined by streams entering the
Foreland from the Jura and flowing through lakes Neuchâtel and
Biel *en route* to the Aare. This river leaves the Bernese Alps at
Meiringen *en route* to the lakes of Brienz and Thun and subsequently
describes a notable loop around the city of Berne before turning
north-eastwards along the base of the Jura, to join the Reuss at
Brugg. These streams then combine to collect the Limmat from
the lake of Zürich and they enter the upper Rhine at Koblenz.
At the foot of the Jura lie the ' finger ' lakes of Neuchâtel and
Biel and along the base of the Pre-Alps lies the piedmont lake of
Geneva, crescentic in form and drained westwards by the Rhône.
The lakes of Thun and Brienz lie within the Pre-Alps and they are
divided by the lake delta of the Lütschine, on which stands the
tourist resort of Interlaken. Other major lakes of the Alpine margin
are the star-shaped lake of Lucerne, drained northwards by the
Reuss; the ' finger ' lakes of Walen, Zug and Zürich, the latter
drained by the Limmat; and, to the north-east, the lake of Constance
(Bodensee), through which flows the Rhine on the Swiss-German-
Austrian frontier.

CLIMATE

Switzerland experiences a Central European type of climate
modified to varying degrees by elevation. Local factors are everywhere significant in determining the daily weather. Aspect is highly
important and the south-facing slopes enjoy high amounts of insolation. The sheltered valleys opening on to the lakes of Lugano,
Maggiore and Como benefit from mild winters and spring comes
early, so that the vegetation assumes sub-tropical luxuriance, as the
dwarf palms and flowering shrubs of Mediterranean type found in
the gardens of Locarno and Lugano bear witness. Elsewhere
winters are cold, with varying amounts of snowfall, Geneva experiencing snow for a fortnight, Basle for a month and the Upper
Engadine for six months; while the observatory on the Säntis records

ten months of snowfall. The lower limit of permanent snow lies at about 9,000 ft. in the western Alps, rising to over 10,000 ft. on the drier eastern slopes. During the winter, the Alps form a barometric divide between the depressions which bring precipitation from the North Atlantic to north-western Europe and the subtropical air masses which give the Mediterranean its winter maximum. In south-east Switzerland, the deep trench of the Engadine has a climate peculiarly its own. High-pressure conditions in Switzerland bring calm weather but may result in prolonged temperature inver-

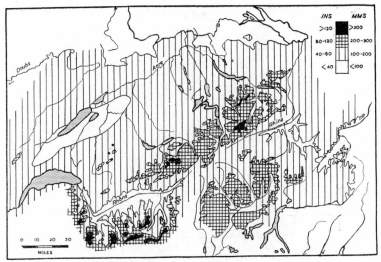

FIG. 25. Switzerland: distribution of mean annual precipitation.

sions over the *Mittelland* and in the deep-cut Alpine valleys, so that a blanket of fog or low cloud may persist; whereas the high-altitude resorts, above the inversion layer, enjoy high sunshine records. Arosa, Davos, Leysin and St. Moritz provide examples but the absence of a cloud blanket in winter is reflected in the very cold nights and wide diurnal temperature range.[1]

In summer, there is often rain of convectional origin with occasional snow on the peaks, and afternoon thunderstorms may occur. Some of the deep-cut valleys experience remarkably low mean annual rainfall totals; the Valais, in the rain shadow of Mt. Blanc and the Pennine Alps, receiving under 24 in. a year, so that irrigation is necessary to guarantee the vine, apricot and strawberry crops, and

[1] W. G. Kendrew: *The Climates of the Continents*, 4th ed., 1953, p. 231.

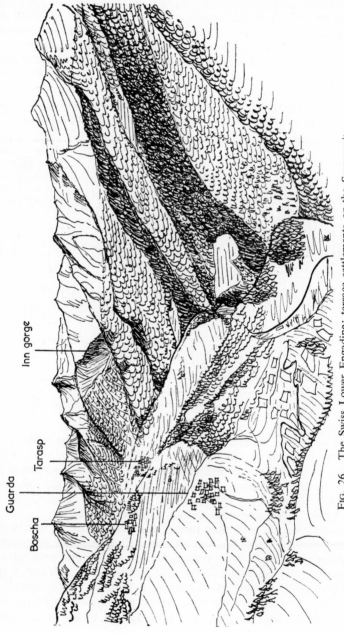

Inn gorge

Tarasp

Guarda

Boscha

Fig. 26. The Swiss Lower Engadine: terrace settlements on the *Sonnenseite*.

maize is excluded. The heaviest precipitation occurs on the Säntis, in Appenzell, where an average of 96 in. a year is recorded, though Sargans, in the upper Rhine valley to the east, has an annual total of 50 in. The *Mittelland* is warm in summer but temperatures may be taken as decreasing at the rate of 1° F. for every 270 ft. of ascent. The diurnal range of temperature is often considerable, especially at high altitudes, and the significance of *adret* and *ubac* (*Sonnenseite* and *Schattenseite*) aspects is highly important. The part played by varying insolation in relation to settlement has long been recognized, especially in the Val d'Anniviers,[1] which opens northwards to the upper Rhône valley opposite Sierre, in canton Valais. The Unterengadin east of Zernez, with a west–east trend, is a less well-known example; the villages and farms along the road to the Finstermünz lying on the sunny 4,000 ft. south-facing terrace, whereas the opposite slope is forested (Fig. 26).

Temperatures vary markedly in response to local winds, though those from the west and south-west predominate. The *Föhn*, like the local *Maloja*, is the type of wind which develops from the south when low pressure lies to the north of the Alpine barrier. This wind is common in the spring, when it brings a sudden rise in temperature and dry conditions, notably in valleys aligned north-south, such as the Reuss. In consequence, it may cause sudden outbreaks of fire, especially in those villages where chalets are built largely of wood and with roofs of wooden shingles. The *Föhn* is also responsible for the rapid melting of snow, notably in the vicinity of Altdorf in the trench of the Reuss, which has a ' canalizing' effect on the wind, so that it is experienced on an average of forty-eight days in the year. Here the summer climate is generally warm and humid, while the mean January temperature is as high as 32° F., as in southern Ticino.

VEGETATION AND SOILS

Switzerland lies in a transitional position between Central Europe and the Mediterranean region, but the high relief means that, in the Alps and to a less marked degree in the Jura, there is a zoning of vegetation according to elevation, the forests of the mountain slopes giving way to alpine flora above about 7,000 ft. As the result of the short growing season in the Alps and of the poor, thin soils found on the steep mountain slopes, coniferous woodland predominates in the Alps, the Jura and on the morainic ridges, as

[1] A. Garnett: ' Insolation and Relief ', *Trans. Inst. Br. Geographers*, Vol. 5, 1937, Chap. 2, pp. 11–21.

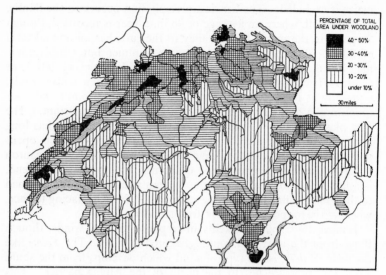

FIG. 27. Switzerland: distribution of woodland.

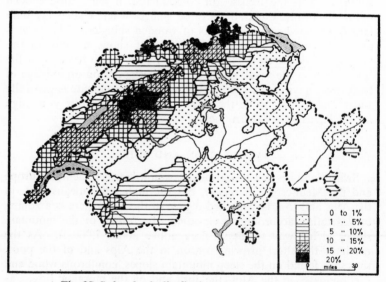

Fig. 28. Switzerland: distribution of permanent grassland.

(a) The Bernese Oberland and the Alpine Foreland from Berne.

5. GLACIAL LANDSCAPES IN THE SWISS ALPS

(b) Rhætian and Bernina Alps with the glacial trench of the Landwasser at Davos.

(a) Natural vegetation of forest trees and alpine pasture preserved in the Swiss National Park.

6. LAND USE IN THE SWISS ALPS

(b) Contrasted north and south facing slopes of the Urnerboden, below the Klausen pass.

(a) Berne, a peninsula site within the incised meander of the Aar.

7. TWO SWISS TOWNS FROM THE AIR

(b) Geneva, at the confluence of the Arve and the Rhône.

(a) The airport of Kloten, showing the modern jet runways and looking southwards over the closely settled Alpine foreland towards Zürich and the lake of Zürich, partly hidden in valley mist, with the Alps on the skyline.

8. ZÜRICH AND ITS ENVIRONS FROM THE AIR

(b) The Altstadt of Zürich on the banks of the Limmat, with bridges linking the Augustinerhof quarter (on rising ground, bottom left) and the Grossmünster Platz.

well as in the Napf region of the *Mittelland*. Spruce and silver
fir are dominant species, though the deciduous larch and birch also
occur. On the slopes below 4,500 ft. mixed woods are found, the
beech intermingling with the coniferous trees. Above 5,500 ft. the
stands of timber thin out and dwarf species of pine (*Krummholz*)
intermingle with juniper scrub and the alpine dwarf rhododendron
(the alpine ' rose '). These give way to the alpine flora of the
mountain pastures interspersed with bare rock below the permanent
snow-line, which lies at about 9,000 ft. above sea-level. One of the
regions where ' natural ' alpine vegetation is best preserved is in the
remote Swiss National Park, between the Lower Engadine and the
Italian frontier, where the wealth of alpine flowers is proverbial.
Elsewhere, in the valleys of the Alps and Jura, the plant cover has
been extensively modified by more than nine centuries of forest
clearance and settlement;[1] while in the *Mittelland* little natural
woodland or meadow remains, for it has been replaced by sown
pastures, cereals (wheat, maize and oats), potatoes and fodder
crops. In the Alps, the hay crop of the valley pastures needs
to be supplemented by that derived from the mountain pastures
or *Alpen* and hay is still cut by hand scythe from incredibly steep
slopes and small fields, often divided by wire fences. Today small
motor mowers are being introduced and hay is carried by tractor-
drawn farm carts, a change necessitated by the shortage of farm
labour in the Alps.

The pattern of vegetation is complicated in the Alps by varying
insolation according to aspect, so that the south-facing slope may
be almost entirely under pasture and peppered with hay barns
(*mazots*) [2] while the north-facing slope is thickly forested, as in the
Unterschächental and in the Pays d'Enhaut regions referred to
elsewhere. The Vorder Rhine valley near Disentis affords another
example. Cereals are grown at remarkably high altitudes where
insolation rates are high, notably at Findelen above Zermatt, at
Chandolin perched above the Val d'Anniviers, and at Cresta above
St. Moritz, where rye ripens at 6,000 ft. These agricultural settlements are three of the highest permanently occupied villages in
Switzerland. In the *Mittelland* and also on the sun-baked terraced
slopes leading to the lake of Geneva, as well as in the upper Rhône
valley at Sion and Sierre and around lakes Como, Lugano and
Maggiore, the vine is cultivated; while maize and tobacco flourish

[1] H. C. Darby: ' The Clearing of the Woodland in Europe '. Contribution
to *Man's Rôle in Changing the Face of the Earth*, ed. by W. L. Thomas, Jr.,
1956.
[2] E. Egli: *Swiss Life and Landscape* (transl.), 1949.

on the better soils of the *Mittelland.* The richest soils occur between the Alps and the Jura, where they are derived from glacial drift, alluvium or occasionally loess. In the Alps and the Jura, the soils are the podsolized forest type, grey, thin and leached, though their composition depends on the local parent rock. In some parts of the Alps there is no soil mantle, frost weathering having produced surfaces partly boulder strewn and partly covered by scree débris, the summit of the Flüela pass between Davos and the Lower Engadine providing a striking illustration (Plate 9a).

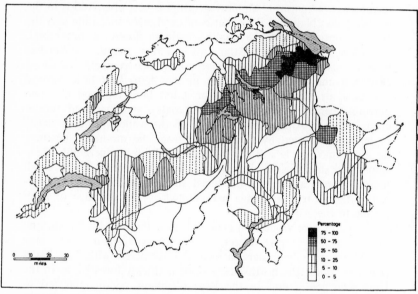

FIG. 29.   Switzerland: distribution of winter cereals as a percentage of grassland.

LAND USE

Because of the mountainous nature of the country, 23 per cent of Switzerland is unproductive and the low mean annual temperatures and heavy winter snowfall above about 4,500 ft. favour the growth of fir forest and mountain pasture rather than crops. The modern tendency is, however, for the area of permanent pasture land to increase in the lowlands and for that under fodder crops to expand at the expense of land under cereals (the ratio of sown meadows to crops being 3:1). Forest land has been increased through systematic afforestation (Fig. 27). During the 1939–45 War, land which had reverted to pasture was brought back under the plough and, in the Engadine, where cultivation terraces had long been abandoned with the import of grain from abroad, crop cultivation was extended to 5,000 ft. (as in the St. Moritz-Samedan region).   Switzerland is a country of small peasant holdings, worked usually as a family unit, with little hired labour.   The average size of a farm is under 14 acres, a reflection of the limited nature of the farm husbandry.   There is little scope for mechanization on the mountain farms, for the fields are too small and there is a general lack of capital, but the mechanical cutting and carting of hay is spreading, where slopes are not too steep.   The output of milk as the basis of cheese production rather than butter is the farmer's main concern, the sale of veal and beef being other important considerations.   The growing of cereals (wheat, oats, rye and maize), root crops (potatoes and sugar beet), orchard fruit and vines is of secondary importance.   Hay is the chief crop, both in the *Mittelland* and the Alpine valleys; for it is the vital winter feed crop and it is stored in the great loft over the dwelling house or in hay barns scattered over the meadows.   It may be carted for storage on the back of a peasant, taken by horse-drawn waggon, tractor-drawn cart, or by a modern lorry.   In the Engadine, the traditional farmhouse is designed so that the hay cart may enter directly into the storehouse through the rounded stone archway or *suler*.   Many examples may be seen in the villages of Scuols and Samedan, and also in the terrace villages of Guarda (Fig. 12) and Sent in the Lower Engadine.

The *Mittelland* is the major crop-producing region of Switzerland but most of the dairy cattle are reared in the valleys of the Pre-Alps and Alps, the Swiss brown cow being almost ubiquitous.   Certain districts in the western Alps are especially noted for their dairy produce, such as the Emmental, for which Fribourg is the market centre, and the Gruyère district in the Sarine (Saane) valley of the Pays d'Enhaut.   A modern development is the buried plastic pipe line conveying milk from the *Alp* by gravity flow to the cheese factory or creamery in the valley.[1]   The production of cream cheese for export is the main activity, and, in Vaud, milk is sent to the chocolate and condensed milk manufacturers in Vevey and Lausanne (Nestlé, Cailler, Tobler, etc.).   Dairy farming is largely dependent upon sown grasses and fodder crops, chiefly clover, colza and lucerne, especially on account of the long period of winter stall-feeding. Narrow footpaths margin the fields and it is an offence to trample on sown pasture.   Supplementary fodder crops include maize and

[1] A. B. Mountjoy: ' Milk Pipelines and Mountain Economies '. *Geography,* Vol. 44, 1959.

sugar beet, while sunflowers are grown for oilseed.   The vine has a specialized distribution and is mainly found in French- and Italian-speaking Switzerland; the Valais (Sierre and Sion), the Geneva region, the upper Rhine valley in Graubünden, and around the shores of the southern lakes being the most important districts.   In the Rhône valley above Martigny, peaches, apricots, strawberries and tomatoes flourish, while irrigation maintains the valley pastures during the long dry summer.   Much fruit is grown in the *Mittelland* and every available space is utilized, the roads and paths being bordered by apple, pear and cherry, while these trees are also scattered through the fields, as in the German Rhineland.

In some of the Alpine valleys, the ' pocket handkerchief ' size of the fields is remarkable and so is the steepness of the cultivated slopes, often without terracing.   Such intensive use of the land is only made possible through the hard labour of the Swiss peasant and his family, whose economic reward is often meagre, particularly in valleys of exceptional difficulty such as the Val d'Anniviers in canton Valais, the Val Calanca in canton Ticino, the Vorder Rhine valley above Disentis and the Landquart valley above Klosters-platz in canton Graubünden.   In such districts much of the land remains in forest; timber forming a major resource of both the Alps and the Jura and covering 25 per cent of the total area of the state.   The preponderance of wood as a building material is very striking, for it is used in the construction of the traditional Alemannic chalet, where the roof consists of wooden shingles and where wooden balconies are sheltered by great overhanging eaves.   In parts of the Engadine, for example in Pontresina, carved slats of timber fill in the spaces of the barns so that air is admitted for the drying of hay, though in this distinctive part of Switzerland, as in canton Ticino, the use of stone covered with plaster and whitewash is widespread.   Many houses in the Engadine, as in Scuols, Guarda, Sent, and Zuoz, show distinctive architectural features which date from the 16th century, when Swiss mercenaries, fighting in Italy, returned with Italian ideas of building and ornamentation.   The houses of the Planta families are especially attractive, for the walls are decorated with murals and *scraffito* work (scratched in the wet plaster) and some houses have ornate iron balconies, festooned with carnations and geraniums in the summer.   Wood is everywhere in general demand as a source of fuel for closed stoves, for it is a cheap and readily available alternative to costly imported coke briquettes, though modern centrally heated buildings in the towns depend increasingly on oil.

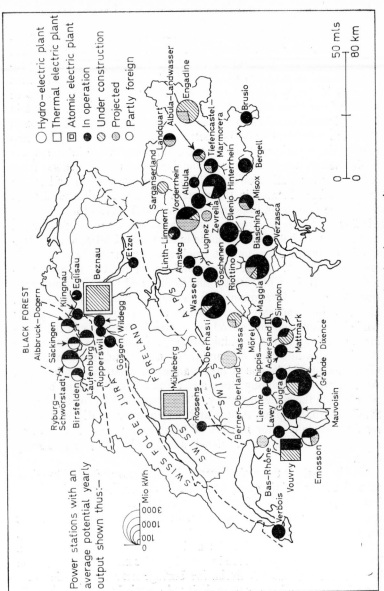

FIG. 30. Switzerland: hydro-electric power sites.

MINERALS, MOTIVE POWER AND RAW MATERIALS

The lack of minerals as well as of fuel and raw materials are great handicaps in the development of industry but, to quote Siegfried, ' Switzerland has been saved from the temptations of mass production and condemned to superiority '.   There is a small amount of coal in the Valais and near St. Gallen, while lignite occurs in parts of the Foreland, as well as peat, both of which are used in thermal power stations to supplement coal imported through Basle from the Ruhr (coke and briquettes) and the Saar.   There are two salt mining districts, at Bex (Vaud) and Rheinfelden in the upper Rhine valley, where there is a chemical works taking power from a local power station on the Rhine.   Some petroleum and marsh gas have been located in the western Alps, but Switzerland relies mainly on petroleum imported by pipe-line from Lavéra to Basle or via Savona to Aigle.   Iron ore and manganese are obtained in small amounts at the base of the Gonzen in canton St. Gallen, at Delsberg-Choindez in the Jura, and at Frick near Olten; while graphite is worked in Ticino.   There is an abundance of building stone, especially in the regions of Jurassic limestones, and there are numerous quarries in the Jura mountains as well as the Calcareous Alps. Cement, lime and gypsum industries also occur in these regions; while building sand and gravel are quarried extensively in the Foreland, especially in the morainic districts.   Marble is worked in the Bernina Alps and also at Landquart, near Chur, both in canton Graubünden; while gneiss and granite are quarried in the High Alps to provide building stone and chips for road making and for maintaining the permanent way.   The great sinuous roads over the St. Gotthard, Simplon, Albula and Bernina passes call for constant repair, especially after months of blocking by snow and ice and subsequent damage from avalanches and rock slides, as well as by frost.

' White coal ' is the main source of motive power for rail traction, as well as for lighting and domestic purposes, but not for heavy industry, which depends largely on imported Ruhr coal.   All but the remotest farms are served by electricity and the domestic market is the greatest consumer, followed by the electro-chemical industries, other manufacturing industries and the Swiss Federal Railways. The oldest power stations are in the High Alps and in the Jura, often in remote sites, like the Barbarine barrage near the frontier with French Savoy, and many were designed especially to serve the railways through the great passes, like the Amsteg station in the upper Reuss valley supplying the St. Gotthard line and that at Visp the

Simplon. Others are located to supply power directly to electro-chemical industries, notably the station which takes power from the Rhine at Eglisau to serve the centre of the aluminium sheet rolling at Neuhausen; while another occurs at Chippis, in canton Valais opposite Sierre, where the steep fall from the Val d'Anniviers to the trench of the upper Rhône provides a high head of water. In recent years older sites have been expanded, notably in the upper Aar valley, and high dams have been built above the Grimsel pass, thus creating an artificial lake over seven miles long below the Aar glacier. This reservoir supplies a modern underground station at Innert-kirchen, completed during the 1939–45 War. Switzerland suffers from a shortage of electricity, especially after a long, dry summer, when the reservoirs run low, and the demand for current is ever increasing. Some power is exchanged with Germany in the frontier region between Schaffhausen and Basle, where there are a number of stations on the Rhine, as at Eglisau, Rheinfelden, Ryburg-Schwörstadt, and Augst-Wyhlen. Further projects are under way, notably just above Basle, where improvements in the Rhine channel are taking place to facilitate navigation, and again at Schaffhausen, using the potential of the Rhine falls. In Graubünden a number of small stations have recently been completed, such as the Marmorera earth dam below the Julier pass, the Rofva barrage on the Hinter Rhein above Zillis, and the high level Albigna dam in the Bergell. Nevertheless Switzerland looks increasingly outside her frontiers for sources of power, and the post-war development of a large hydro-electric project on the upper Adige, below the Rescia (Reschen-Scheideck) pass, on the Austro-Italian frontier, has been largely financed by capital from Zürich. The total output of the Swiss electrical power plants in 1964 was 22,864 million kWh.

INDUSTRY AND MANUFACTURE

Switzerland is one of the most industrialized of the smaller countries of the world, with over 10 per cent of her population engaged in industry (compared with only 4·7 per cent in 1882). The rapid progress from highly skilled domestic and craft industries to large-scale production in factories, often located in rural and somewhat remote Alpine valleys so as to absorb local labour, has been made necessary by a rapidly growing population in an Alpine environment. There has been some loss of Swiss citizens by emigration, for example to Paris, London and the U.S.A., but the high standard of living enjoyed by the bulk of the population is the outcome of strenuous effort, inherent thrift, highly skilled labour, and ability

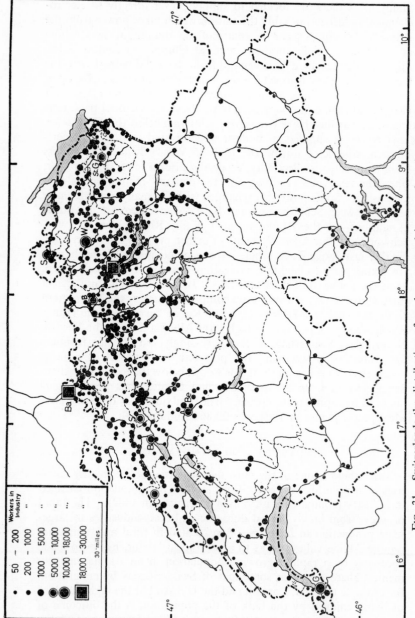

Fig. 31. Switzerland: the distribution of workers engaged in manufacturing industry.

to use the minimum of raw materials to provide articles which command a high price on the world market on account of precision, reliability, artistic merit and fine quality. Dispersal of industry is typical of Switzerland, in view of its dependence on private enterprise which has often determined the location of plant, and of the desire to absorb rural labour, though man-power in Swiss factories is often reinforced today by Italian and other 'Mediterranean' immigrants. Although many of the industrial centres are small, there is also a marked concentration of industry into over thirty of the larger towns. Only Zürich's industrialization is perhaps disproportionate to such a small country. With a total population of 440,600 in 1960, over 81,000 were workers in industry. Various kinds of engineering are carried on in Zürich, for example the production of all types of turbines, pumps and refrigerating machinery by the firm of Escher Wyss; while the suburb of Oerlikon is world famous for its naval guns and modern armaments, as well as aero engines, electronic equipment and machine tools. Again in Basle, the third great metropolis of manufacturing industry in Switzerland, there were over 20,000 industrial workers in 1960, out of a total population of 233,500, mainly engaged in the engineering, chemical and textile trades. Other major centres of manufacturing, apart from their other urban functions, are Geneva, the headquarters of the clock and watch industry; Baden, the site of the Brown-Boveri electrical engineering works; Winterthur, where the firm of Sulzer produces diesel and now jet engines; St. Gallen, the home of the Swiss lace and embroidery industry; together with the federal capital of Berne, and also the Jura foothill towns of Biel, Neuchâtel and Solothurn.

A striking feature of Swiss industry is the large number of small factories and workshops. The creation of factory industries in fairly remote valleys in the Alps and Jura has served to check rural depopulation and to raise the standard of living in these places. The textile industries of the Linthtal valley between the Klausen pass and the Walensee offers one example, while the dispersed distribution of the lace industry in canton St. Gallen provides another. Today, of the 727,711 employed in manufacturing industry, over 44 per cent are engaged in the engineering, metal, machine and watch-making trades, the latter accounting for nearly 10 per cent of this total. Textile industries have fluctuated in importance, employing over 9 per cent in 1964, as a result of changes in fashion, especially in the world demand for Swiss hand-made lace and embroidery, although there is now some revival of the trade often using nylon in place of the traditional cotton and silk. Food processing, especially the manufacture of cheese and chocolate for both the home and export market, is of growing importance, on account of the high quality of the produce. The chemical industry, both electro-chemical, such as the production of aluminium and aluminium ware, and the manufacture of pharmaceutical drugs as in Basle, has greatly expanded, while woodworking, printing and publishing employ most of the rest of the population. There is little scope for women in Swiss industry, apart from the manufacture of textiles, lace and embroidery and in the making of watches;

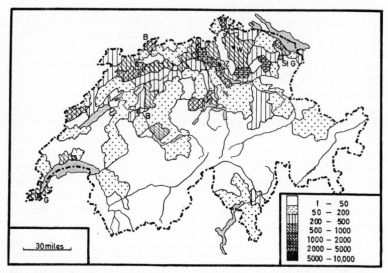

	1 — 50
	50 — 200
	200 — 500
	500 — 1000
	1000 — 2000
	2000 — 5000
	5000 — 10,000

30 miles

FIG. 32. Switzerland: the distribution of workers engaged in the manufacture of machinery.

for other light industries, notably engineering, depend on skill and precision in metal working, etc. There is a marked dependence on imported raw materials, ranging from silk, cotton and modern synthetic fibres, to bauxite, precious metals, raw steel and non-ferrous metals. Most of these imports are handled through Basle, a great rail terminal and also the present limit of barge navigation on the Rhine. Some goods are also imported at high cost from northern Italy *via* Genoa and the St. Gotthard and Simplon routes; while bauxite comes from the south of France *via* the Rhône valley and Geneva.

Mechanical Engineering. Iron and steel production is largely out of the question in Switzerland, except for the electric-arc production of alloy steel, but the processing of various metals is a major activity. Skilled labour is often derived from peasant stock or from craftsmen whose traditional skill dates from the Middle Ages, as in Zürich, St. Gallen and Berne. Today Swiss workmen and technicians command high wages and salaries. The range of products is wide and typically Swiss, ranging from electro-turbines to watch parts, from stereo-plotters to diesel engines. Today electric-arc furnaces are used for the production of alloy steels, as at Biel (*von Roll'sche Eisenwerke*), Winterthur (Sulzer) and Schaffhausen (Fischer). The

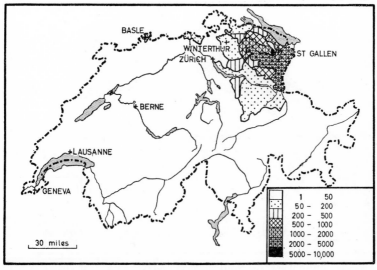

FIG. 33. Switzerland: the distribution of workers engaged in the lace and embroidery industry.

smaller centres of steel consumption are at Baden (Brown-Boveri,) Brugg (steel cables) and Oerlikon (machine tools). Specialization, quality and diversification typify Swiss products, which are the antithesis of those of the U.S.A., with its mass-production methods and standardization of products.[1]

Textile Manufacture. The textile industries, together with clothing and knitwear, occupy about a third of the working population, and Swiss lace and embroidery find a high-priced world market, though subject to the vagaries of fashion. St. Gallen is the chief centre of the textile trades and here is the technical school which trains workers in these highly skilled occupations. The linen industry,

[1] A. Siegfried: *Switzerland*, 1950, pp. 76-7.

which is the oldest, has declined in recent years in favour of cotton and synthetic fibres, but linen mills remain in St. Gallen, Berne and Burgdorf, the linen still being bleached in the open. The woollen industry is also traditional but today the wool is almost entirely imported *via* Basle and Genoa. Schaffhausen, Solothurn and Interlaken carry on the spinning and weaving of wool; while the ancient silk industry survives in Zürich, as well as in Lucerne and in Basle-Lörrach, the spun silk coming from Milan, Lyon and the Far East. Cotton spinning and weaving depend on fine

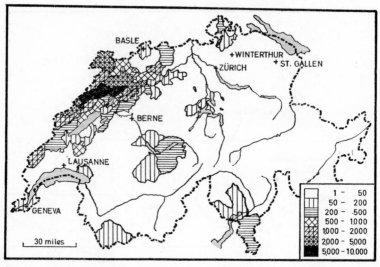

Fig. 34. Switzerland: the distribution of workers engaged in the clock and watch industry.

imported Egyptian cotton and also on coarser cotton from the U.S.A. and India, most of the mills being in Basle and in the cantons of Aargau and Thurgau, while Glarus carries out printing and dyeing, mainly in the Linth valley. Embroidery and lace manufacture are synonymous with St. Gallen, where the traditional hand-made lace industry has now become largely mechanized. Much of the work is still done on a piece-work basis and is semi-domestic. The hand embroidery of handkerchiefs, etc., is a typical domestic craft carried on in canton Appenzell, where the traditional peasant costume is one of the most elaborate in Switzerland. The famous Stoffel handkerchiefs are, however, made in a factory near Sargans in the upper Rhine valley.

Watches and Clocks, etc. Specialized branches of the metal trades, such as clock and watch making, jewellery and musical instruments, are found in many parts of the *Mittelland* and the Jura. These highly skilled industries began as a domestic and winter occupation and were later carried on in small workshops under a master craftsman. The influx of skilled French workmen from Alsace after 1871 led to a marked expansion of the industry. Today the modern factories of the Jura valleys include such world-famous names as Omega at Biel, Longines at St. Imier, Zénith at Le Locle; while others are grouped in La Chaux-de-Fonds, Solothurn, Schaffhausen and Geneva. Geneva is also noted for its related crafts, such as the cutting of precious stones, engraving watch cases, coins and silver plate; while Zürich, Basle, Lausanne and Lucerne handle much of the jewellery trade. Musical instruments are made in the Jura at Le Locle, and also in Berne, Basle and Zürich, a town also renowned for its precision instruments, textiles and electrical equipment.

Food Processing. Switzerland is noted for its production for export of high-quality foodstuffs, especially involving the processing of milk and dairy produce. Winterthur is an important market for dairy produce in the north-east but, apart from Appenzell, most of the processed cheese comes from the Emmental and is sold to cheese factories around Fribourg; while the Pays d'Enhaut produces the Gruyère type of cheese, as do the Jura valleys. Vevey is the centre of the condensed milk industry and of the various Nestlé products; while the chocolate industry is partly concentrated in the region of lake Geneva, though the Suchard factory is at Neuchâtel and that of Lindt at Kilchberg, near Zürich. A modern development has been that of making soups and meat extracts (Knorr and Maggi) and these firms have their works at Kemptthal near Zürich, and at Thayngen, near Schaffhausen, respectively.

The Chemical Industries. The manufacture of chemical dyes came as an adjunct to the textile trades and is especially associated with Basle and Rheinfelden, which takes its power from the plant on the upper Rhine at Ryburg-Schwörstadt. Basle is also noted for its pharmaceutical products, especially those of La Roche, Ciba, Sandoz and Geigy. With the development of hydro-electric power in the Valais and along the Rhine below Schaffhausen, the electro-chemical and electro-metallurgical industries have greatly expanded, notably the production of aluminium from French bauxite. Lausanne is the headquarters of the industry but the main reduction plants are at Chippis, opposite Sierre, and at Visp, both in the Valais; while Neuhausen maintains a research plant, using power from the Eglisau station.

The Foreign Trade of Switzerland. Switzerland's Central European position between Italy, France and the Rhineland, her command of the major Alpine routes, together with her stable currency, have favoured a considerable foreign trade, mainly with her neighbours, Germany, Italy and France, as well as with the U.S.A. and Great Britain. Swiss exports in 1962 amounted to 9,580 million Swiss francs, compared with 12,986 million Swiss francs of imports, the balance being maintained by such ' invisible ' items as the lucrative foreign tourist trade (valued at 1,500 million Swiss francs in 1964) and by Swiss banking and insurance services. The exports consist partly of high-priced manufactured articles, especially watches, clocks, jewellery and precision instruments, as well as cheese, packaged soups and chocolate, etc. In addition, Switzerland exports locomotives, diesel engines, pumps, turbines and machine tools. The imports are largely coal, coke and briquettes, petroleum, raw steel, textile raw materials and various foodstuffs, including wheat, coffee, cocoa and vegetable oils. Basle handles most of the foreign trade, as the result of its frontier position at the head of navigation on the Rhine, and its function as a transit town for goods travelling by rail, road or river barge. Geneva, also near the French frontier, handles some foreign trade, as does Zürich, on account of its worldwide air connections, as well as its function as a great railway node.

POPULATION DISTRIBUTION

Of a total population of 5,870,000 in 1960, probably three-quarters is to be found in the towns and rural districts of the *Mittelland* (Fig. 35). The most densely populated regions occur along the northern shore of the lake of Geneva, in Berne, in Lucerne, in greater Zürich, in the Basle region, and also south of lake Constance around Winterthur and St. Gallen. In these districts the density often exceeds 1,000 to the square mile. In the Alps and the Jura the density falls to under 100 per square mile, while many areas, including those above the permanent snow-line, are uninhabited. Between these population deserts and the Alpine valleys are the regions of seasonal occupance (Fig. 36). Alpine centres such as Interlaken, Lucerne and Lugano, as well as St. Moritz, Davos and Arosa, owe their modern growth to the tourist industry. The capitals of cantons, such as Chur (Graubünden) and Bellinzona (Ticino), are small Alpine towns and there are a few centres of industry in the Alps, such as Visp and Brig (Brigue). The large centres of population are, however, in the piedmont lake zone, in Berne and in the upper Rhine valley, with Zürich by far the largest Swiss urban centre, with a population of 440,600 in 1960. Basle is the second largest town, with 233,500; followed by Geneva, with 175,000. The federal capital of Berne is small compared with most other European capital cities, for its population was 166,600 in 1966. The population density distribution map closely reflects the three great physical regions of Switzerland, for the Foreland varies from 200 to the square mile in the prosperous rural areas to 500 where the population is mainly industrial. In the Pre-Alps and Jura valleys, however, it falls to between 60 and 130, and it is less than 60 in the rest of the Jura and in most of the Alps. In the prosperous agricultural and industrial region of the Valais, it rises to over 260, as in parts of the upper Rhine and Inn valleys, as well as in the overpopulated canton Ticino.

Switzerland has seen a considerable amount of rural depopulation during the last century; people leaving the mountain valleys with their frequently meagre resources for the towns and industrial centres of the *Mittelland*, where Zürich, Berne, Geneva, Basle and Schaffhausen have attracted the greatest numbers. Switzerland also includes a considerable number of foreigners, for the prospect of high wages in factory work and in the hotel business attracts a number of Italians, Spaniards, Austrians and French people, while; since the war, Switzerland has received a relatively large quota of refugees from all over Europe. In 1960, there were 584,739 foreigners (largely Italian workers) resident in Switzerland, compared with 160,774 Swiss living abroad, especially in France (Paris), West Germany, the U.S.A., Italy and Great Britain. The number of visitors to tourist centres was 2,900,498 in 1961, compared with 2,569,646 in 1930, and in addition there were 5,353,210 foreign visitors, a valuable source of revenue to the country, where the business of catering for visitors is a fine art. The fact that Switzerland has today the highest cost of living in Europe (second in the world to the U.S.A.) is reflected in high living standards, especially in such cosmopolitan cities as Zürich, Geneva and Basle. Its rôle as a world banking and insurance centre reflects its economic stability. It is a member of the ' Outer Seven ' or E.F.T.A. (European Free Trade Area).

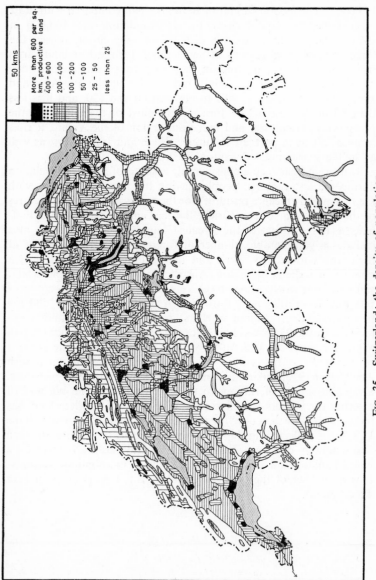

Fig. 35. Switzerland: the density of population.

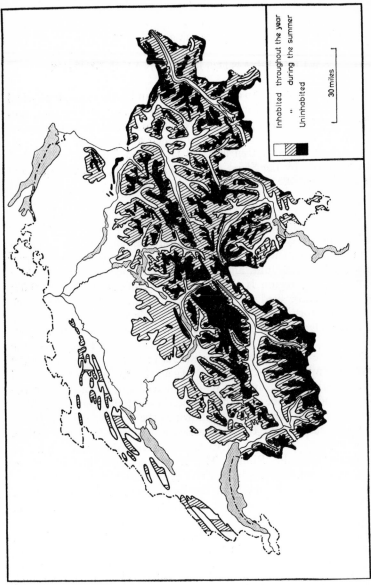

Fig. 36.   Switzerland: the three zones of settlement.

Inhabited throughout the year
   "   during the summer
Uninhabited

30 miles

CHAPTER 6

SWITZERLAND: REGIONAL STUDIES

IT IS CONVENTIONAL to consider Switzerland in three major physical regions, namely the Jura, the *Mittelland* or Alpine Foreland, and the Swiss Alps. It is possible to recognize a number of sub-regions within these major units, some of which are indicated in Fig. 24. The following description is based largely on the detailed regional studies made by the Swiss geographer, J. Früh, and incorporated in his *Geographie der Schweiz*, Vol. 3, 1938.

THE JURA

The Swiss section of the Jura comprises part of the ' Plateau Jura ', which extends from France across the Rhine at Schaffhausen into the Swabian Jura, and a large part of the folded Jura.[1] The centre of this region is the frontier town of Basle (*French*, Bâle; *German*, Basel), sited mainly on the left bank of the Rhine as the river turns northwards into Germany. Basle lies between the region of the Sundgau, at the head of the Rhine rift valley, and the Dinkelberg limestone plateau in the south-west of the Black Forest. To the west lies the Belfort gap between the Jura and the Vosges and to the east is the upper Rhine valley, offering a route to eastern Switzerland and Austria. Basle is thus readily linked with Germany and the Netherlands, France and the Mediterranean, the Danubian lands and south-east Europe. It is known as the ' golden gate ' of Swiss international traffic. Here has arisen a major nodal centre for the great routeways of western Europe and also the present limit of navigation on the Rhine. The river port lies downstream at Kleinhüningen, where wharves and grain elevators line the water-front and where barges from the Netherlands, the Ruhr and the Saar unload the various cargoes of grain, petroleum, coal and coke. Basle also has a small airport. The oil pipe-line bringing refined petroleum from Lavéra (Marseilles) to the Rhineland *via* Belfort, has a branch to Basle. Another pipe-line bringing crude oil links the Italian oil importing port of Savona to Aigle in Valais. Eventually, Dutch natural gas will be piped to Switzerland. Basle is a bridge town, linking the Swiss and German side of the Rhine; while the

[1] H. Gutersohn: *Geographie der Schweiz*, in 3 vols., Vol. I: ' Jura ', 1958.

industrial centre of Lörrach, in the lower Wiese valley opening
south-westwards from the Black Forest, is an integral part of the
Basle manufacturing region across the German frontier. The city
takes its name from the Roman settlement of *Basilia*, though *Augusta
Raurica* (modern Augst), a little to the east, was the more important

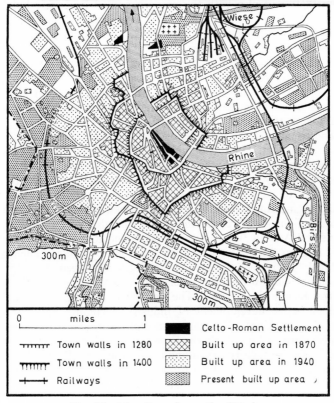

FIG. 37. The site and growth of Basle.

site in Roman times. Today, Basle, with a population of 233,500,
is the second city of Switzerland and it is a highly prosperous centre
of commerce and industry. It is a major centre of the Swiss
engineering industry and it also specializes in chemicals, both dyes
and drugs being well known (for example Ciba, Geigy and La Roche
products). The silk industry was introduced by Huguenot refugees
from France and textile production is carried on here and in a
number of neighbouring villages and small towns, such as Lörrach
with its cotton mills. The core of the town, the *Altstadt*, resembles

that of Berne and pre-war Freiburg-im-Breisgau, for all these 12th-century towns were laid out as part of the Habsburg domains. The cathedral and town hall are of local Bunter sandstone and they contrast with the highly modern steel and concrete structures of the recent extension of the University, the foundation of which dates from 1460, and also with the modern annual trade fair building. Basle is a great banking centre, the commercial node of the town being near the Exchange in the *Altstadt*.   The stages in the growth of the town are indicated in Fig. 37. The major development of the town, especially after the coming of the railways which linked Basle with the rest of western and central Europe, has seen it spread far beyond the limits of the medieval walled town. Today, its residential suburbs extend on to the higher ground to the west, south-west and south of the town.

The countryside to the west of Basle supports a high density of rural settlement.   In the Sundgau, the *Molasse* is partly covered by loess and this highly fertile region is intensively cultivated, with vine terraces on the *adret* slopes.   The region is drained by the Birs river to the Rhine and the valley is highly industrialized; silk mills, engineering works, cement works and chemical factories extending along it.   Between this valley and that of the Aar lie the Basle and Aargau Jura.   Between Basle and Rheinfelden, *Muschelkalk* overlies the Bunter sandstone and is cut by faults.   The region is highly cultivated, the land being divided between dairying and arable farming, with some viticulture, especially on the limestone scarps facing the Rhine.   The settlement is agglomerated and there is some development of industry, including knitwear and also clock making.   The main centre of the region is the medieval walled town of Liestal, on the Ergolz river, where the knitwear industry (Hanro factory) lies along the railway from Basle. This line continues towards the Olten tunnel, constructed through the Jura between 1912 and 1915, and part of the St. Gotthard route.   The main towns of the Aargau Jura are Brugg, Laufenburg on the upper Rhine, and Rheinfelden.   These are all modern industrial centres.   Brugg, the bridge town over the Aar, is noted for its manufacture of steel cables, machinery, textiles and chemicals.   Rheinfelden, formerly an outpost of the Habsburg domains, is also a bridge town, where islands in the Rhine have facilitated the crossing. Today, the walled medieval town has become a thriving centre of industry; local salt from the Triassic rocks being the basis of a chemical industry, and hydro-electric power from the Rhine (Ryburg-Schwörstadt) supplying the aluminium plant.   Rheinfelden is also a noted spa.

The folded Jura extend south-westwards from the neighbourhood of Olten in a series of parallel ranges and longitudinal valleys. This region, of relatively simple Oligocene-Miocene folding of Jurassic rocks, lies in the region of the Franco-Swiss frontier. It was settled in the 5th century by tribes of Burgundians and Alemanni and in the later Middle Ages the monastery of Moutier (Münster) was founded. There is a lack of water on the limestone heights but strong springs break out along the valleys, where villages and small

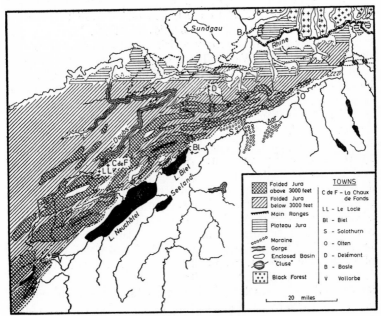

FIG. 38. Physiographic features of the Jura.

industrial towns, such as Delémont, are located. Although the valleys have long been cleared of forest in favour of dairy farming and cultivation, fine stands of fir, beech and elm remain on the slopes. These valleys saw the growth of industries using local wood by the end of the 18th century and today these small Jura towns are famous for clock and watch manufacture, as well as for other related industries, such as gem cutting and the carbing of objects of ivory. La Chaux-de-Fonds, near the French frontier, is the home of Tissot, while the clock and watch factories of Biel (Bienne), at the north-eastern end of lake Biel, employ over 5,000 workpeople. The main centre of the watch and clock industry in this part of the Jura is, however, Grenchen, with a population of 17,000 in 1960. Solothurn is a medieval bridge town which has developed where routes converge on the crossing point over the Aar river, as it turns away north eastwards following the outer edge of the Jura.

The south-western ranges of the Swiss Jura extend between the Doubs valley, which forms the frontier with France, and the long narrow lake of Neuchâtel. Within the folds of the Jura are a number of synclinal valleys, some of which contain morainic material from the Riss glaciation. In the trench of the Orbe, between the French town of Morez and Vallorbe, lies the 'finger' lake of Joux, overlooked by the Mont Tendre which rises to over 5,840 ft. To the north-east lies the Val de Travers, which carries the traditional 'salt road' to Pontarlier. The lower section of this valley, drained by the Areuse, is devoted to viticulture. The gorge where the stream breaks through a 'combe', in the last of the Jura ranges before the lake of Neuchâtel is reached, is known locally as the 'Trouée de Bourgogne'. A devious route leads from the lake-side town of Neuchâtel through La Chaux-de-Fonds into Burgundy. Lying at 3,000 ft., this important centre of clock making and jewellery is said to be the highest manufacturing town in Europe. It was destroyed by fire in 1794 and the modern town has been laid out on the grid plan. La Chaux-de-Fonds is an important crossing point of routes from Besançon, Basle, Neuchâtel and Le Locle, and its population in 1960 totalled 38,900. The nearby townships of St. Imier and Le Locle are also centres of clock and watch production of world-wide renown, St. Imier being the site of the Longines factory and Le Locle that of Zénith. Specialization in clock manufacture in these centres dates from the early 18th century, when many parts were made by hand in small workshops. Today, over 12,000 workers are employed in watch and clock manufacture in Le Locle alone.

The last subdivision of the Jura region lies between the north-eastern folds of the Jura ranges and the Rhine Falls at Schaffhausen. Here the plateau Jura end in the fault-line scarp of the *Klettgau*, south-east of the Black Forest, and to the east rise the isolated volcanic stumps of the *Hegau*. This transitional region, lying along the northern margin of the drift-covered *Mittelland*, is richly cultivated; cereals, including maize, fodder crops, orchard fruit and viticulture being widespread. The typical Alemannic type of farmstead, with its massive wooden roof, is found here. Eglisau, once a market centre for corn, wine and salt, on the road from Swabia to Zürich, is a small route centre for the region. The main town

is, however, Schaffhausen, the bridge town over the Rhine, where
the river pursues its post-glacial course in a gorge cut through the
Jurassic limestones. Much of the hydro-electric power generated
at the power station at Rheinau, some distance below the Rhine falls,
is taken by the aluminium rolling mill at Neuhausen, though Schaffhausen also uses the power for its engineering industries. The
proposal to develop the potential of the Rhine falls at Schaffhausen
has recently been accepted, in spite of much opposition on æsthetic
grounds.

THE MITTELLAND

The Swiss *Mittelland* or Alpine Foreland lies between the Pre-
Alps and the Jura. Although Tertiary formations outcrop locally,
especially in the sandstone hill country of the *Napf*, the *Molasse*
and *Nagelfluh* formations are largely covered by Pleistocene drift.
Towards the edge of the Alps, the *Molasse* is highly contorted,
but it is not often significant as a relief feature compared with the
great terminal moraines of the Riss and Würm periods which lie
around the lower ends of the piedmont lakes, especially those of
Constance, Zürich and Geneva. This region, once covered by
Alpine valley glaciers, has since been heavily eroded by streams
with an Alpine régime, such as the Limmat, Reuss and Aar. It
presents the appearance of a highly dissected landscape, hence the
term 'plateau', frequently used by the French geographers, appears
a misnomer. The *Mittelland* is the major human region of Switzerland, for not only is it the chief region of crop production and
of stock rearing, but it contains three of the four largest towns in
Switzerland, namely Zürich, Berne and Geneva, and it is served by
a thick network of communications. A number of modern 'national' roads are now under construction. These are designed as
dual carriageways, by-passing built up areas, and designed to carry
fast traffic. Some sections of the N1 are already in operation,
particularly between the Walensee and Chur, Zürich and Richters-
wil. The *Mittelland* is also cross by the modern *Trans-Europa*
electrified express trains, linking Geneva *via* Lausanne with Basle,
Lugano with Zürich and Basle, etc.; while the *Transalpin* connects
Basle *via* Zürich and the Aalberg tunnel with Linz and Vienna.
The *Mittelland* also supports a high density of rural population,
as well as small towns and industralized villages; for manufacturing
activity is widely dispersed through the region, deriving its motive
power from hydro-electric sites in the Alps, the Jura and from
the German-Swiss Rhine, as well as from imported coal and coke
from the Ruhr and Saar fields.

It is possible to distinguish various parts of the *Mittelland* according to their distinctive features. They are:

The Region of Lake Constance (Bodensee)

This great expanse of water on the Swiss-Austro-German frontier is the site of the Rhine valley glacier, evidence of which are the Riss and Würm moraines around the lower end of the lake. There is also much ground moraine, together with drumlin ridges. To the south of the lake plain rise the *Molasse* hills of Thurgau. This is prosperous farming country, with an abundance of fruit orchards, wheat, maize and rotation grasses such as clover and lucerne. It has been thickly settled since Carolingian times, but some villages, such as Arbon, on the road from Chur to Constance, are of Roman origin. Frauenfeld is the chief market town but there are also the early monastic sites of Radolfzell and Bischofszell. Rorschach is a small industrial centre, noted for lace and machinery, and it comes within the industrial zone of influence of St. Gallen. This latter city, on the site of the hermitage founded by the Irish monk, St. Gallus, in 614, is a rare example of a modern centre of textile manufacture with no obvious advantage of site. It lies in a rather narrow trench, aligned south-west to north-east between *Molasse* ridges. This Steinach valley, which opens to the lake of Constance, is not a main routeway and its supply of water is meagre. The linen industry was introduced into St. Gallen as early as the 13th century and cotton was added in the 18th century. With the mechanization of the cotton industry and the development of specialization in lace and embroidery in the latter part of the 19th century, the products of this ancient Swiss town achieved international repute. Since the war, the lace and embroidery industry has been depressed as the result of foreign competition, especially Japanese but there has been a recent revival with the demand for nylon lingerie of fine quality. Training in the lace-making craft is given in the embroidery school where skill is achieved in design and in the manipulation of the complex machines which produce the most delicate patterns in the world. Much lace making and embroidery are still carried out as domestic activities and the industry is distributed widely through the canton of St. Gallen and through neighbouring Appenzell, as well as spreading into the Austrian province of Vorarlberg, across the Rhine. St Gallen offers an interesting contrast as a town between the *Altstadt*, within the circular walls, where the baroque cathedral, with its magnificent library, is the centre, and the modern town which spreads along the valley. The towers of St. Lawrence and St. Mangen dominate the medieval *Oberstadt*, with its narrow market street and high, gabled house fronts, so that the core of the old town appears remote from modern industrial activity, which, however, thrives all around the town. Here, however, a ' new town ' type of shopping centre has recently been opened, to the south-west of the *Altstadt*, with a pedestrian precinct.

The Zürich Region

Between the lake of Constance and the Reuss valley lies a diversified and prosperous countryside, where intensive agriculture is mingled with rural and urban industry. This section of the *Mittelland* is drained by streams such as the Töss and Limmat across a glacial drift-covered landscape. Winterthur, in the Töss valley,

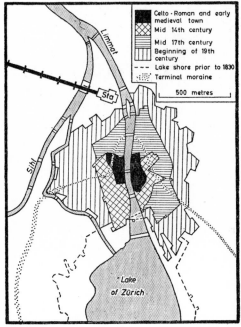

FIG. 39.   The site and growth of Zürich.

is a site of Celto-Roman origin (*Vitu*—forest, *dur*—water), on the road from Windisch (*Vindonissa*) to Arbon (*Arbona*). It developed first as a centre of textile manufacture (linen, silk and wool) but today it is world-renowned as the site of the Sulzer engineering

works and for its technical institute.   The town is also a market for
cereals, wine and cattle.   The whole of this region is, however,
dominated by the great city of Zürich, which, with a population of
438,800 in 1966, is the most important town in terms of size, industry
and commerce in all Switzerland.   The conurbation, however, totals
645,301, this figure including the ' new town ' around the airport
of Kloten and former villages, like Oerlikon, now part of greater
Zürich.

Zürich originated as the Celto-Roman fortified site of *Turicum*
on the Lindenhof.   By the 8th century it had become an important
bridge point over the Limmat and by Carolingian times it had the

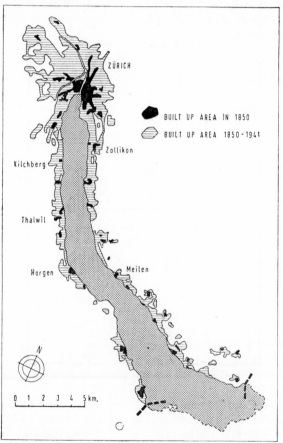

FIG. 40.   Expansion of settlement around the Lake of Zürich since 1850.

right to exact tolls, as a market town, and to mint coins. Zürich became a free city in 1218 and its silk industry developed on account of its position on the 'silk road' *via* Zug from Milan. The medieval core of the town may be traced today around the Augustinerhof (Fig. 39) where a maze of narrow streets slopes steeply to the Limmat. It is estimated that Zürich had between 7,000 and 8,000 inhabitants in the 14th century and within the walls were the monasteries of the Augustinian and Dominican friars. Medieval Zürich spread on both sides of the banks of the Limmat, below its exit from the lake of Zürich, over the moraines of the Linth glacier which may be traced today along the steep streets leading to the University quarter of the town. Modern Zürich has spread over the Sihl tributary of the Limmat on to the *Molasse* slopes of the Uetliberg to the west and the Zürichberg to the east. To the north, the boundaries of the town were extended in 1934 to include the industrial suburb of Oerlikon. Today, Zürich, symbolized by the elegant stores of the Bahnhofstrasse and the Talacker shopping centre, is a major European centre of commerce and industry. It lies where the route from Basle to the St. Gotthard is crossed by the line from Berne to the Arlberg. It also has connections with the cities of southern Germany such as Stuttgart, Ulm and Munich, *via* Schaffhausen and St. Gallen. It has world-wide connections by air through its modern airport of Kloten, to the north-east of the town. Zürich has its notable memorials: to Zwingli, the religious reformer; to Pestalozzi, the educational reformer; and to Escher, the promoter of the St. Gotthard line. Its industrial activities are represented by long-established firms such as Escher-Wyss and Georg Fischer, and its significance as a centre of world insurance by the magnificent offices by the lake of Zürich. Zürich is rapidly expanding and its most modern housing development is in the form of narrow skyscraper flats which have arisen especially in the south-western suburbs, as well as of garden estates.

The Lucerne Region

The central *Mittelland* region is drained northwards by the Reuss and the Aar towards the foot of the Jura. Traces of Mindel-Riss interglacial material have been found at the lower end of the lake of Lucerne and, in the Reuss valley, the Würm terminal moraines assume considerable significance as relief features. Inside this girdle of hills was a former marshy region where the Reuss was liable to flood until modern regulation. Lucerne, as the centre of lake and pre-Alpine scenery, represented by Pilatus and the Rigi, originated as a bridge town over the Reuss, and its wooden medieval covered bridge is still a feature of the town which today is increasingly dominated by tourism. Lucerne owes some of its popularity as a resort to its accessibility from Basle on the St. Gotthard route. To the west of the Reuss valley lies that of the Aar, densely populated for many centuries. Its strategic importance in medieval times is shown by the number of bridge point settlements, such as Aarburg and Aarau, defended by castles on bluff sites. In this valley lies Langenthal, the most noted centre of Swiss porcelain manufacture, an industry providing employment for the local population, as an alternative activity to farming.

The Berne Region

The western part of the Swiss *Mittelland* slopes from the foot of the Alps towards the line of the Jura and the upper Rhine valley. The main valleys are these of the Aar (Aare) and the Emmental, both of which show marked terrace development and incised meanders. A striking relief feature is that of the Napf, a *Molasse* plateau deeply dissected by streams, with the local development of deep, wooded gorges. This district is rich in names ending in *-rüti*, *-schwand* and *-brand*, indicating medieval settlements in forest clearings. To the west of the Napf lies the Emmental valley, famed for its dairy farming and cheese production. Settlements occur here on terraces above the rich meadows of the valley floor, and surrounded by cultivated land and fruit orchards. Farm buildings are generally dispersed and are typical of canton Berne, with huge wooden roofs, balconies, overhanging eaves, green painted shutters and window-boxes made bright in summer with red geraniums. This is the Swiss expression of the Alemannic farmhouse.

Berne became the federal capital of Switzerland as recently as 1848. Its foundation, however, dates from 1191, when the site was selected by Count Berthold IV of Zähringian for its strategic value on a long, narrow peninsula surrounded by the incised valley of the Aar. The site of this bridge settlement survives in the Nydeck, where a stone bridge replaced the first wooden bridge in 1250. The Zähringian town, laid out between 1191 and 1250, extended from the bridge over the Aar to the Clock Tower. Its parallel medieval streets have such significant names as *Gerechtigkeitsgasse* (Justice Street) and *Kramgasse* (Street of the Traders). The town hall, with the painted shields of each canton displayed on the walls, was erected between 1406 and 1416, and the Gothic cathedral was begun a few years later. During the period 1250 to 1345 the town was extended to the *Käfigturm* (prison tower) and subsequently to the limit of the 17th-century fortifications across the neck of the

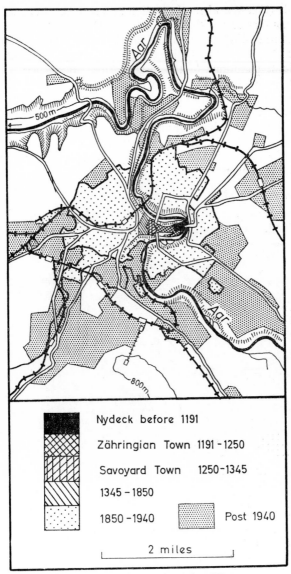

Fɪɢ. 41. The site and growth of Berne.

peninsula (Fig. 41), where the station now stands.   In contrast with the medieval streets, with their *Lauben* or arcades, statues, fountains and colourful window-boxes and flower stalls, is the modern town and the *Bundeshaus* or parliament building, from which there is a magnificent panorama of the distant Alps.   Berne lies where the railway route from Geneva to Constance is crossed by that from Basle *via* Olten and the Lötschberg tunnel to the Simplon.   It is a centre of light industry, including spinning, knitwear, furniture making, printing, publishing and the manufacture of Tobler chocolate.   As federal capital, it has grown to be a city of over 163,000 people, the fourth city of Switzerland, without losing any of its medieval attractiveness.

The Geneva Region

The western part of the *Mittelland* is part of French-speaking Switzerland.   It is drained partly by the Aar and the Sarine (Saane)

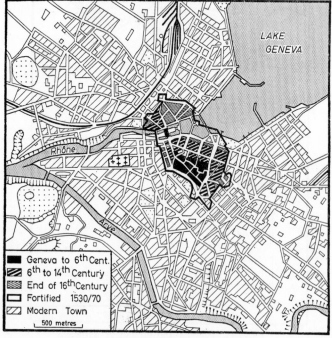

FIG. 42.   The site and growth of Geneva.

towards the Jura and partly to the lake of Geneva and the Rhône valley.   Here the Würm moraines of the Rhône valley advanced to the foot of the Jura so that the soils are generally of glacial origin. Parallel with the Jura foothills is the *Seeland*, a trench including the lakes of Neuchâtel and Biel (Bienne). Overlooking these lakes are sunny slopes terraced for viticulture, and the rich soils of the lake shores produce potatoes, cereals, sugar beet and specialized crops such as asparagus. At the upper end of lake Neuchâtel lies Yverdon, a centre noted for its manufacture of rolling stock. In the Sarine (Saane) valley lies Fribourg (Freiburg), comparable in site with Berne, for the town was also founded by Berthold IV of Zähringen in 1175 on a peninsula site overlooking the incised valley of the Aare (Aar). The little town is an important centre of cheese production. Its Roman Catholic Gothic cathedral of red sandstone is a dominant feature.

Geneva is the focal point of western Switzerland and the upper Rhône valley. Its Roman origin is commemorated by the site of the temple of Apollo built in A.D. 170. It originated as a confluence town, where the Arve enters the Rhône. It is a bridge town like Zürich, at the lower end of lake Geneva. Its modern growth and development, especially as the centre of the Swiss jewellery, watch and clock industries, have been favoured by the settlement of Protestant refugees from France in the 18th century. Geneva has become a symbol of reform and humanism beginning with the leaders of the Reformation, especially Calvin, continued by the French refugee philosopher, J. J. Rousseau, to modern international organizations represented by the Red Cross, the International Labour Office and various branches of U.N.O. which are found here. Geneva functions as a ' window ' on the western world. Its population now exceeds 196,000.

THE ALPS

The Swiss section of the Alps falls almost entirely within the western Alps, west of a line from the lake of Constance along the Rhine to Chur and thence over the Splügen pass to the lake of Como. The general trend from south-west to north-east is represented by the outer line of Pre-Alps, including those of St. Gallen and Appenzell. Behind these lower ranges rise the High Calcareous Alps of the Bernese Oberland, with the narrow zone of the Fribourg Alps cutting off this massif from the outer zone of *Flysch*. East of the Reuss, the Graubünden Alps extend to the Austrian border and are succeeded north of the Vorder Rhein valley by the Rhætian and Albula ranges. In the extreme south-east of Switzerland, the peaks of the Bernina Alps lie along the Italian frontier, as do the Albula, Ticino and Lepontine Alps to the west. Apart from the high central massifs

of the Aar and St. Gotthard, which form the hydrographic core of
Switzerland, the other great ranges lie in the Pennine Alps, where
the permanent snows of Monte Rosa, the Mischabel, and the
Matterhorn rise to the greatest heights of the Swiss Alps.

The St. Gallen Alps

Between the lake of Constance and Sargans, the great trench of the
Rhine offers a major routeway into eastern Switzerland.   This wide
flat-floored trough is also the product of the Rhine valley glacier,
as the numerous *roches moutonnées* bear witness.   The Rhine is
embanked and regulated as a protection against the floods which
formerly devastated the plain of St. Gallen in late spring.   The valley
is also open to the *Föhn* and the mild temperatures in spring make
viticulture possible on the slopes.   The region was settled in the early
Middle Ages by Alemannic tribes and much forest clearance was later
carried out by the Walser.   Rheineck is the key town to the Rhine
valley on the route to canton Graubünden. The streets have ancient
arcades or *Bögen*, while the town hall has a Germanic crow's foot
gabled façade.   The town is a market for fruit, wine and vegetables,
while some commodities come *via* lake Constance, such as cereals,
timber from Germany and salt from Lindau. This is a well-
preserved lake-side town of ancient half-timbered houses, squares
and fountains, ornamented with flowers.   In the small centre of
Buchs, with its star-shaped street plan, is the station used by the
Orient Express route to the Arlberg tunnel.   Near by, the foothill
settlement of Azmoos had developed industries such as cotton
manufacture, drawing partly on Italian labour.   Across the Rhine,
Vorarlberg and Liechtenstein have come under the influence of St.
Gallen, with textile manufacture and embroidery industries.   Liechtenstein came into a customs and currency union with Switzerland in
1919.   The centre of the principality is Vaduz, where the medieval
castle stands perched on a bluff above the town.

The Alps of St. Gallen and Appenzell have a marked south-west
to north-east trend, as the result of their anticlinal folding.   The crests
are often formed in *Nagelfluh* but the Toggenburg is part of the
Molasse zone.   This is a region of abundant precipitation, with over
150 in. on the Säntis, and the slopes are extensively forested.   This
massif, with its great statified rock face, derived its name from the
Latin *sentis*, a spine.   It is developed on Cretaceous rocks which overlie *Flysch* as the result of the erosion of the *nappe* folds here.   It has
been the site of an observatory since 1887.   Between it and the Churfirsten massif lies the valley of the upper Thur.   This massif is forested
on the northern slope up to 3,000 ft., when the alpine pastures begin.

(a) The summit of the Flüela pass at 7,737 ft. carrying the road from the Engadine to Davos. This route is closed for about seven months each year.

9. TWO SWISS ALPINE PASSES

(b) The Julier pass at 7,448 ft. with Roman columns marking the route from northern Italy to Chur (*Curia Raetica*). A new road has recently been completed here.

(a) House at Pontresina.

10. SWISS ENGADINE ARCHITECTURE

(b) Hay barn at Pontresina.

(a) Houses at Fang, perched high above the Navigenze gorge, looking towards the Rhône trench and the Wildstrubel.

II. SETTLEMENT IN THE VAL d'ANNIVIERS, CANTON VALAIS

(b) Hay barns (*mazots*) and chalets on steeply sloping terrace at St. Luc on the west-facing aspect of the Val d'Anniviers at over 5,000 ft.

(a) Village of Guarda on south-facing bench above the Inn trench, Lower Engadine.

12. SWISS ENGADINE TERRACE SETTLEMENT

(b) Village of Guarda on sky-line at 5,415 ft. with fields of rye and pasture in foreground.

On the southern slope there is a precipitous descent, marking a line of faulting, to the Walensee. This lake lies in a fertile, sheltered trench between Weesen at the lower end of the Linth valley, and Wallenstadt, at the head of the lake on the canalized Seez river. Today a modern road, cut partly through rock tunnels, follows the south shore of the lake. The vine and magnolia flourish by the shore of the lake which is followed closely by the railway which has linked Zürich with Chur since 1859.

The Pre-Alps from the Walensee to the Lake of Lucerne

To the west of the Walensee rises the heavily eroded Cretaceous and Jurassic folds of the Alps of Glarus, drained north-eastwards by the Linth. This valley is still heavily forested, with magnificent stands of beech on the lower slopes below the fir zone. Above the forest zone lie the alpine pastures and then the needle-like peaks, known often as *Stock*. The valley is part of the route to the Klausen pass, where the modern road was opened in 1899. For many years the lack of arable land and the general poverty of the Linth valley has led to a heavy drain of emigrants, especially to the dairying state of Wisconsin, U.S.A. The construction of the Klöntal barrage has made possible the development of local industries, such as saw milling and cotton spinning and weaving based on hydro-electric power.

In canton Schwyz, to the west of Glarus, the main valleys are those of the upper Linth, the Sihl and the Muota. The Linth drains from the divide on the summit of the Klausen pass at 6,400 ft., several hundred feet above the tree-line and where the snow lies until late July. Above the alpine pastures, the Helvetic *nappes* are sometimes weathered into dolomitic land forms. From the Klausen pass, the Schächental continues the road to Altdorf and this east–west valley offers a striking example of *adret* and *ubac* effects, for the villages and pastures are mainly on the south-facing slope, while that facing northwards remains almost entirely forested. There are a number of medieval monastic sites in this Roman Catholic canton both in the Brunnital, a side valley of the Schächental, and notably at Einsiedeln with its great 18th century baroque monastic church. Here it is said that there are ' six months of winter and three months of cold '. At this height of 2,700 ft., the temperature range is from 25° F. in January to 59° F. in July, and potatoes, beans and rye grown in strips are the only possible crops. There is also some peat digging here. The third valley, that of the Muota, opens on to the town of Schwyz, with its ornate town hall. This valley has an alpine economy but its scenery is generally that of a karst limestone landscape. Over all this region the Reuss glacier has left its mark.

The Lake Lucerne Region

The nucleus of the Swiss confederation lies around the shores of the lake of Lucerne, the *Vierwaldstättersee* (Fig. 19). Here lie the towns of Lucerne, Altdorf and Brunnen, with Schwyz nearby. This historic lake and mountain region lies on the route up the Reuss valley to the St. Gotthard pass and so to Italy. Though the mountains which rise from the shores of the branching lake are not high by Alpine standards, the combination of lake and mountain scenery has made this a tourist region of world renown, so that today tourism is the main activity of Lucerne and of many of the lake-side resorts, especially along the *Axenstrasse*. Many of the settlements are on detrital cones below steeply wooded slopes, above which rise pyramidal masses, such as the Bristenstock, which appears to fill in the head of the Reuss valley as seen from Flüelen. The river enters the lake through a great delta. The valley is fully open to the *Föhn* and the mild spring is reflected in the sweet chestnuts, fig trees and laurels which flourish by the lake shore. The Reuss valley, which leaves the central Alpine furrow at Andermatt in the Urserental and leads northwards from the St. Gotthard pass *via* the Schöllenen gorge to the lake of Lucerne at Altdorf, is quite spectacular. At Andermatt, it lies in part of the central Alpine furrow before turning through the great defile at the Devil's Bridge, where its gradient is as much as 1 : 6 (approx.). An underground power station has been built at Göschenen; while at Amsteg a rock bar occurs and here is the power station which was built to supply current to the St. Gotthard line.

The Bernese Oberland

This is one of the best known regions of the Swiss Alps on account of its accessibility from the tourist resort of Interlaken, which lies on the lake delta built up by the Lütschine between the lakes of Brienz and Thun. The range, which culminates in the Finsteraarhorn (14,009 ft.), flanks the zone of the Pre-Alps extending from the Pays d'Enhaut north of the lakes of Thun and Brienz to Pilatus overlooking Lucerne. It is a region of *nappe* structures, developed on limestones and *Flysch* and cut by deep transverse valleys, such as the Simme, Kander, Lütschine and Aar. The great glacial trench of Lauterbrunnen leads from the Jungfrau to Interlaken and above the *auge* lie Wengen and Mürren on great benches, down which plunge such waterfalls as the Staubbach and Trümmelbach. The Oberland was a region of early Germanic penetration, as the place names suggest, for example Frut*igen* and Wilders*wil*. In this valley there is little crop cultivation but there are rich meadows of clover and sown grasses interspersed with orchards of apple, pear and plum. The valley experiences the *Föhn*, as does the neighbouring Kander valley. This latter valley carried the private line from Berne through the Lötschberg tunnel to Brig and the Simplon. To the west lie the Col de Pillon and the Col des Mosses which link the *Pays d'Enhaut* with the Diablerets and the Rhône valley above Martigny. To the east, up the Haslital, lies the road to the Grimsel pass *via* Meiringen, Innertkirchen and the Handegg falls on the upper Aar. This river emerges from the Aar glacier on the eastern side of the Finsteraarhorn and in recent years the river has been damned at two points in the region of the Grimsel lakes to form a lake reservoir over seven miles long, supplying a modern underground power station at Innertkirchen, completed during the last war. Most of the settlements in the region of the Bernese Oberland have developed from small agricultural communities into centres of tourism, notably Grindelwald, Interlaken and Brienz with its famous wood-carving craft, while to the west lie the mountain resorts of Kandersteg, Lenk and Gstaad. Medieval castle sites, such as Spiez and Thun on the lake of Thun, are less frequented tourist resorts. The valleys of the Oberland retain their importance as centres of dairy farming, the Simmental being famous for its dappled red cattle. The upper Sarine (Saane) and Jaunbach valleys make cheese of the *Gruyère* type. In this *Pays d'Enhaut* region there are many prosperous villages, of which Château d'Œx is the chief. The valley slopes are under meadow grasses and the fields are small and fenced, in each of which there is a hay barn. Above the forest lie the *mayen*, where there are cattle sheds and a temporary dwelling. These alps are usually privately owned and seasonal transhumance is a traditional feature. South of Château d'Œx, the gorge of the Estival leads to the open pastoral country of the Col des Mosses and the name of this valley is derived from the Latin *æstiva*, summer pasture.[1] The *Pays d'Enhaut* forms a distinctive regional unit in French-speaking Switzerland, where dairy farming remains the main source of income, without much addition from tourism. The winter sports resort of Gstaad near the head of the valley and on the route to the Col de Pillon and the Diablerets is an international centre of growing importance.

The Graubünden Alps

In eastern Switzerland, the Grisonide Alps mark the limit of the Swiss Alps against the upper Rhine valley. The great trench of this

[1] J. Früh: *Geographie der Schweiz*, Vol. II, 1938, p. 459.

river, with its formerly ill-drained flood plain between St. Gallen and Liechtenstein, was followed by the Roman road from Constance past Sargans to Chur and *via* Thusis and the fearsome Via Mala gorge to the Splügen pass and so to Italy. Today, a modern road has been completed, involving rock tunnels, above the site of the Roman and medieval bridges across the Rhine at the Via Mala. An alternative route to the Engadine and so to Italy over the Maloja pass is that of the Julier pass, on the summit of which Roman columns mark its ancient significance, though it carries little tourist traffic today. The strategic importance of the Roman settlement at *Curia Rætica* depended upon its command of routes converging from these passes on to the Rhine as it turns northwards. The medieval town of Chur developed on the upper slope of the great detrital fan built up by the Plessur torrent which now pursues a regulated course between stone walls before joining the Rhine, opposite the great limestone mass of the Calanda. Chur became a market and cathedral city inside defensive walls, part of which are preserved in the Martins-tor, Obertor and Untertor which mark the limit of the medieval town. Today, Chur serves as the administrative centre of canton Graubünden and as a small centre of industry. The Roman Catholic baroque cathedral is somewhat dwarfed by the Protestant Martins-kirche, for Graubünden adopted in the main the doctrines of Calvin and Zwingli at the time of the Reformation.

Below Chur is a region of fairly dense rural settlement, partly concerned with viticulture, especially around the defensive site of Maienfeld. Across the Rhine has arisen the modern spa of Bad Ragaz. Above this point, Landquart is a local railway junction at the entrance to the *Prätigau*, a valley noted for its rich meadows and leading to Klosters. It is a region of fairly dense rural settlement lying on the steep slopes below the Rhätikon. This limestone range culminates in the Scesaplana or Alpstein which rises to 9,712 ft. The valley enjoys marked shelter and much sunshine, for the mountain rampart protects it from north and east winds. In consequence, maize and the vine are cultivated on the terraced slopes and the farms are surrounded by garden plots, with fruit trees and vegetables. This region was settled by the Walser from the Valais (Wallis) in the later Middle Ages, and some of the place names show this recognition of sunny and shady slopes. Above Klosters the character of the Landquart valley changes, and the upper valley, which lies within the Silvretta range, is one of marked impoverishment. The high-altitude resort of Klosters lies on the circular route *via* Davos and the Landwasser valley to Tiefencastel and so to Chur. Around this settlement are ancient farm buildings constructed of timber on a stone foundations often with wooden balconies, and these rise to several stories below great over-hanging eaves. Electricity is supplied to the valley from the small power station at Küblis, on the Landquart below Klosters. From the Flüela pass on the divide, the Landwasser flows in a spectacular valley below steep wooded slopes to Davos, which lies at 5,118 ft., hemmed in between the rock-strewn mass of Parsenn, the Weissfluh, where stone walls like scars have been built to check avalanches, and the Hoch Ducan. This valley, partly cleared of forest by the Walser, as the figure of the *Wilde Mann* by the *Rathaus* in Davos suggests, later developed a trade in grain, salt and wine with the Valtelline. There was also some mining of iron, lead and silver ores. The urban appearance of modern Davos, with a population which exceeds 10,000, further increased during the winter sports season, results from its growth since the late 19th century as a high-altitude health resort, especially for the cure of tuberculosis, and the healing properties of the mountain air were first exploited by Dr. Spengler from Mannheim in 1865. Both Davos-Dorf and Davos-Platz also owe their international fame to their amenities for winter sports and summer tourism, for the ski slopes are made accessible by funiculars to Schatzalp, the Weissfluhjoch and Parsenn on the western side of the valley, where gondola cars continue to Strela, while similar ski-lifts ascend to Bräma-Büel on the east.

The valley in which the high-altitude resort of Davos lies is a tectonic trench, overdeepened by ice and lying between the crystalline Alps of the Silvretta group to the east and the Triassic rocks of the Rhætian Alps to the west. Drainage at the head of the Landwasser valley has been diverted artificially, in a region of former river capture,[1] so that some water is supplied to Klosters, another ski resort, while, below the lake of Davos, drainage is to the Landwasser. To the west of this trench is the upper Plessur valley, opening on to the Rhine at Chur, and at its head lies the high-altitude and winter sports resort of Arosa, ' an oasis in the midst of wild mountains '. To the east, a devious road strikes off from Davos-Dorf to the Engadine over the Flüela pass, which lies above the tree-line at 7,737 ft. Below the pass are alpine pastures strewn with hay barns, from which hay may be carted at the end of the winter, when supplies of fodder for the stall-fed cattle in the valley are running short. On the summit of the pass, however, the moraine-dammed lake is margined by scree-covered slopes and below it lies a chaotic mass of *roches moutonnées*. Below the pass, the Flüela stream cuts through a series of rock bars on its way to join the Landwasser at Davos.

[1] H. J. Mackinder: *The Rhine*, map on p. 41.

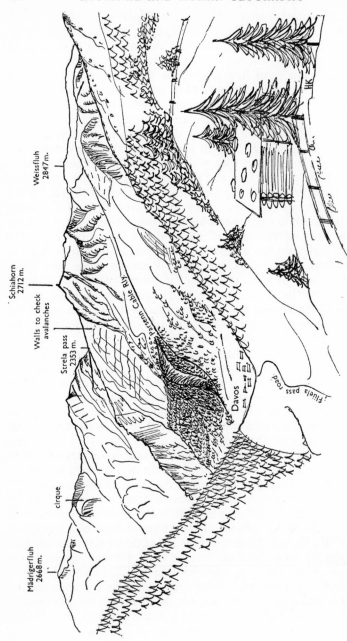

FIG. 43.   Glaciated Alpine landscape: Davos and the Landwasser valley from the Flüela pass road.

The *Postauto* route over the pass is only open during the brief summer and the lake remains frozen until late June. In contrast with the *Föhn*, which brings warm dry air from the south to melt the snow rapidly in spring. The *Bise*, a cold wind from the north which brings snow in late spring is frequent in this region but more particularly at Chur.

The Valley of the Vorder Rhine

The great trench of one of the two great headstreams of the Rhine extends from the Oberalp pass to the confluence with the Hinter Rhine at Reichenau. To the north are the steep slopes of the Oberalpstock, while those of the St. Gotthard and the Adula group rise wall-like to the south. This valley is part of the structural furrow of the Central Alps and is also ice-eroded, high terraces extending throughout its length. At Flims, a great inter-glacial landslide has served to divert the Rhine through a deep gorge at Conn. Although the total mean annual precipitation is not high (generally under 40 in.), the slopes are mainly covered with red fir, white pine and larch, with the silver fir mantling the sunny, south-facing slopes from Disentis to Flims. Above the forest zone occurs a belt of dwarf pines and alpine rhododendrons and this in turn gives way to high alpine pastures. The settlement density is low compared with the Valais and traditional ways of life persist. The predominant language is Romantsch. Disentis (Mustér) originated as a medieval monastic site on the routes to the Oberalp and Lukmanier passes. Many of the village settlements were originally made by the *Walser* and their wooden chalets on a stone foundation are typical. Today, the farms are set amidst small garden plots where vegetables and fruit trees are grown, surrounded by arable fields and meadow land. Orchard fruits, such as apples, pears and plums, are found up to 3,000 ft., while rye, oats and potatoes persist up to 4,500 ft., the approximate limit of permanent settlement. On account of the low summer rainfall, irrigation of the hay meadows occurs, especially around Disentis, and the harvest also comes late. The Vorder Rhine valley is served by the line which operates all the year from Chur to Disentis and there is a summer service to Brig (Brigue), and thence to Zermatt, but its importance is mainly local compared with that of the great through routes across the Alps.

The Rhætian Alps and the Hinter Rhine Valley

The Rhætian Alps derive their names from the Roman province of *Rætica* and the passes which today carry only the Swiss *Postauto* and summer tourist traffic between the Hinter Rhine valley and the Engadine were of major importance in Roman times, as links between Chur, lake Como and northern Italy. The Splügen pass carried the Roman road *via* the Via Mala gorge above Thusis (*Roman* Tusauna), while another led *via* Tiefencastel to the Julier pass and so to the Upper Engadine and the Maloja pass route to Italy, as already described. Today, *Postauto* services are run between Thusis and the Engadine village of Silvaplana, and also to St. Moritz, while an alternative route is *via* Filisur and the Albula pass to the Inn valley below Samedan. Other routes through the Rhætikon strike off from Chur up the Plessur valley to Arosa and through Churwalden and Lenzerheide to the Landwasser valley and so to Davos. The only railway routes through the region are the Rhætic lines, formerly privately owned, and these run from Chur *via* Thusis to the Albula valley and from Landquart *via* Klosters and Davos to Filisur. The Albula line is a spectacular engineering feat, for it attains a summit level of 6,000 ft. by means of eighteen tunnels between Bergün and Preda and was completed in 1896, the highest ' normal ' railway line in Europe.

These remote valleys of the Rhætic Alps were largely settled by the *Walser* in the 13th century and these people from the Valais were responsible for much forest clearance, especially in the upper valley of the Hinter Rhine called the Rofna and in the section between the Rofna and the Via Mala known as Schams, for example around the village of Zillis. The highest permanently settled village in Switzerland lies above the Rofna valley at 7,000 ft., but few houses remain occupied today and these burn peat in winter. Its name, Juf, derived from the Latin *jugum*, a ' col ', is significant. A recent development in this region has been the completion of the Marmorera earth dam across the Julia river above Tiefencastel and also that of the Lei barrage above Thusis on the Hinter rhein.

The Engadine

Between Chiavenna in Italy and Kufstein in the Austrian Tyrol a great trench extends from south-west to north-east, drained below the Maloja pass by the Inn tributary of the Danube. The regional name of Engadine is derived from the Celtic *Engiadina* and denotes the valley of water. It divides into the Upper Engadine, extending from the Italian frontier on the Maloja pass to Süs below the Flüela pass, and the Lower Engadine which lies between Süs and the gorge of Finstermünz on the Austrian frontier.

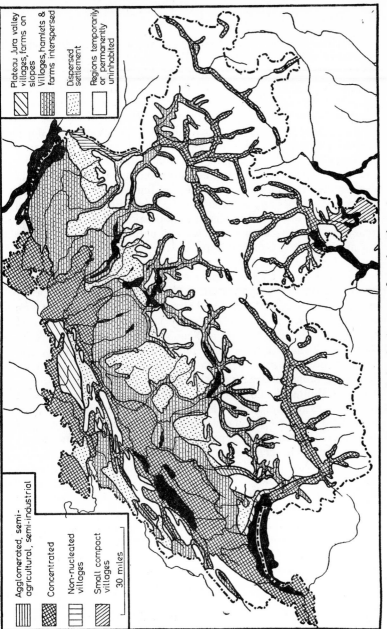

Fig. 44. Switzerland: types of rural settlement.

The Upper Engadine and the Bernina Alps

The Inn rises below the Maloja pass and flows through a series of 'paternoster' lakes known as the Silsersee, Silvaplanersee and the lake of St. Moritz, before being joined by the Morteratsch from the Bernina Alps. This latter stream rises in the Morteratsch glacier on the north-eastern slope of the snow-capped and accidented massif which culminates in the Piz Bernina (13,288 ft.) and the Piz Palü (12,829 ft.), on the Italian frontier. Below the snow-line are slopes covered with juniper scrub and alpine rhododendron but this zone gives way to fine stands of pine and larch, intermingled with birch, and these woodlands remain not only on the valley slopes but also on the terminal moraines of the Inn valley floor, notably between St. Moritz and Samedan. The Upper Engadine is exposed to the Maloja down-valley wind and both spring and harvest times come late, the hay crop not being cut until late August. There is a marked absence of hay barns on the slopes and, above Zuoz, that is above 5,000 ft., there is no crop cultivation, though artificial terraces at Cresta, Celerina and Samedan mark the former upper limit of potato and rye cultivation. The region saw much voluntary emigration to Italy in the past and also as mercenaries. Those who settled in Venice in the 17th century later returned as banished Protestants. In such villages as Scuols and Zuoz the great Planta houses mark the wealth of these returned emigrants. The typical Engadine house is a *maison unitaire*, a single detached house constructed of stone, under a vast sloping roof of shingles. The windows are shuttered and recessed and frequently ornamented with iron grills, as in Pontresina. Entrance to the house is by the *suler* or rounded stone archway, which admits a hay cart over a cobbled entrance. The walls are generally faced with plaster and whitewashed, the plaster being ornamented with *sgraffito* work, of Italian type. Many houses are built round a central square, where stands the ornamental fountain. In Pontresina, a striking feature is the hay barn built as part of the house, with great apertures filled with open wooden slats for the free admission of air. Superimposed on the traditional mode of pastoral economy involving seasonal transhumance, there has been a century of tourism and winter sports, bringing additional sources of wealth which have changed St. Moritz and Pontresina into cosmopolitan resorts.

The Lower Engadine

Below Zernez, the Inn describes a marked bend through a gorge cut into the crystalline rocks of the Silvretta massif, the culminating peak of which is the Piz Linard (11,188 ft.). To the south-east of Zernez lies the Swiss National Park, a region of unspoilt beauty, where the local flora and fauna are carefully preserved. Here the marmot and the stag roam wild and there is a rich display of alpine flowers as well as of forest trees. The park is traversed by the road from Zernez leading to the Ofen (Fuorn) pass, thence to Italy over the Stelvio pass, with its multiplicity of hairpin bends. At Santa Maria, another route strikes off to the upper Adige valley and returns to the Inn valley in Austria over the Rescia (Reschen Scheideck) pass. The local language is generally Romantsch, so that the settlements have double names, such as Scuols (*German*, Schuls). The old village, though partly destroyed by fire in 1921, offers fine examples of Engadine architecture, though tourism has left its mark in the newer part of the town which is a growing summer resort and spa. Another village exemplifying *sgraffito* work is Guarda, perched high on a bench above the main valley and remote from the main stream of traffic. Above Scuols lie the health resorts of Tarasp-Vulpera, where mineral springs occur; a Catholic village dominated by the Habsburg Castle. The Lower Engadine exemplifies a striking contrast between the south-facing slopes, with their cultivated terraces of barley, rye, oats and potatoes, and the forested north-facing slopes. Irrigated meadows occur adjacent to the Inn and fruit cultivation increases towards Martinsbruck. The cutting of timber has long been important and logs were formerly floated to Solbad Hall below Innsbruck, for use in the salt mines. The entrance into Austria *via* the Finstermünz gorge, cut into the highly resistant rocks of the Lower Engadine ' window ', is highly spectacular, as are the lateral valleys of Samnaun and Sinestra.

Ticino

This Italian-speaking canton, with its ' Mediterranean ' aspect, joined the Swiss Confederation with the opening of the St. Gotthard road in 1803. It falls into two contrasting regions, the Ticino Alps or *Sopraceneri* and the southern Ticino lake region or *Sottoceneri*, where the lake margins of Maggiore and Lugano enjoy a sheltered and quasi-Mediterranean climate and where vegetation is luxuriant.

The Ticino Alps or ' Sopraceneri '

This region lies south of the St. Gotthard massif and is one of worn relief developed on crystalline *nappe* structures. The valley land forms are the combined result of ice and river erosion. Terraces, rock bars and waterfalls abound and above the valley floor

bare rock walls often rise.   Some of the steep slopes are artificially
terraced for cultivation, notably between Bellinzona and Locarno,
for example at Brione, above Minusio on lake Maggiore.   About
a third of the slopes are forested but the rather low and markedly
seasonal precipitation is reflected in the fact that alpine pastures
descend to 5,500 ft., compared with 6,700 ft. in the Valais and
6,500 ft. in the Engadine.   The southern slopes are poor in timber
compared with those facing north.   Both avalanches and rock falls
have reduced the area of forest.   This is a region where traditional
ways of life persist and the holdings are really too small to be
economic, being divided into small fields under crops, rotation
grasses and vines.   The pasture land is mainly in the hands of
corporations and there is some modern development of irrigation
and drainage, as in *Malcantone*.   Settlement is impossible in the
narrow valleys and is found on detrital cones, terraces and stream
deltas, on sites free from the risk of avalanches and floods.   In the
upper valley of the Ticino, there is little settlement on account of the
risk of avalanches and floods, except for Bedretta, a village of
wooden houses and barns on stone foundations.   At the entrance
to the Leventina valley, Airolo marks the end of the former hairpin
bends of the St. Gotthard pass road and of the railway tunnel, and
below here lies the Ritom power station.   Below Biasca, where the
St. Gotthard pass route is joined by that over the Lukmanier
from Disentis, the section of the Ticino valley known as the Riviera
is entered.   Here more than half the land is cultivated and a
' Mediterranean ' type of flora occurs.   Sweet chestnut woods
extend up to 2,700 ft.; above that comes the beech, and finally the
fir forest.   Here cereals are grown and the vine is trained along
pergolas.   Stunted mulberries mark the formerly important silk
industry.   Bellinzona, at the confluence of the Moèsa and the
Ticino, is at the end of the electrified St. Gotthard line.

To the west lies the *Valle Maggia*, narrow and partly gravel filled.
This is a region of scattered farms, with wooden hay barns dispersed over the pastures, as in the Valais.   In fact, the language,
customs and costumes mark the historic connection which dates
from the medieval settlement by the *Walser*.   The lower valley
supports rich meadow land and woods of sweet chestnut, together
with vineyards, peach and apple orchards, but the region is one of
modern depopulation, emigration to France, Italy and the U.S.A.
being frequent.   Stone cutting and polishing for the Swiss clock
and watch industry is a local activity.   In 1923, a line was built
between Bellinzona and Locarno, thus linking the Simplon and
St. Gotthard routes *via* the Centovalli.   Locarno, at the head of lake

Maggiore, is the nodal point on this route. It lies to the north of the lake delta of the Maggia and is sheltered by steep slopes to the north. It is a town of gardens, where the magnolia, palm, eucalyptus, cypress and olive flourish. Vines occur on the terraced slopes and there is a luxuriance of flowering shrubs in the spring. The town is dominated by the Madonna del Sasso monastery. Nearby lies another tourist resort, Ascona, a centre of citrous fruit cultivation and of orchard fruits and vines. Originally a fishing village, Ascona is today a small town of villas, with industries using local produce in the manufacture of liqueurs and preserves. There are also modern textile mills.

The Southern Ticino Lake Region or ' Sottoceneri '

The Alps of the Lugano lake region mark Switzerland's only point of contact with the north Italian plain. This is the Ivrea zone, dividing the Pennine from the Dinaric Alps, and culminating in the Monte Ceneri, whence the name *Sottoceneri*. Around the shores of lake Lugano, there is a remarkable parallelism of pre-glacial valleys, at the lower ends of which gravel deltas occur. This is a region of high mean annual temperatures and the vegetation attains a sub-tropical luxuriance. Rhododendrons form thickets interspersed with sweet chestnuts and olive groves, while *maquis* scrub occurs on the hill slopes. Viticulture is very extensive, space being saved by training the vines along pergolas, with crops of maize, tobacco and beans beneath. The region is overpopulated and many people migrate seasonally or seek work as stone masons, sculptors or painters. Most of the population is Italian-speaking, but dialects vary from one valley to another. Under a fifth of the total population is employed in agriculture but nearly 60 per cent find work in industry, trade and transport. The growth of the modern tourist industry, especially since the opening of the St. Gotthard line, has brought much prosperity, especially to Lugano. This resort is sheltered by Monte Brè and by the dolomitic block of San Salvatore to the south. It is a lake-side resort, with local industries such as silk weaving and the making of furniture, leather goods and alimentary pastes. South of lake Lugano lies Mendrisio, on the road from Lugano to Como. It, too, has silk mills and manufactures alimentary pastes.

The Valais and the Pennine Alps

This partly French-speaking canton, which joined the Swiss Federation as recently as 1815, extends from the great peaks of the Bernese Oberland to those of the Pennine Alps. Its main artery is the transverse valley of the Rhône, which opens on to lake Geneva, so that St. Maurice marks the gateway to the Alps from the west. The Valais (*German*, Wallis) is a region of marked individuality and of traditional ways of life. It is largely Catholic, while Mediterranean influences on modes of life and economy are well marked, for example in the development of transhumance and irrigation agriculture, in a region of low rainfall. The trench of the Rhône is of minor importance as a through routeway, though it contains sites of defensive value in medieval times, such as Martigny, Sion and Sierre. Today, the region derives its importance from the fact that it is utilised by the Simplon route and it is also approached by a number of ' internal ' passes, such as the Grimsel, Furka and Col des Mosses. The development of hydro-electric power has also made possible the growth of an aluminium industry at Chippis opposite Sierre, the main centre of bauxite reduction, using high voltage electricity available directly from the Val d'Anniviers power station.

The Rhône rises in a glacier north of the Furka pass and flows as a meandering stream along the overdeepened trench between the St. Gotthard and Aar massifs. This upper section of the valley is known as the valley of Conches (Goms), a name derived from the Celtic *cwm* or *combe*. The steep slopes traversed by the Furka and Grimsel roads are broken by terraces, said to be Pliocene. Below the zone of bare rock, the forested slopes are scarred by the sites of avalanches. The Rhône glacier is now revealing a great rock bar in its recent retreat, comparable with that down which the Furka pass road descends. This latter road was built in stages between 1820 and 1867, following the completion of the Simplon road in 1805, constructed at the order of Napoleon. The railway tunnel under the Simplon pass was built between 1898 and 1906 and the Lötschberg tunnel was completed in 1913. The use of the passes is limited to the summer months for, at 6,000 ft., they are completely snow-blocked in winter. Both the Simplon and the Great St. Bernard passes were open in medieval times, the St. Bernard hospice being world renowned; while the Stockalper palace, built out of profits from the transit trade over the Simplon, replaced the medieval hospice founded by the Knights of St. John of Malta. In 1964 a road tunnel was opened under the St. Bernard pass and thus makes possible all the year traffic.

The Rhône valley appears to have been settled first by the Celts, as names such as Brig or Brigue (*Celtic*, Brigwa, a bridge) suggest, but the main wave of Germanic settlement took place in the *Rodungs-*

zeit of the 9th and 10th centuries. There are some early place name endings, such as ' *-ingen* ', as in Reckingen, but the attack on the forest is represented by such names as Oberwald, below Gletsch. In the 12th and 13th centuries the people of the Valais, namely the *Walser*, spread over the divides into northern Italy, Graubünden and Vorarlberg, as has already been shown.

The Rhône valley trench enjoys a sunny climate but the rainfall is generally inadequate for crop cultivation and the maintenance of pasture without irrigation. Summer drought and heat favour the vine, the ripening of orchard fruits and the cultivation of market garden crops, such as tomatoes and strawberries, but the price of these crops is high compared with Italian produce and comes later on to the market. The valley of Conches must therefore be regarded as an overpopulated region, in spite of its apparent fertility when compared with the Vorder Rhine valley, with its predominance of pasture and forest.

The valleys which open on to the Rhône valley from the Pennine Alps and from the Wildstrubel and the Bernese Oberland each have their distinctive features. At Visp, the combined streams of the Saas and the Mattervisp enter the Rhône over a steep bench. These are both spectacular valleys leading to such climbing centres as Saas-Fee and Zermatt. Both these resorts were little more than a collection of primitive chalets a century ago, Saas-Fee being the centre of the summer pastures for Saas Grund. The 'Golden Age of Alpinism ' was from 1850 to 1866, pioneered by the Swiss Alpine Club, culminating in Edward Whymper's ascent of the Matterhorn in 1866. Life remains traditional, apart from the hotel centres. Rye, barley and wheat are grown, as well as potatoes, especially on the valley terraces, with the aid of a primitive plough and with one year of fallow. The summer village of Findelen above Zermatt records the upper limit of rye cultivation in Switzerland at over 6,000 ft. Nut trees ascend to 3,600 ft., apples to 4,500 ft. and cherries to 5,400 ft. Transhumance is traditional; cattle, sheep and goats ascending in thousands to the mountain pastures in late spring, returning to the valley farms for stall feeding as autumn begins. Access to the Gornergrat has been made by rack and pinion railway, and from this vantage point a unique panorama may be obtained of the snows and glaciers of the Matterhorn, Monte Rosa and Dufourspitze, all with an elevation of about 15,000 ft.

To the north of the Rhône valley, the Lötschberg route climbs from Brig (Brigue) on to the rock terrace which it follows to a point opposite Visp. Here it enters the Lötschental *en route* to the tunnel which carries the line to Kandersteg and so to Thun and Berne. This valley lies to the south-west of the peaks of the Bernese Oberland and is one of the driest in Switzerland. Agglomerated settlements occur on detrital cones, often accessible to irrigation ditches. The care of sheep and goats is mainly the concern of women and children, while the men work in the fields and in the vineyards of the Rhône valley. There is some spinning and weaving of wool. Leukerbad, below the Gemmi pass, is a high-altitude health resort.

The valleys of central Valais which open northwards to that of the Rhône are d'Anniviers and d'Hérens.[1] The Val d'Anniviers has been studied on account of its special settlement features, especially in relation to the insolation factor,[2] for it includes the agglomerated village of Chandolin at 6,335 ft., one of the highest permanently settled villages in the Alps, above the limit of cereals and growing only potatoes and vegetables during the brief summer months. Zinal, at the head of the valley, is a summer settlement amidst alpine pastures. St. Luc, at the upper limit of rye cultivation, is a collection of primitive wooden chalets on stone foundations, where wooden hay barns are scattered over the tiny fields on very steep slopes. Peasants from this village, as from Vissoie, the main centre of the valley, *descend* in summer to work in the vineyards around Sierre. At lower levels, as around Fang perched on a narrow ledge overlooking the gorge of the Navizanze, irrigated meadows and fields of cereals and orchards occur on steeply sloping terraces. The approach to the Rhône is through a fearsome defile, marking a post-glacial gorge cut by the Navizanze, known as the ' Combe de Rechy '. The road from St. Luc and Vissoie descends by a series of narrow hairpin bends to Chippis, where the penstock from the high-level reservoir supplies water to the power station serving the aluminium works.

The Val d'Hérens, to the west, shows similar features, ending in the snow and ice fields of the Dent Blanche. Here the terminal moraines have been eroded into earth pyramids at Euseigne. Settlements such as Evolène, at 4,538 ft., are on sunny terraces receiving the maximum insolation. At the head of the valley lies Arolla, a small tourist resort surrounded by irrigated meadows. In this valley, rye, potatoes, flax and hemp are grown up to 4,725 ft., while the cherry is found up to over 4,000 ft., and the forest ascends to over 7,000 ft. Settlements extend to the limit of the alpine pastures and many of these grazing grounds are owned by peasants in Sion.

[1] E. H. Carrier: *Water and Grass*, 1932, Chap. 34.
[2] A. Garnett: ' Insolation and Relief ', *Trans. Inst. Br. Geographers*, Vol. 5, 1937, Chap. 2, pp. 11–21.

(a) Cattle shed and summer dwelling in the Bernina Alps near the Roseg glacier.

13. TRANSHUMANCE IN THE SWISS ALPS

(b) Cattle migrating from summer alpine pasture in the Tuoital near Guarda in the Lower Engadine.

(a) Solbad Hall in the Inn valley trench, on the medieval 'salt road' to the Brenner pass and Italy.

14. THE BRENNER ROUTE

(b) The Wipptal south of Innsbruck, with the Brenner road and railway.

Between Sion and Martigny, the Rhône flows over a gravel bed with a steep gradient. This is a region of ' steppe ' flora, with heath and juniper scrub. The sunny terraces are utilized for viticulture, especially around the monastic site of Sion. Meadows need to be irrigated during the prolonged summer drought. To the north of Sierre, below the limestone wall of the Wildstrubel, a series of terraces occurs and in the midst of these is the health resort and cure station of Vermala Montana, enjoying a sun-trap site, surrounded by fir forests.

The middle Rhône has been regulated from Sierre to the bend at Martigny for over a century, whereas previously it had been liable to flood and was bordered by unhealthy marshes between islands of sand dunes. Today the water-table is low and irrigation is necessary for the successful cultivation of peaches and apricots and also for market garden crops. Sion is the market centre for this produce, as well as for wine and table grapes. Until 1830, it remained a walled town, with gates on the roads leading to Martigny, Sierre and the bridge over the Rhône. Downstream, Saxon is also a centre of viticulture and of almond and fig cultivation; while the appearance of the beech suggests the penetration of Atlantic influences. Below the limestone peaks of the Diablerets to the north lie the alpine pastures, succeeded by a belt of forest and then by settlements surrounded by fields of wheat and rye. Towards the bend of the Rhône, canals divert water into irrigation ditches supplying water to plots of vegetables and maize. Here poplars and fruit trees provide wind breaks.

There are a number of streams converging on the Dixence or Drance (*Celtic*, Duana, a wild stream), which, as the Val d'Entremont, leads to the Great St. Bernard pass, set in a rock-strewn and heavily glaciated region, today avoidable by means of the all-the-year-round road tunnel. In the Middle Ages, Martigny, the seat of a bishopric founded in the 6th century, profited by traffic over the pass to Italy *via* Aosta, a route which has declined in importance since the opening of the Simplon and St. Gotthard tunnels. Today, Martigny, at the bend of the Rhône, is a centre of viticulture and orchard fruit cultivation. Above Orsières, where the Val Ferret converges on the Val d'Entremont, red pine and larch mantle the slopes up to 6,000 ft. and at Bourg St. Pierre is the Linnæan Alpine garden. To the east, vast hydro-electric developments have taken place in two valleys leading from the Pennine Alps to the Rhône trench. One, the Mauvoisin barrage, lies above the village of that name in the Val des Bagnes. The other, the Grande Dixence, which incorporates the highest dam in the world (934 ft.), is above

C.E.—F

Motôt in the Val d'Herémence, a valley which joins the Val d'Hérens at Euseigne. The project was completed in 1965 and it is estimated that the Grande Dixence scheme will eventually supply 16 per cent of Switzerland's electricity.

To the west of the Dixence lies the Trient valley, cut in the highly resistant rocks of the Aiguilles Rouges. The river rises in a glacier near the French frontier and above Finhaut it is joined by the Barberine, a river which has been dammed to form a high-level reservoir behind a rock bar in a typical Alpine setting, supplying water power to the plant at Châtelard for the supply of the electrified Chamonix–Martigny line and for the electro-chemical plant at Vernayaz, below the terrace cut through by the Trient *en route* to the Rhône, a site comparable to that at Chippis, opposite Sierre.[1]

Between Martigny and the lake of Geneva, the Rhône follows an epigenetic course between the Dents du Midi and the Dent de Morcles. The Rhône enters the lake through a large delta, across which the river now flows in a straight and artificial channel. In contrast with the water meadows of the flat valley floor are the forests of larch, fir and beech on the steep slopes on each side. The Roman site of St. Maurice marks the gateway to the upper Rhône valley and on the slopes across the river lies the spa of Bex, long noted for its salt working. At the foot of the *Flysch* slopes of the Fribourg Alps lies Aigle, the starting point for the high-altitude cure place of Leysin, where the sanatoria enjoy a sunny aspect on a terrace cleared of forest at 4,760 ft.

REFERENCES

The standard reference work, available in French and German, is that of J. Früh: *Geographie der Schweiz*, published in three volumes, 1930–45. A comparable modern compilation is that of H. Gutersohn: *Geographie der Schweiz*, of which Vol. I: 'Jura' was published in 1958 and Vol. II, Part I, 'Alpen' in 1961. E. Egli: *Die Schweiz, eine Landeskunde*, 1954, and also 'Swiss Life and Landscape' (transl.), 1949, are shorter but invaluable studies. A series of local studies, on a variety of topics, appears continuously in the *Heimatbucher* series. E. de Martonne: *Les Alpes*, 1926, is a model study in French. L. W. Collet: *The Structure of the Alps*, 1927, is a useful summary in English. M. Newbigin: *Southern Europe*, 3rd ed., 1949, includes the physical geography of the Alps, and her *Frequented Ways* contains a study of the Valais. E. H. Carrier: *Water and Grass*, 1932, deals in detail with pastoral life in the Alps. The political geography of Switzerland is analysed in A. Siegfried: *Switzerland*,

[1] G. J. Fuller: 'The Trient Valley: An Introductory Study', *Geography*, Vol. 40, 1955, pp. 28–39.

1950. There are a number of books which provide splendid illustrations of Alpine scenery, beginning with *Switzerland from the Air*, 1926, and including Frank Smythe's *Alpine Ways*. E. Whymper: *Scrambles in the Alps*, 1860, is a classic on early Alpine mountaineering. Switzerland has excellent topographical maps, ranging from the original Dufour hachured quarter sheets, on a scale of 1 : 50,000, to the modern *Landeskarte* series on scales of 1 : 50,000 for the whole country and 1 : 25,000 for the *Mittelland*. Staub's geological map of the Alps on a scale of 1 : 1 million is invaluable for reference and so are the four sheets which cover Switzerland on a scale of 1 : 200,000, with useful inset maps, entitled *Geotechnische Karte der Schweiz*. There is complete geological coverage on a scale of 1 : 200,000 and four detailed vegetation maps have also been published. A relief model, scale 1 : 500,000 was produced by Kummerly and Frey in 1962. H. Boesch: 'Die Industrie der Schweiz', on a scale of 1 : 300,000, is a useful economic map of Switzerland.

CHAPTER 7

AUSTRIA: HISTORICAL AND
ECONOMIC SURVEY

AUSTRIA, WITH a population of 7·2 million (1964 estimate), is an impoverished and mainly Alpine state, but maintaining, as for centuries past, the position of a bulwark, however weakened, against south-eastern Europe and the lower Danubian lands. De Martonne has said that, in referring to Austria, the past must always be recalled.[1] The end of World War II saw freedom from the domination of Germany which reached its climax with the *Anschluss* in 1938, but it was not until 1955 that a separate peace treaty was made after Austria had been occupied for ten years by the Four Powers, Today, apart from Austria's Alpine frontiers with Germany, Switzerland and Italy, the State lies in the pincers formed by Communist Czechoslovakia, Hungary and Yugoslavia. Whereas Vienna has for centuries played the rôle of the last outpost of Germanic urban life and culture against Slavonic and Magyar Europe, today the city is shut off from eastern Europe by the Iron Curtain.

The modern Republic of Austria experienced only twenty years of political independence (1918–38). During this inter-war period, Austria attempted to build a democratic state out of the remains of the Austro-Hungarian Empire, shorn of all its non-German-speaking elements, which had been incorporated in Czechoslovakia, Yugoslavia, Polish Galicia and Upper Silesia, and the Italian district of the Trentino and South Tyrol. As Clemenceau expressed it in 1919, ' le reste, c'est l'Autriche '. Greater Austria, the realm of the Habsburgs, had grown from the original nuclear duchies of Austria and Styria, granted by Rudolf of Habsburg, Holy Roman Emperor, to his sons in 1282. These German *Länder* developed during the next century as the defensive frontier outposts of the Ostmark, to which were added in the 14th century the adjacent duchies of Carinthia and Carniola, and the Margravate of the Tyrol. Each of these *Länder*, however, retained a strong sense of individualism, and, since this characteristic has been preserved to a large degree until the present day, it is perhaps justifiable to adopt each province as a unit for purposes of regional description. Moreover, their number and size also make this convenient, as

[1] E. de Martonne: *Europe Centrale*, Géog. Univ., 1931, Vol. 4, p. 451.

well as the fact that each province corresponds approximately with the upper part of a river basin.

In 1526, when the Ottoman Turks defeated the Magyars at Mohács south of Buda Pesth, Bohemia and the remaining Hungarian lands were added to Austria. Vienna was twice unsuccessfully besieged by the Turks, in 1529 and again in 1683, but the lands of the Magyars remained submerged under the Ottoman Empire until 1699, when Hungary was freed by the Treaty of Carlowitz. During the religious strife of the Thirty Years' War (1618–48), Bohemia, stirred by the teachings of the reformer Jan Hus, sought to establish a Protestant king in place of its Catholic Habsburg ruler,

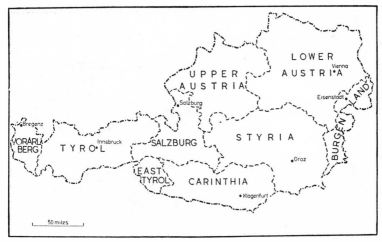

Fig. 45. Austria: provinces and provincial capitals.

and, as the result of defeat at the Battle of the White Mountain, 1621, the Czechs became largely Germanized. The 18th century saw some social and economic reform under the 'enlightened despots', the Empress Maria Theresa and her son, the Emperor Joseph II. Decadence, however, characterized the period following the Congress of Vienna, in 1815, for the Austrians had suffered defeat by Napoleon at Austerlitz in 1805 and the domination of the House of Habsburg by that of Hohenzollern was determined by the Prussian victory at Sadowa in 1866. The Dual Monarchy was established the following year, the Emperor Franz Josef ruling both Austria and Hungary from Vienna. In the Empire, the language of the majority, especially in Vienna and the Alpine provinces, was German, but Czechs, Slovaks, Magyars, Slovenes, Serbs, Croats and Italians formed minority groups.   Over all was a certain unity imposed by allegiance to the Roman Catholic Church. Today, except for small groups of peasants speaking Slovene in southern Carinthia and Styria (totalling 22,500 in 1951), and for the Magyars and Croats of the Burgenland (totalling 5,000 in 1951), accounting for a total minority of only 0·3 per cent, Austria is entirely German in language and culture.   The pre-war Jewish element, which played so large a part in the life of Vienna, has also been largely eliminated.

Austria is mainly a mountainous state, with few centres of urban life, apart from Vienna.   Most of the other large towns are the regional capitals of the provinces; Linz, with a population of

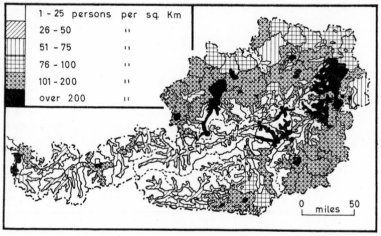

1 - 25 persons per sq. Km
26 - 50   ,,
51 - 75   ,,
76 - 100   ,,
101 - 200   ,,
over 200   ,,

0   miles   50

FIG. 46. Austria: density of population in relation to improved land.

195,978, is the chief town of Upper Austria; Innsbruck, with 100,695, is the administrative centre of the Tyrol; Klagenfurt, with 69,218, of Carinthia; Graz, with 237,080, of Styria; and Salzburg, with 108,114, of the province of Salzburg.   Vienna, with its present population of 1·76 million, dominates, to an overwhelming degree, the urban life and thought of the country.   A cosmopolitan city, it epitomizes the centuries of resistance to non-Germanic advance from the lower Danube valley and also the modern ' Drang nach Osten ' of Greater Germany.   In contrast stand the conservative and Catholic peasantry of the Alpine *Länder*, where traditional modes of life, adapted to a mountainous environment, are still maintained.   In these regions of strong relief, with little space for settlement, the land is cultivated on the traditional strip system, where physical circumstances permit, though most of the land cleared of forest is under pasture.   In the Tyrol, the massive farmhouse is dominated by a large wooden roof, a typical Teutonic feature, contrasting with a more primitive thatched roof, a Slovene feature, in the frontier province of Carinthia.   Each province maintains, as in the Swiss Alps, its traditional style of dress and custom. Vienna, on the other hand, with over 23 per cent of the total population of the country, remains, in spite of its recent internal division and impoverishment, a great European city, rich in its cultural and artistic heritage.

The importance of the modern Austrian Republic, as indeed in the past, has been out of proportion to the economic resources of the State.   Her position astride the eastern Alps and the upper Danube valley is that of a cross-roads.   Apart from the fact that the Danube valley has been a major routeway into Central Europe since the Bronze Age, Vienna's nodal significance lies in its position at the point where the Danube routeway is crossed by that from the loess lands of Polish Galicia and the Moravian or March corridor to the Adriatic coastlands.   Moreover, within the eastern Alps lie such historically significant passes as the Brenner, at only 4,495 ft., since 1919 on the Tyrolean divide between Austria and Italy.   To the west, there is fairly easy access to Switzerland and Liechtenstein by means of the Arlberg route; in the south-east, the Pontebba and Tarvisio passes provide long-frequented ways between Italy and Carinthia, with minor passes such as the Loibl and Seeberg, as well as the Drave valley itself, offering links between Carinthia and Carniola.   Internally, the wide barrier of the eastern Alps is breached at a number of points, so that the Inn valley may be reached from Bavaria over the Fern, Seefeld and Achen passes, as well as directly through the gorge at Kufstein.   Eastwards, the upper Salzach valley may be approached from the Zillertal over the Gerlos pass, at 4,856 ft., and the Salzach valley is linked with the Enns over the Mandling pass, at 2,357 ft.   In modern times, the Drau lowlands have been made accessible from Salzburg and the Tyrol by the construction of the Hohe Tauern tunnel and by the completion of the summer tourist road from Salzburg and Zell-am-See to the Gross Glockner and Villach.   In the north-east, the Semmering pass provides an historic, possibly prehistoric route from Klagenfurt and Leoben to Vienna, following in part the Mur-Mürz trench.

ECONOMIC SUMMARY

Austria can never hope to be economically self-sufficient. Since the extinction of the Austro-Hungarian monarchy in 1918, the federal republic has suffered from economic 'malaise'. Only 34·5 per cent of the total area is productive farm land and the total crop production is steadily falling. In all 37 per cent is under forest (mainly coniferous), and 16 per cent under alpine pastures, while vineyards and gardens account for 1·5 per cent, leaving 10 per cent waste land. In view of the fact that 70 per cent of the total area lies in the Alps, much of the farm work is seasonal and there is the problem of winter feeding the stock, mainly on dried hay. Everywhere the continental climate means long cold winters, with abundant snowfall, especially in the mountainous areas (Fig. 4), and warm summers with considerable rainfall, often from brief storms. The system of farming in the Alps is that of polyculture, in contrast with the general practice of stock rearing characteristic of the Swiss Alps, and the economy is more primitive, traditional methods persisting everywhere. Many of the holdings suffer from over-division, through the system of inheritance, so that only 2·7 per cent exceed 125 acres, 42 per cent are between 12 and 1·2 acres and 10·3 per cent are of less than 2·47 acres (one hectare). The persistence of methods of land use evolved through centuries of adaptation to an environment of rugged relief, steep slopes and thin soils, makes the use of machinery impracticable, except in regions external to the Alps, such as the Danube valley and the Vienna basin. The upper limits of cultivation vary from 6,000 ft. in the Örtler massif to 4,265 ft. on the northern slopes of the Hohe Tauern but 5,400 ft. on the southern. Below 3,300 ft. vines, maize, fruit trees and tobacco are grown, especially in Carinthia, Styria and the Vienna basin. In view of the total population of 7·2 million (23 per cent of which consists of the urban market of Vienna), Austria has necessarily to import much of her food supplies. In the past, trade with Hungary, the lower Danubian lands and the Balkans was vital, especially in wheat, maize and meat. Today, these sources of supply are made difficult of access by the Iron Curtain.

So far there has been no serious attempt at agrarian reform, peasant holdings of under 12 acres persisting, except where vineyards have been established or grain farms created, as on the loess lands of the Vienna basin. It is estimated that 48 per cent of the total population lives on 6 per cent of the land, while 36 per cent live on 22 per cent of the area on medium-sized holdings.

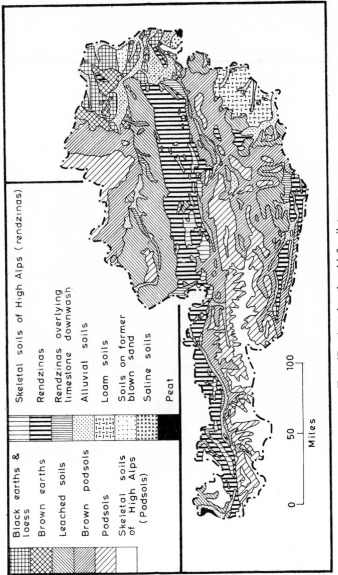

Black earths & loess

Brown earths

Leached soils

Brown podsols

Podsols

Skeletal soils of High Alps (Podsols)

Skeletal soils of High Alps (rendzinas)

Rendzinas

Rendzinas overlying limestone downwash

Alluvial soils

Loam soils

Soils on former blown sand

Saline soils

Peat

0   50   100

Miles

Fig. 47. Austria: the chief soil types.

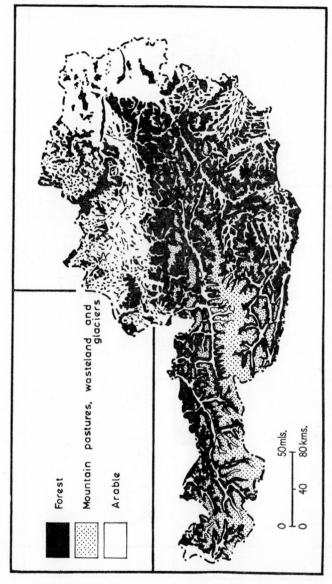

Fig. 48. Austria: the chief types of land use.

Forest

Mountain pastures, wasteland and glaciers

Arable

50mls.
80kms.
0   40
0

Large estates of over 250 acres account for 45 per cent of the total, these belonging to the nobility, the church, bankers and business men. The outcome of this archaic system of land holding is large-scale rural depopulation in favour of industrial occupations either within the Alps or in the marginal lowlands and cities, especially Vienna.

The best arable land lies in the Burgenland (39 per cent of the total area) and the Vienna basin (47 per cent); Upper Austria returning 28 per cent, and Styria and Carinthia 15 and 12 per cent each respectively, in spite of their extensive share of the Alps. The provinces in the western and northern Alps have the lowest percentages of arable land; Vorarlberg, with its economy akin to the adjacent Swiss cantons, recording only 1 per cent; while the Tyrol returns 3 per cent, mainly accounted for by the cultivated river terraces above the Inn, and Salzburg has 7 per cent. Most of the land under arable produces wheat as well as maize, potatoes and fodder crops. Sugar beet is grown only outside the Alps and the vine is restricted to the slopes of the Danube gorge (the Weinviertel), the terraces of the Leitha hills and the Wienerwald, the Graz region and the southern slopes of the Alps and terraces in southern Carinthia. Conversely, the pre-eminently pastoral regions lie in the Tyrol, Vorarlberg and Salzburg, where the practice of seasonal transhumance is practised. The number of stock decreased during the war, though the number of sheep increased, to meet the demand for wool.

Austria is rich in resources of timber, especially softwood, ranking fourth in Europe in this respect. Over 84 per cent of the timber is coniferous; 10 per cent consisting of beech, 2 per cent of oak and the remainder of other broad-leaved trees. Firs account for 58 per cent of the forested area and the most heavily forested provinces are Styria (with 19 per cent under timber) and Carinthia (44 per cent). Before the 1939–45 war the amount of forest land privately owned was 44 per cent, 15 per cent belonging to the state, the rest being the property of the communes and parishes. Much of the timber is preserved as a precaution against rock slides, avalanches and soil erosion, and also to protect mountain reservoirs. The timber which is cut is mainly marketed as sawn timber, about a quarter of the cut being used for fuel, but this figure is decreasing. A subsidiary industry is that of resin extraction from the black pines of Lower Austria and the larches of Carinthia and Styria, while oil of turpentine is distilled in Wiener Neustadt and elsewhere in Lower Austria. The output of sawn timber and of forest products from the Austrian forests is sufficient to supply the home market as well as to provide an export commodity.

Industrially, Austria has greater potentialities than her Alpine neighbour, Switzerland, and also greater mineral resources, but their development has been retarded by lack of capital and modern economic depression and instability. The chief coalfield is at Grünbach-am-Schneeberg in Styria, and the total output of anthracite coal in Austria in 1964 was 1000,000 metric tons, compared with 230,000 tons in 1937, but to this figure must be added an output of lignite totalling 5·7 million tons (1964). Some Tertiary lignite occurs in Styria near Leoben, as well as in the Lavant valley of Carinthia, but the main deposits lie in and around the Hausruck plateau of Upper Austria, in the Alpine Foreland. Petroleum and natural gas occur in the northern part of the Vienna basin, especially at Zistersdorf, as well as to the west in the Marchfeld. Production in these fields increased rapidly after the *Anschluss* in 1938 (1937 : 32,000 tons of oil; 1944: 1·2 million tons; 1963: 2·6 million tons). The output of petroleum in Austria is sufficient for the home market but, as the Zistersdorf oilfield lies in the former Russian Occupation Zone, much of the oil is still being sent to Eastern Europe. In all, Austria has some 30,000 people employed in the mining industry, including, in addition to the above minerals, iron, zinc, copper, lead ore and other metals. Most of the iron ore comes from the Erzberg mines in Styria, the total output of iron ore and manganese being 3·7 million tons in 1963, compared with 1·8 million tons in 1937. Non-ferrous metals also occur in the Austrian Alps, notably copper at Mittelberg, near Salzburg; lead and zinc at Bleiberg in Carinthia; while magnesite is found in Styria, as well as in the Tyrol. Antimony has long been mined in the Burgenland and bauxite is worked in Vorarlberg.

The development of heavy industry in Austria, based largely on the traditional smelting of Styrian iron ore with local charcoal and more recently on imported Ruhr or Silesian coke, is of growing importance, though there is not much specialization for export. Before the war, Austrian heavy industry came to be largely dependent on the investment of German capital in a relatively ' safe ' strategic region, especially where the *Ostalpine Montangesellschaft* was concerned. After the *Anschluss* in 1938, Austria was regarded as virtually German semi-colonial territory, the Styrian iron and steel works being re-named the Hermann Göring plant. Today, a modernized industrial ' conurbation ' extends from Donawitz-Leoben to Bruck along the Mur-Mürz valley, in the direction of the Semmering pass. For many years during the Habsburg monarchy, these blast furnaces and steel mills were subsidiary to the Skoda works in Bohemia and Moravia, but by 1938 the *Ostalpine Montan-*

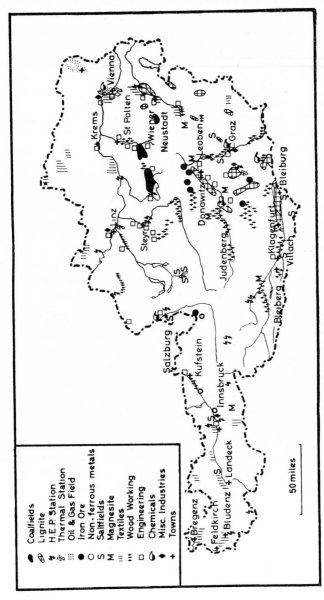

FIG. 49.   Austria: distribution of mineral resources, power and manufacturing industries.

gesellschaft monopolized 95 per cent of the total steel output.   After the war, much of the plant was removed by the Russians.   Under the stimulus of American capital, modern developments have taken place, not only in Styria but also at Linz, on the Danube.   The major producing plants are at Donawitz, where the three blast furnaces yield pig iron used in the production of blooms, billets and bars. At Judenberg, higher up the Mur valley, there are now both open-hearth and electric-arc furnaces producing alloy steel.   In Upper Austria, the four plants at Linz are being completely integrated, with a capacity of 2 million tons of pig iron and 2 million tons of basic Bessemer and open-hearth steel.   In view of Austria's lack of

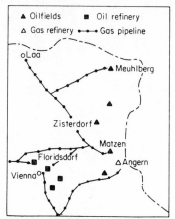

FIG. 50.   Oil and natural gas in Austria.

coking coal, it is planned to develop hydro-electric power for use in the production of alloy steel as well as in the reduction of non-ferrous metals, such as nickel (at Saalfelden) and copper (Salzburg), as well as chromium and molybdenum.   Nevertheless, Austrian heavy industry remains unbalanced, primary production being too great compared with that of finished metal goods.   The output of raw steel in 1963 was 2·9 million metric tons.

Hydro-electric power is not yet developed as much as in Switzerland, though it now totals 18 million kWh. per annum, and so it assumes national and supra-national importance.[1]   Before the war, power stations in the Vorarlberg, as well as at Achen-See and Gerlos in the Tyrol, supplied electrical current to Bavaria and thus to the Ruhr industrial region.   Today a super grid scheme is planned

[1] R. Sinclair: ' Austria's Place in Europe's Electric Power Exchange ', *Geog. Review*, Vol. 54, 1964.

to serve a wide market in Central Europe, in view of the potential surplus beyond the domestic demand.   There is little development of industry in the Alps directly related to power supplies as in the Swiss Alps.   The great Kaprun-Hohe Tauern scheme[1] is primarily designed to supply current to the grid which already sends electricity from Gerlos, etc. to Vienna. New power stations have been built on the Enns, at Ternberg and Staning, and others have been completed, as at Ybbs-Persenbeug, which will send current to Czechoslovakia in summer in return for thermal electricity in winter (Fig. 51).   Much of this current finds a market in Linz, where, in addition to steel produced in modern electric-arc furnaces, a heavy chemical industry has been established for the production of nitrates, using atmospheric nitrogen and chemical fertilizers. Further power developments are also taking place on the Danube. In Salzburg, the aluminium industry at Lend, as well as at Ranshofen on the Inn, takes electrical current off the grid.   Most of the bauxite

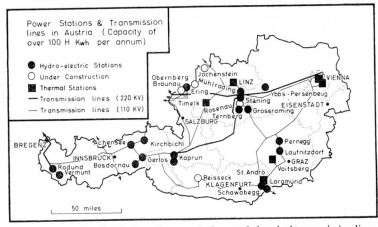

FIG. 51.   Austria: distribution of power stations and electrical transmission lines

now comes from Yugoslavia.   The output of aluminium was increased to 77,700 metric tons in 1957.

Apart from isolated centres of metallurgy, mainly in remote Alpine valleys and at Linz, there is little development of manufacturing industries in Austria outside Vienna.   Many Alpine towns, such as Innsbruck, Klagenfurt and Graz, have their traditional craft industries, and the embroidery work of Vorarlberg, originally stimulated from St. Gallen, is well known.   After the war, the rôle

[1] A. F. A. Mutton: ' The Glockner-Kaprun Hydro-electric Project, Hohe Tauern, Austria ', *Geographical Review*, Vol. 41, 1951, pp. 332–4.

of Vienna as a producer of luxury goods and as a fashion centre suffered through its division into the four occupation zones and by its difficulty of access from western Europe.   Competition from Czech textiles, glass, leather and porcelain, already keen before the war, has again asserted itself.   The international importance of Vienna as a banking centre has declined since the Nazi persecution of the Jews, who once formed a large element in the population of the city.   Until 1955, the tourist industry in Vienna was very seriously hampered by travel restrictions but it has since revived fairly rapidly.   In Austria as a whole, the organization of the tourist industry has been on a small scale compared with Switzerland but it is now rapidly expanding partly on account of lower costs than in neighbouring Switzerland.   The number of foreign tourists exceeded 5 million in 1961.

CHAPTER 8

AUSTRIA: REGIONAL STUDIES

Vorarlberg

THIS most westerly province of Austria marches with Germany through lake Constance and with Switzerland and the Principality of Liechtenstein along the upper Rhine valley. Broadly diamond shaped, Vorarlberg drains northwards to the Ill, the highest elevations being reached in the Silvretta Range, where the Piz Buin rises to 10,864 ft. The province includes a cross-section of the western Alps, for, in the south, the frontier regions of the Rhätikon and the Silvretta Range form part of the Austride folds, while to the east the transverse ranges of the Lechtaler Alps and the Bregenzerwald are part of the calcareous and *Flysch* zones of the Pre-Alps. The outlook of the province is partly westwards towards the neighbouring Swiss cantons of Graubünden, St. Gallen and Appenzell, the famous embroidery and textile industries of Vorarlberg developing under the stimulus of Swiss enterprise in St. Gallen, notably in the Bregenzerwald and the Walgau region of the Ill valley. These industries have served to draw labour from the Alpine valleys, but the chief occupation of the population is pastoral farming, the more gentle slopes of the Alps providing hay pasture in a region of thickly dispersed chalet settlement. The chief urban centres are the lake-side town of Bregenz, at the head of lake Constance, and also Dornbirn, Feldkirch and Bludenz, all lying in the broad Rhine-Ill trench. Eastwards, Vorarlberg is linked with the Tyrol through the Arlberg pass, between the Klostertal and the Rosannatal. This is the route utilized by the Arlberg tunnel which serves the Arlberg Express line from Paris *via* Buchs to Vienna. It offers the most direct route from the upper Rhine valley, which it leaves at Feldkirch, to the longitudinal trench of the Inn below Landeck. The line was completed from Zürich in 1884.

The Tyrol

The entirely Alpine province of the Tyrol (*German*, Tirol) extends from the Swiss and Italian frontiers in the south-west and south to the German frontier in the north. To the west lies Vorarlberg and, to the east, Salzburg. The Tyrol lies on the northern slope

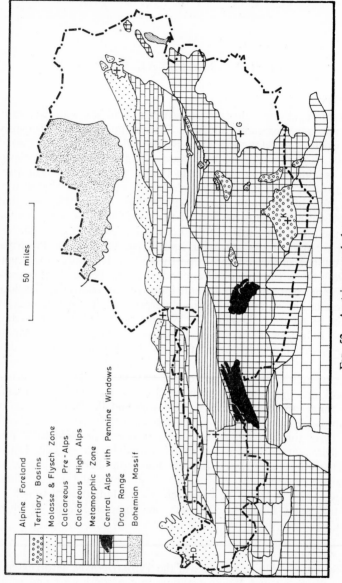

Fig. 52. Austria: morphology.

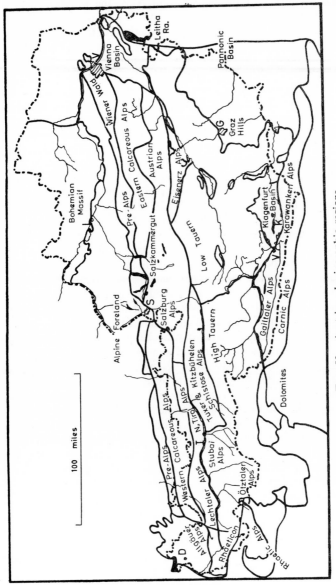

Fig. 53.   Austria: physiographic regions.

of the western part of the Austrian Alps, the province being, in large measure, the basin of the upper Inn, though the trench of the upper Lech is also included.   Structurally, the Tyrol comprises within its wide limits part of the Lower Engadine ' window ' on the Swiss border; the central Alpine crystalline ranges, high enough to be permanently snow-capped, as in the Ötztal, Stubai and Ziller Alps; the metamorphic zone of the Tuxer and part of the Kitz- bühler Alps; the calcareous High Alps of the North Tyrol; and the *Flysch* zone along the borders of Vorarlberg and Bavaria.

Some of the finest Austrian Alpine scenery is to be found in the rugged, ice-sculptured mountain country of the Ötztal, Stubai and Ziller Alps.   All these ranges are dissected by a number of valleys of glacial form, opening out northwards to the great furrow of the Inn.   In the west, the Ötztal forms a major trench, walled in to the south by the Wild Spitze (12,369 ft.), the Hochwilde (11,385 ft.), and the Zuckerhütl (11,516 ft.).   At the head of this valley lies the summer resort of Obergurgl.   To the east, a number of valleys lead down to the main trench of the Wipptal and of these the Stubai is, perhaps, the best known and most accessible.   All these valleys, except the Wipptal which leads to the Brenner pass, end in *cul de sacs*, and all are settled up to 6,000 ft.   The lowest breach in the Austrian High Alps lies at the head of the Wipptal, in a region of beheaded drainage, where the Brenner pass, at 4,495 ft., lies on the narrow water parting between drainage northwards by the Sill to the upper Inn and southwards by the Eisack to the Adige.   The Brenner pass also lies where the width of the Tyrol from the German to the Italian frontier is only 34 miles.   It is crossed by both a motor highway and a double-track railway and, although the use of the pass declined in the latter part of the last century with the cutting of the Simplon and St. Gotthard tunnels through the Swiss Alps, today it forms a major link between Central Europe and the Mediterranean.   On the summit of the pass, fragments of the Roman paved road have been uncovered, revealing the ruts worn by the chariots.   During the Middle Ages, this pass was frequented by traders from Salzburg and the ' fair ' towns of southern Germany, such as Augsburg and Ratisbon, on their way through Innsbruck to the cities of northern Italy.   The road over the pass was known as the ' salt road ', on account of the importance of that commodity, obtained especially from the Hallein district near Salzburg and from the Inn valley at Solbad Hall, above which a number of ancient villages are located on the terrace known as the *Mittelgebirge*, such as Rinn and Igls.   Here the dusky peach blossom adds a colourful touch to farmsteads surrounded by arable strips left bare in spring below the edge of the retreating snow line. The stepped valley of the Sill which ends at the Brenner pass has steep slopes which remain largely forested, except where clearance and settlement have occurred, often on detrital fans where side streams debouch on to the main valley. The Stubaital, which opens north-eastwards to the Sill, provides striking examples of the importance of the insolation factor in relation to village settlement, notably at Neustift and Mieders, in a valley penetrated in pre-Germanic times, possibly on account of its minerals.[1]

To the east of the Brenner region, the Ziller valley offers an easy route between the Tuxer and Kitzbühler Alps, followed by the local railway from Jenbach as far as Mayrhofen. This village, with its growing tourist industry, lies at a point where a marked change in the landscape occurs, for below it the wide, flat-floored, steep-sided trench of the Ziller valley extends for about 20 miles before opening on to the Inn valley opposite Jenbach. Above Mayrhofen, the rich meadow lands and orchards give way to steep, forested, gorge-like valleys, drained by mountain torrents known as the Tuxer, Zemm, Stillup and Ziller. Towards the Zillertal Alps, these valleys broaden again, to end in *cirque* heads. Warm springs have led to the development of Hintertux as a small Alpine resort in the upper Tuxer valley, while Ginzling is a centre for the Zemm-tal glacial scenery. Below Mayrhofen, a road strikes off from Zell-am-Ziller for the Gerlos pass, which provides a connection eastwards at 4,856 ft. between the Tyrol and Salzburg, though the road is closed by snow in the winter months.

The upper Inn valley is a complex feature, partly structural in origin. It leaves Switzerland and the Lower Engadine 'window' at the spectacular defile of Finstermünz, above which an ancient high-level route leads from the Inn valley through Nauders to the Rescia or Reschen-Scheideck pass and so to the upper Adige and northern Italy. In this upper section of the Inn trench, the valley sides are wall-like, that facing north-eastwards (on the *Schalten-seite*) remaining long in deep shadow and mostly under forest. On the south-eastward-facing slope or *Sonnenseite*, with much more favourable insolation, villages occur on the 4,000-ft. bench above the main glacial trench of the Inn, as at Serfaus and Fiss, near the limit of wheat cultivation. The Inn leaves the Austrian Engadine at Landeck, where it describes a wide sweep before being joined by the Rosanna headstream from the eastern foot of the Arlberg pass. This valley, which carries the main route from Switzerland into

[1] A. Garnett: *Insolation and Relief*, 1937, Trans. Inst. Br. Geographers, Vol. V, 1937, pp. 22–33.

Austria *via* Vorarlberg, continues westwards the main direction of the trench of the Inn. East of the Arlberg tunnel, the villages of St. Anton and St. Jakob have become tourist and winter sports centres. Between Landeck and Imst, the upper Inn trench runs parallel with the Lechtaler Alps which extend in a wide arc from Bludenz, in the province of Vorarlberg, to the Fern pass, to the north-north-west of the Inn. At Imst, the course of the Inn has been diverted by valley ice advancing from the Ötztaler Alps. The pyramidal-ended block of Tschirgant rises between the former course of the Inn, now followed by the little stream of the Gurgl, and that which it follows today. Below this point, the Inn occupies a structural divide between the crystalline High Alps to the south and the metamorphic zone of the Karwendel Alps to the north. It is thought that stagnant ice was responsible for the striking terrace fragments, with their morainic débris, preserved at about 2,700 ft., along this west-east section of the Inn valley. They are represented north of Innsbruck by the terrace below the Hafelekar Spitz, followed by both the ancient road, now a modern highway leading to the Fern pass and Bavaria, and by the railway which ascends from Innsbruck to the Seefeld tunnel *en route* to Munich, and also by the *Mittelgebirge*, south of Innsbruck. Here the terrace is in places nearly a mile wide, providing the site of a number of prosperous agricultural villages, where the climate is sufficiently favourable for maize to ripen and for orchard fruits to flourish. The thick cluster of villages on this terrace may also be related to the importance of the salt trade which formerly passed along here from Innsbruck to the Brenner pass.

Innsbruck, the ' bridge town on the Inn ', is the regional and historic capital of North Tyrol and today it has a population of 100,695. It lies 1,500 ft. above sea-level, on a gently sloping detrital fan built up by the Sill tributary of the Inn. This stream divides the town of Innsbruck and its ancient southern suburb of Wilten from Pradl to the east. The gravel fan of the Sill has deflected the course of the Inn to the north-west and here the main river cuts into the edge of a much deeper cone built up by the Weissenbach which joins the Inn from the north. The general setting of the town is the glacially over-deepened trench of the Inn, dominated by the Karwendel range to the north, with its markedly even sky line at 7,500 ft. To the south the Wipptal carries the sinuous route towards the Brenner pass, the South Tyrol and Bolzano (*German*, Bozen). Northwards, this historic route between Italy and Germany is continued over the Seefeld and Fern passes into southern Bavaria. Eastwards it continues as the ' salt road ' from the

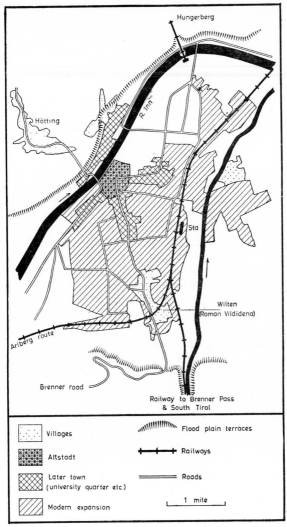

FIG. 54. The site and growth of Innsbruck.

Brenner to Solbad Hall, a few miles below Innsbruck, and to Hallein in Salzburg. The commercial importance of Solbad Hall is commemorated in its *Munt Thurm,* where coins were minted in late medieval times. Although the longitudinal trench of the Inn has been of importance in the growth of Innsbruck, its significance has never compared with these transverse routes linking the 'fair' towns of southern Germany with northern Italy over the Brenner pass. Iron copper and silver ore mining have also contributed to the importance of the Innsbruck region in the past, in addition to the local extraction of salt.

The significance of the site of Innsbruck is indicated by the antiquity of settlement here. To the north-west of the town, there is evidence of Neolithic occupation. The Roman town of *Vildidena* survives in Wilten, on the gravel fan of the Sill to the south of Innsbruck, where the medieval monastery was built. In Innsbruck, the *Altstadt* formed a compact unit east of the medieval bridge and was surrounded by defensive walls by 1180.[1] The site of the moat may be traced along the thoroughfares known as the Marktgraben, Burggraben and Herrengraben. Within these medieval limits survive the Hofburg, the open market place and the *Goldenes Dachl* (Golden Roof), together with the Patricians' houses and the arcaded streets known as the *Lauben*. The architectural splendour of the medieval town reflects the importance of its guild crafts and industries, its international trade, especially in salt, cloth, metal work and jewellery, as well as its political importance as a residence of the German Emperors. It was incorporated as a city in 1239. Across the bridge, another market centre developed, known as Hötting, around the ecclesiastical nuclei of the churches of St. Nicholas and St. Maria. Innsbruck suffered from the decline of traffic over the Brenner after the opening of trade with the New World, but the University was founded in 1677, adjacent to the baroque Hofkirche. A century later the town was linked with the Neustadt by the impressive thoroughfare named after the Empress Maria Theresa. The modern town has spread beyond the Inn and the Sill to include a number of outlying villages and the coming of the railway from Munich to the Brenner in 1861 brought much traffic and stimulated new industries in the town, especially that of catering for tourists visiting the North Tyrol.

The lower Inn valley begins below Innsbruck, where the Inn takes a generally north-easterly course between the Tuxer and Kitzbühler Alps and the Calcareous Alps of the North Tyrol. Its broad, flat-floored trench contrasts with the precipitous slopes on both sides, cut through at a number of points by tributary valleys, some of which, like the Zillertal, are also deep-cut, flat-floored, glacial trenches. On the opposite side of the Inn valley, hummocky moraines block the high-level trough in which the Achen-See lies to the north of Jenbach, so that it drains northwards to the Isar in

[1] N. Krebs: *Die Ostalpen u. das Heutige Österreich*, Vol. 2, 1928, p. 81, etc.

Bavaria. The lake forms a reservoir for the Achen-See power station. Its marginal slopes are so steep and frequently subjected to rock slides from the Karwendel mountains that forest usually extends to the water's edge. Only at Pertisau is there space for a small settlement and resort on an alluvial fan. The intense turquoise colouring of the lake in summer bears comparison with many of its Swiss counterparts and it is visited by a number of tourists from both Bavaria and the Tyrol. Further down the Inn valley, at Wörgl, the route to Salzburg over the Thurn pass strikes off through Brixen and the winter sports resort of Kitzbühel. The Inn finally leaves Austria through a spectacular gorge cut through the limestone folds of the Pre-Alps of North Tyrol below Kufstein, where the valley closes in and is dominated by high limestone craggy peaks.

The Pre-Alps of North Tyrol separate the Inn valley from Bavaria by means of a series of ranges trending generally parallel with the Inn, the upper Lech and Isar tributaries of the Danube. Apart from the metamorphic zone of the Karwendel range extending north of the Inn from Innsbruck to Jenbach, the mountains consist mainly of highly folded Triassic and Jurassic rocks, with limestones predominating. Sharply accidented ridges characterize the Lechtaler Alps in the west as well as the ranges of North Tyrol. Between these two features, the Fern pass, at 3,630 ft., is followed today by a modern motor road between Innsbruck, Füssen and Augsburg. To the east lies the Scharnitz pass, above the upper Isar, on the Bavarian frontier above Mittenwald. The Achen pass, at 2,823 ft., offers a minor route between the Inn valley at Jenbach and southern Bavaria, the main connection being along the Inn valley itself through Kufstein. In the Pre-Alps, the culminating peak is the Zugspitze, rising to 9,711 ft. on the Austro-German frontier, at the western end of the Wetterstein range. It is an ice-sculptured mass, rising well above the tree-line into a region of arêtes, scree-covered slopes and *cirques* in which snow lies all the year. To the north of the main Pre-Alps lies a belt of *Flysch*, forming a narrow, mountainous border on the northern frontier of the Tyrol. This Tertiary conglomerate forms the Allgäu Alps in the west, where the feature expands westwards into Vorarlberg. These outer folds of the Alps form a continuous east-west barrier except where they are crossed by the great stream of the Lech, which flows in a series of alternating open basins, as at Reutte, and narrow transverse gorges, as above Füssen. To the east of Reutte, in a longitudinal trough further eroded by ice, lies the remote Plan-See, where scree mantles much of the slope to the lake.

Salzburg

The province of Salzburg is carved out of that part of the Austrian Alps which is drained by the Salzach river system.   In the south, the watershed is formed by the Hohe Tauern and by the western end of the Niedere Tauern ranges.   To the north, the trench of the Salzach forms part of the diagonal furrow through the eastern

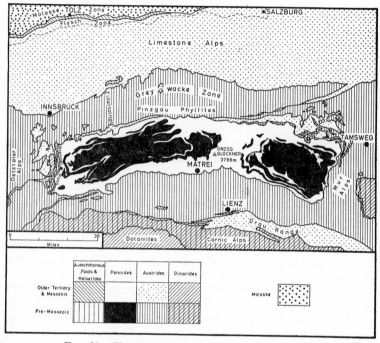

FIG. 55.   The Pennine window of the Hohe Tauern.

Alps, followed by the Inn to the west and the Enns to the east. Below the Klamm pass, the Salzach turns northwards along the gorge cut across the Salzburg Calcareous Alps, below which the river forms the frontier with Germany until it joins the Inn in the Foreland region.

The Hohe Tauern 'window' in the south is a complex region in which the older Pennine folds are surrounded by the Austrides,[1] the crystalline rocks of the 'window' being exposed by the erosion of the former covering of younger rocks and forming the highest peaks in Austria.   This is the region of the Austrian High Alps,

[1] E. Bailey: *Tectonic Essays, mainly Alpine*, 1935, pp. 129–41.

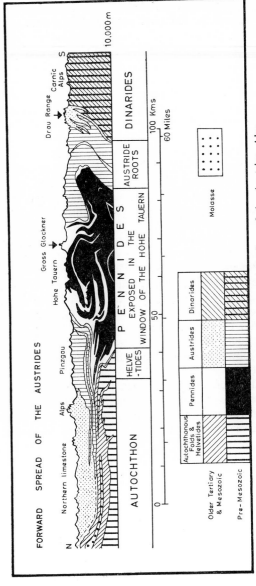

Fig. 56. Section across the Central Region of the Austrian Alps.

with the Gross Venediger, rising to 12,041 ft. on the boundary
with the East Tyrol, and the Riffeltor, attaining 10,203 ft. on the
Carinthian boundary. Glaciers descend from these snow-capped
peaks and form the source of a number of streams which flow in
parallel trenches to the Salzach. At the western end of the range,
the valley of the Krimml is of special note on account of the three
spectacular waterfalls which occur above the junction of the stream
with the upper Salzach. Glaciation has considerably modified the
drainage here and only the narrow Gerlos pass, lying at 4,856 ft.,
divides the upper Salzach trench from that of the Gerlos tributary
of the Ziller in the Tyrol. In this region is to be found one of the
largest of the older Alpine power stations, the Gerlos plant having
an annual capacity of 920,000 kWh. A valley of note is that of
Kaprun, above the village of that name. Its glacial form, especially
its stepped longitudinal profile and its steep gradient, make it very
suitable for hydro-electric power development, and the valley is now
the centre of the Glockner-Kaprun hydro-electric development.[1]
This was carried out through three stages: the dam at Limberg was
completed in 1951; the upper dam at Mooserboden marking
the second stage in the creation of a series of reservoirs to serve the
power house at Kaprun. The third involved diverting the upper
Möll drainage from the Carinthian side of the slope to the
Stausee reservoir north of the Gross Glockner. The precipitous slopes of the Kaprun valley enable water to be carried
through penstocks down a concentrated drop of 3,937 ft. above
the Kaprun power station. There is as yet no development of
industry in this typical Alpine valley and the current will be fed
into the grid which supplies Vienna from the Alps. East of the
Kaprun valley lies that of the Gastein, which is followed by the
Hohe Tauern railway up to the Klamm pass, which it ascends in
a sudden curve from the Salzach valley, and so makes for the
tunnel through the divide lying beyond the high-altitude resort of
Bad Gastein. This electrified line is a vital link between Switzerland, southern Germany and south-eastern Europe. To the east,
the general altitude of the Niedere Tauern is lower, the Radstädter
Tauern rising to only 8,169 ft., but the range is little penetrated.
The only road through the region ascends from the upper Enns
valley to follow the upper Mur below Tamsweg. This part of the
Mur valley, known as the Lungau, is a region of isolation and
retarded development when compared with the rest of Salzburg.
    In the upper Salzach valley, regional *gäue* are denoted by the

[1] A. F. A. Mutton: ' The Glockner-Kaprun Hydro-electric Project, Hohe
Tauern, Austria ', *Geographical Review*, Vol. 41, 1951, pp. 332–4.

local names of Pinzgau and Pongau. Upper Pinzgau is the name of the Salzach valley below the Gerlos pass and the village of Krimml. It forms a broad structural trench lying between the slopes of the Hohe Tauern and the Kitzbüheler Alps in which villages, such as Mittersill and Niedernsill, are located on terraces or detrital fans above the ill-drained floor of the valley. Middle Pinzgau lies north of Zell-am-See and drains independently of the upper Salzach by means of the Saalach. This stream first flows eastwards from the Kitzbüheler Alps along the Glemmtal and then northwards past Saalfelden, where it begins its transverse section across the dazzling white limestone ranges of the Salzburg Pre-Alps to join the Salzach below Salzburg. A strip of marshland marks the region of indeterminate drainage between the elbow of the Saalach and the lake of Zell. Moraines at the lower end of the Glemmtal appear to have blocked the escape northwards of drainage from the lake. The Pinzgau provides the easiest route from the Hohe Tauern region to Salzburg and is followed by the Gross Glockner highway. In contrast, the lower Salzach valley is cut through a post-glacial gorge, known as the Pongau, and the defile begins below Bruck. Both road and railway follow a narrow bench above the rushing torrent of the Salzach, and at St. Johann the river turns northwards to break through a gap between the Hagen and Tennen Mountains, the road following the bend of the river through the fierce defile known as the Pass Lueg. In the section of the valley between this pass and Salzburg is the ancient salt-working centre of Hallein, where rock salt is obtained from the Trias. Its importance in the Middle Ages gave rise to traffic along the road from Hallein over the Brenner pass to Italy. A modern industry in upper Pongau using local water power is the reduction of alumina imported from Yugoslavia and treated at Lend.

Salzburg, the ' salt town ' and the capital of the province, has a population of over 108,114. It lies in a beautiful site at the foot of the Salzburg Calcareous Alps, with foothills of *Flysch* rising on each side of the Salzach river which flows through the centre of the city. These residual buttes are the Mönch Berg (1,500 ft.) and the Kapuziner Berg (1,980 ft.), and they form an amphitheatre of hills around the lowland in which Salzburg lies. These hills provided the Celtic settlement sites in the region but the Romans founded the city of Juvavum at the foot of the Mönch Berg. This town was destroyed during the period of the *Völkerwanderung*. Medieval Salzburg dates from the founding of the bishopric in 788, after which the town became the centre of dispersal of Christianity across southern Bavaria and into the Tyrol. Salzburg also flourished commercially, like Hallein (a Celtic settlement), as centres of the salt trade with northern Italy and these two aspects of the town's history are still reflected in its dual character. During the 16th and 17th centuries, Salzburg enjoyed considerable prosperity and much of the town was rebuilt in baroque style, the flamboyant

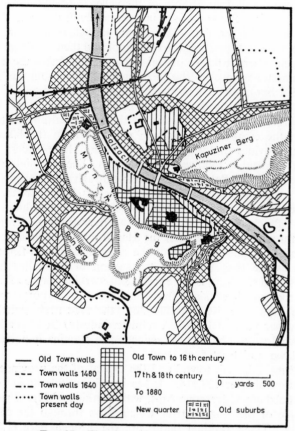

FIG. 57. The site and growth of Salzburg.

expression of which is well exemplified by the cathedral and bishop's palace. The late 19th century saw the revival of Salzburg as a traffic node, for the Orient Express line from Munich to Klagenfurt and the Balkans was routed through the town. In 1908, a line was opened to Zell-am-See, thus opening up a new area of the Salzburg Alps to tourists, a process which was carried further by the completion of the Gross Glockner Alpine road before the last war. Salzburg's international significance is also the outcome of its association with the early life of Mozart, a fact commemorated in the annual Music Festival, which attracts many visitors to the town.

East Tyrol

This small province lies between the South Tyrol, ceded to Italy in 1919, and Carinthia, the province of Salzburg forming the northern boundary. Hemmed in by the snow-capped peaks of the Hohe Tauern to the north, East Tyrol offers an east–west passage between the Trentino region of Alpine Italy and the valleys of southern Carinthia. The main and historic routeway follows the trench of the upper Drau, utilized by the railway from Bolzano (Bozen) and Brixen through Lienz, the regional capital of East Tyrol, to Villach in Carinthia. The Drau valley is known here as the Pustertal, and at Lienz, where it is joined by the Isel from the north, the river turns sharply south-eastwards towards the Tyrolean ' gate ' and Carinthia. The Lesachtal offers a minor alternative route from the Pustertal to Carinthia over the Kartitsch saddle and then along the Gail valley to the Carinthian ' gate '.

The relief features of the East Tyrol continue those of the adjacent provinces. To the north, the Hohe Tauern ' window ' includes two of the highest peaks of the range, the Venediger, rising to 12,042 ft., and the Granat Spitze, to 10,106 ft., while the three provinces of East Tyrol, Salzburg and Carinthia meet in the Eiskogele, at 11,254 ft., north-west of the Gross Glockner. This region provides some of the most splendid glaciated mountain scenery in Austria, with its permanent snow, its glaciers radiating from the high peaks, its hanging valleys and rushing mountain torrents. To the south of this Pennine ' window ', the metamorphic rocks of the Austride folds form the east–west ridge of the Defereggen Alps, the Drau following a line of faulting along the southern margin. This valley, like that of the Isel and the Defereggen, is markedly overdeepened by the passage of valley ice, two lobes of which coalesced in the region of the Lienz basin. Access to the Defereggental is made difficult by the great rock step at its junction with the Isel and through which the Defereggen has cut a deep ravine. To the south, the limestones of the Italian Dolomites sweep round into the east–west ridge of the Lienzer Dolomites. This range occupies a triangular block of rugged relief between the Pustertal and the Lesachtal, drained eastwards by the Gail. The frontier with Italy is defined by the west–east ridge of the Carnic Alps.

The climate of East Tyrol, and the lack of extensive lowlands and general inaccessibility, hamper settlement, so that the region is one of marked impoverishment, little touched by the tourist industry. The high-level valleys, such as the Defereggen and the Virgental which lies parallel to it to the north, experience severe winters, with much snowfall and cool summers, though they lie in the lee of the Hohe Tauern and so are dry compared with those to the north. Late frosts are common and snow may fall late in the spring. On the north-facing slopes of these valleys forest extends to the valley floor, and on the south-facing slope, the *Sonnenseite*, wheat reaches its upper limit and rye and barley are the more important cereal crops.[1] These valleys were settled in comparatively late medieval times, mainly by Slavonic colonizers entering along the Drau and Gail valleys; while German names are not so frequent, except in the Lienz basin and the Isel valley; St. Jacob and St. Leonard in the Defereggental forming exceptions. This valley has been studied in detail on account of the significance of the insolation factor in the location of settlement and in relation to land use.[2] Here permanent settlement is pushed to extreme limits, the highest farmstead which is permanently occupied lying at 5,612 ft., and wheat reaches its upper limit at 5,560 ft. In the upper part of the valley, the older Slavonic settlements are high up the slope where they receive the maximum insolation, the newer farmsteads and villages, such as St. Jacob, once a copper mining centre, are on the lower and gentle slopes of the valley. As the result of a change in the form of the valley in its lower section, settlement avoids the narrow floor and is again found high on the *Sonnenseite*. The importance of the east–west orientation of the Defereggental may be seen when it is contrasted with the north–south trench of the Isel, for, although this main valley lies much lower, below 3,000 ft., little land is under cultivation, wheat being rarely grown. The steep slopes are mainly under forest, like the *Schattenseite* slopes of the Pustertal. It is not until Lienz is reached that the valley opens out into a fairly wide basin under intensive cultivation.

Carinthia

The province of Carinthia (Kärnten) forms Austria's southern frontier province with Italy and Yugoslavia[3] and it owes its historical

[1] N. Krebs: *Die Ostalpen u. das heutige Österreich*, Vol. 2, p. 66.

[2] A. Garnett: *Insolation and Relief*, Trans. Inst. Br. Geographers, Vol. V, Chap. 4, 1937, pp. 34–71.

[3] A. F. A. Mutton: ' Carinthia. A Province of Austria's Southern Frontier ', *Geography*, Vol. 38, 1953, pp. 83–94.

(a) Village of Hintertux, with hay drying on stakes in fields, Tuxer Alps.

15. ALPINE SETTLEMENT IN AUSTRIA

(b) Village of Krimml at the head of the Salzach, province of Salzburg.

(a) The Kaprun valley, the site of the Glockner—Kaprun project, from the Salzach valley.

16. HYDRO-ELECTRIC POWER DEVELOPMENT IN THE HOHE TAUERN

(b) The Westsperre under construction in April, 1950. This dam impounds the Mooserboden reservoir at 6,640 ft.

importance to its function as a passage land between Mediterranean Europe and the middle Danubian lands.   The two foci of these cross routes are Villach and Klagenfurt, both important centres of railway communication, as they have been the destination of over-land routes converging on the Drau lowlands from the Adriatic coastlands and Alpine passes since Roman times.   From the north-west the Hohe Tauern railway penetrates the divide between the Salzach and Drau drainage at 3,675 ft., and, on leaving the 5½-mile long tunnel, it follows the Möll valley to Villach and so to Klagenfurt, thence along the Drau (Drava) valley to Belgrade, with a branch line using a tunnel through the Karawanken Alps to reach Ljubljana and Trieste and another using the Tarvisio gap to Udine and Venice. Apart from the modern Gross Glockner tourist road from Villach to Heiligenblut and so over the Hohe Tauern to Zell-am-See and Salzburg, an ancient road follows the trench of the Drau westwards to the Tyrolean ' gate ' and so along the Pustertal to each Tyrol, where it meets another from the Gail valley and the Carinthian 'gate'.

Carinthia is a diversified province, including in the north-west the permanent snow and ice of the Hohe Tauern peaks, notably the Gross Glockner and the Pasterze glacier on its north-eastern flanks, and, in the south-east, the intensively farmed lake basins of Villach-Klagenfurt and the Drau lowlands.   De Martonne compares this region of the Pre-Alps with the Carpathians.[1]   There is the same general east–west alignment of the Alpine ranges (the ' Drau ' trend of the German geographers), the same broad accordance of summit levels, the same prevalence of forests of fir and beech, with settle-ment in the cleared river valley trenches.   The Hohe Tauern ' window ' compares with that of the High Tatra, and both are heavily glaciated massifs, unlike the other lower ranges.   There is, however, no vulcanism in Carinthia, as there is in the Slovak Carpathians.

The unifying feature of Carinthia is the drainage of the Drau and its headwaters, the Möll and the Gail.   Both these valleys experienced the advance of the Pleistocene ice from the Hohe Tauern as far as the Klagenfurt basin, where the Würm moraines may be traced around St. Veit and Völkermarkt and across a line of peninsulas and islands in the Wörther-See.   In the Klagenfurt basin deposits of loess also occur.   In the Hohe Tauern region, the erosive action of ice has done much to sharpen the landscape features, though the relief was already strong.   Much of the attrac-tion of southern Carinthia lies in the harmony of glacial and moun-tain lake scenery, especially in the Wörther-See and Millstatt regions,

[1] E. de Martonne: *Europe Centrale*, Géog. Univ., Vol. 4, 1931, p. 470.
C.E.—G

where summer lake-side resorts have been created, such as Velden and Pörtschach, like Strebské Pleso in the High Tatra. In the Hohe Tauern, the completion of the Gross Glockner road just before World War II has made a spectacular part of the Austrian High Alps accessible to the tourist. This region has also been involved in the Glockner-Kaprun hydro-electric development, previously described (p. 164).

The Hohe Tauern massif, the region of maximum relief in the eastern Alps, rises to 12,440 ft. in the Gross Glockner. Here the Pennine *nappes* have been exposed by the erosion of the Austride folds and a ' window ' of older rocks is exposed, as in the Lower Engadine on the Swiss-Austrian border of the Inn valley. The rugged grandeur, arêtes, pyramidal peaks, hanging valleys and waterfalls of the Hohe Tauern region contrast with the less spectacular relief of the Drau ranges, carved in the Austride folds, and structurally less complex. Here the scenery is glaciated only locally and most of the slopes are covered with forests of fir and beech. In the south-west, the limestone folds of East Tyrol are continued eastwards into the Lienzer Dolomites, rising to nearly 9,000 ft. To the east lie the Gailtaler Alps, with the Erzberg and Villacher Alps forming minor ranges. In the latter the Dobratsch, known locally as ' the Rigi of Carinthia ', dominates the town of Villach. To the north of this range lies Bleiberg with its lead-mining industry, in a remote and notably sunless valley.[1]

In contrast with the relief of inner Carinthia, the frontier ranges of the Carnic and Karawanken Alps are narrow and spine-like, seldom more than 9 miles wide and rising to about 6,500 ft. The Carnic Range forms the divide between streams draining to the north Italian plain by the Tagliamento system and to the Danube by the Drau and the Gail. The only breaks are formed by the Plöcken and Nassfeld passes, over which roads lead to Udine and Venice. Between the Carnic and the Karawanken Ranges, the Tarvisio (Tarvis) water gap is used by the railway from Villach to Italy as well as by a modern road. To the east, the Karawanken Range presents steep limestone slopes towards the Drau lowland, frequently mantled with beech forests and dissected by ravines, down which waterfalls plunge. Road communication is made with Yugoslavia by means of the Loibl pass, at 4,463 ft., and also by the Seeberg pass at 5,650 ft.; the first connecting with Ljubljana and the second with Kranj (Krain) in the Sava valley. To the west of the Loibl pass, a 5-mile long tunnel carries the railway from Klagenfurt to Ljubljana and Trieste.

[1] N. Krebs: *Die Ostalpen u. das heutige Österreich*, Vol. 2, p. 114.

The valley lowlands of Carinthia trend from west to east in sympathy with the Alpine fold ranges and the ' Drau ' trend. Settlements show a marked concentration on terraces above the floodplains of the meandering Drau and Gail rivers and also on the south-facing slopes, that is the *Sonnenseite*. In these districts, with their high insolation, the forest was cleared by the *Rodungszeit* and today these grassy slopes are peppered with farms and hay barns. The north-facing slopes, however, remain largely forested, with pines and birches, in contrast with the sweet chestnut found on the opposite slope. Place names bear out the fact that valleys such as the Gail were settled by German colonizers in early medieval times, as at St. Lorenzen, as well as by Slovenes from the east, as at Hermagor. Settlements avoid the valley floor, with its high watertable and winter temperature inversions, and are agglomerated on detrital fans, such as Spittal, in the Drau valley. Between Villach and Klagenfurt, the Drau appears to have been diverted by ice from its pre-glacial course across the Klagenfurt basin, for it swings away from its natural continuation in the Wörther-See through the Rosental, to be joined by the Gurk east of Klagenfurt, where it enters the Jauntal. Finally, the Lavant joins the Drau from the north at Lavamund and the Austrian section of the valley ends where the Drau enters Yugoslavia by means of an impressive defile, forming an ' Iron Gate ' in miniature.

Carinthia was the meeting ground of two advancing types of settlement in medieval times and both the Germanic and Slavonic colonizers have left their mark on the cultural landscape. Whereas the typical Slovene settlement is the hamlet or dispersed farmstead, the German colonizers founded agglomerated villages and small towns, the latter frequently occupying defensive sites. The rich soils of the Klagenfurt lake basin developed from lacustrine silts and loess, and also those of the Rosental to the south, favoured crop farming on the traditional strip system. On the other hand, the steep slopes of the Alps, with their poor, thin, podsolised soils, are able to sustain chiefly a pastoral economy, based on hay as winter feed and involving the seasonal migration of flocks and herds to the mountain pastures or *Almen* above the tree-line. Transhumance is still practised; farmers in the Klagenfurt basin owning grazing rights on the *Almen* as far away as the Möll valley.

The most prosperous farming regions of Carinthia are the lake basins and river lowlands of the lower Drau, especially the Rosental and the Lavant valley; the latter known locally as ' the Paradise of Carinthia '. In this latter region, shelter and sunny aspect, together with the stimulus of medieval monastic houses, have long favoured

viticulture.   In south-eastern Carinthia, the season is long enough
and the summer rainfall adequate for the cultivation in rotation
of maize, wheat, lucerne and tobacco.   Much of the land is under
either sown or natural pasture and fruit trees line the roadside,
especially the walnut, cherry and apple.   The Germanic farmers
are more frequently concerned with stock farming, as in the other
Alpine provinces of Austria.

Carinthia is poor in minerals, except for some lignite and iron
ore in the Lavant valley and the lead and zinc of the Bleibergtal
in the Erzberg, and there is little development of industry.   Urban
settlement is mainly concentrated in the two major towns of Klagenfurt and Villach, apart from the medieval defensive sites in the
Metnitz valley, such as the medieval walled town of Friesach, ' the
Rothenburg of Carinthia ', and St. Veit, north of Klagenfurt, one-
time capital of the province.   Klagenfurt, with a population of
69,218 in 1961, replaced St. Veit as the capital in 1518.   The limits
of the medieval town may be traced along the broad thoroughfares
which form an inner ring, on the site of the former walls, as in
Vienna (Fig. 59).   The modern town has spread outside this central
Altstadt within the outer ring or *Gürtel*, and part of it spreads westwards towards the Wörther-See.   Klagenfurt and Villach, apart
from their international importance as railway foci, serve a rich and
comparatively densely populated agricultural region, where a
Slovene type of peasant life and economy prevails.   Elsewhere, the
province has become entirely Germanized, in spite of the difficulty
of access from the north-west, that is from the Tyrol and Salzburg,
until the opening of the Hohe Tauern railway in 1909 and the Gross
Glockner road some thirty years later, two factors which have
brought new life and contacts to this Alpine province otherwise
remote from Western Europe.

Styria

This is the most easterly of the Alpine provinces of Austria and
is called in German, Steiermark.   Along its southern margin lies
the Yugoslav frontier and the general orientation of the province
is south-eastwards towards the Drava lowlands and the Pannonic
basin, a feature which is emphasized by the Mur drainage.   On
the contrary, the diagonal trench of the upper Mur and its tributary
the Mürz offers a route to Vienna over the Semmering pass at
2,940 ft., at right angles to the route through Graz to Yugoslavia.
In the north-west of Styria, the trench of the upper Enns lies parallel
with that of the Mur-Mürz valley and provides a route from Salzburg
over the Mandling pass to Steyr and Upper Austria.   As the result

of the way in which the Alpine valleys of Styria open on to the Danube lowlands, penetration and settlement came in the early Middle Ages from Slavonic rather than Germanic Europe. The province remains one of isolation and retarded development, apart from the city of Graz and the growth of the important iron and steel industry of the Donawitz-Leoben region of the Mur valley. Here the extraction of iron ore from the Eisenerz range dates back to the early Iron Age. It was also an important source of supply to Roman Italy.

The general trend of the Alpine folds in Styria is from south-west to north-east, a direction followed by the main drainage lines and in sympathy with the western Carpathians. The oldest rocks are exposed in the crystalline massif of the Niedere Tauern, the range which divides the upper Enns from the Mur drainage, but the greatest elevation occurs in the Dachstein, 9,810 ft., the snow-capped peak of which lies where the boundaries of Styria, Salzburg and Upper Austria meet. These eastern Calcareous Alps continue across the northern part of the province, where they are known by such various names as the Totes Gebirge, Ennstaler Alps and the Styrian Limestone Alps. Their general height is of the order of 6,500 ft., their relief is comparatively subdued and the ranges are largely forested, with settlement and cultivation ceasing at about 3,000 ft. The main drainage feature is that of the upper Enns, which flows in a flat-floored trench between the crystalline massif of the Niedere Tauern and the Calcareous Alps to the north. At Hieflau the Enns abandons its longitudinal furrow to cut through the Ennstaler Alps in a great gorge incised in the limestone rocks, on its way to the Alpine Foreland of Upper Austria which it enters below Altenmarkt.

The Totes Gebirge region, in the north-west of the province, lies in highly glaciated mountain country, with several large finger lakes lying in deeply cut valleys, a region for which the resort of Bad Aussee is the centre. As its name suggests, the Totes Gebirge is a desolate mountainous district, with much bare limestone, rock waste, scree and subterranean drainage. Between the Ennstaler Alps and the Niedere Tauern lie the Eisenerz Alps, which derive their name from the local iron ore. The *Erzberg* or Ore Mountain rises to 7,090 ft. and to the south-east of it lies the industrial ' conurbation ' of Donawitz-Leoben, with Bruck and Judenburg as other iron-smelting centres, all in the trench of the upper Mur, where the local forests provided charcoal for the smelting of the iron ore in medieval times. The importance of the iron and steel industry here today, based on imported (Ruhr) coke, is dealt with elsewhere

(p. 148).   In modern times, the existence of a lignite field at Fohns-
dorf near Knittelfeld in the upper Mur valley has also favoured
industrial development, as has access to Vienna and Upper Silesia
via the Semmering and Moravian ' gate ' routes.

To the south-east, the land slopes generally towards the Mur
(Drau) lowlands and the relief is much more subdued than to the
north-west.   Flat-topped hills, such as those around Graz, characterize the region.   Below Bruck, where the Mur is joined by the
Mürz, the combined rivers flow south-south-eastwards towards the
Yugoslav frontier, the landscape becoming increasingly steppe-like
as the Alps are left behind.   Both the Mur and the parallel stream
of the Raab have cut deeply incised valleys in the Miocene gravels
which lie at the foot of the Alps.   These fertile terrace lands are
known as the Grazer-Feld or Leibnitz-Feld below Graz, and the
intensively cultivated and well-drained slopes contrast with the
narrow strip of alluvial flood-plain with its alder swamps bordering
the river, and again with the forests of mixed pine, fir and beech
which mantle the foothills.

Graz, the provincial capital of Styria, lies in a rich agricultural
lowland, noted, like the western Pannonic basin, for its wheat and
maize production, fruit orchards, poultry and stock.   It originated
as a fortified settlement on a bluff site, but Neustadt developed as
the ' new city ' on the plain, where alpine and lowland produce
could be exchanged.   Graz is a cathedral town and its university
was founded in 1586.   Today, with a population of 237,080, it
ranks as the second city of Austria, in spite of extensive damage
during the second world war.   It is a centre of a variety of small-
scale industries, including mechanical engineering, chemical production, textiles, paper, leather, milling and brewing, and the recent
development of hydro-electric power in the Alpine section of the
Mur valley, making possible the transmission of current to Graz, has
been a further stimulus to industry.   The town is a route centre of
some importance, especially in view of its position on the main
railway from Vienna to Trieste.

Upper Austria

Lying between the German frontier along the Inn to the west,
the Czech frontier to the north and the High Alps to the south,
the province of Upper Austria consists of a lowland traversed by
the upper Danube from Passau to the Enns confluence.   Upper
Austria's main function, therefore, is that of a corridor along the
Danube valley from Bavaria to Vienna, but the province includes
four contrasted features, namely; the Pre-Alps, the western section

of the Alpine Foreland, the Danube valley, and the western part of that section of the Bohemian Massif which lies in Austria. In contrast with Alpine Austria, movement is easy along the Danube valley and the region has functioned for many centuries as a passage land between the lower Danubian lands and Central Europe.

In the south, the Pre-Alps form an irregular belt of mountain country, developed on limestones, *Flysch* and *Molasse*. Upper Austria reaches its culminating point in the Dachstein (9,810 ft.), on the borders of Styria, and, north of this limestone peak, with its snowfields and glaciers, lies the Salzkammergut. This spectacular glaciated limestone country is drained northwards by the Traun, a stream which rises on the south-western slope of the Totes Gebirge and flows in turn through the Kammer and Grundl lakes in Styria before turning northwards through the lake of Hallstatt *en route* to Bad Ischl and so to the Traunsee which lies above Gmunden, at the northern foot of the Alps. Much interest attaches to the history of settlement in this region, in view of the Early Iron Age finds at Hallstatt, but the main permanent penetration into the region came in the forest-clearing period of the 11th century, a period associated with the founding of a number of monastic houses, as at St. Wolfgang and at Zell; while place names, such as Gschwandt, also suggest the destruction of forested land for settlement. In modern times, with the coming of the railway lines from Salzburg and Linz and the construction of motor roads, the Salzkammergut has become a famous Alpine resort and its tourist industry is a major asset to the province and to Austria. Bad Ischl, with its mineral springs, is a well-known spa, and St. Wolfgang, Traunkirchen and Altmünster serve as summer resorts.

To the north of the Pre-Alps, the Austrian Foreland slopes gently north-eastwards to the Danube valley. Here the general features of the Alpine Foreland of Switzerland and southern Germany are represented on a restricted scale. In general, the Foreland is part of the geosyncline lying between the Alps and the Bohemian massif, filled in with Oligocene and Miocene sands, gravels and marls, with *Molasse* and *Schlier* forming local ridges but with the greater part of the Tertiaries masked by Pleistocene drift. In the Alpine piedmont zone, large trough lakes lie in deep glacial trenches, notably the Traun, Atter or Kammer-See, and forested morainic ridges impede drainage at the lower ends of these lakes. In contrast, the drainage of the Enns and Steyr across the eastern part of the Foreland in Upper Austria flows unimpeded by moraines across open lowlands, the streams cutting through broad Pleistocene gravel terraces. To the west, between the Innviertel and the Traun valleys, the Foreland is diversified by the east–west ridge of the Höllen-Gebirge, developed on *Flysch* and rising to 5,545 ft. It forms a detached range between the Atter and Traun lakes. To the north of this ridge and finger-lake region lies the ill-drained Vöckla depression, floored with boulder clay and with peat-filled hollows. It is drained eastwards by the Vöckla and Ager streams. To the north of this region the Hausruck plateau rises to 2,400 ft. and is developed on *Schlier*. Lignite is worked in the neighbourhood. Towards the Danube, the older river terraces are capped with loess and provide soils which are suitable for arable farming and viticulture. Along the margin of the Foreland, the Danube follows a sinuous course from Passau through the Sauwald and past Linz to the Enns confluence. Northwards the crystalline rocks of the Bohemian massif approach close to and in places cross the Danube, and here the region is one of poor, thin soils, mainly under forest. The Danube valley varies from a narrow epigenetic gorge, where the river flows between high rock walls, as in the Sauwald, and open basins across which the river follows a braided course between islands of gravel and where floods are liable to occur, as below Linz. This section of the river ends at Mauthausen, where the Archæan granites reach the river and where kaolin is worked. Between Grein and Ybbs in Lower Austria, the Danube valley is known as the Strüdengau, again an extension of the Bohemian massif, rising in the Hengstberg to 1,866 ft.

To the north of the Danube, Upper Austria extends across the southern part of the Bohemian massif to the Czech border. This region is known as the *Mühlviertel* and consists of a flat-topped and dissected plateau, cut by deep valleys which are in places gorge-like, such as that of the Mühl. On account of the raw winter climate and the poor, acid soils weathered from granitic rocks, the primeval forest cover largely remains uncleared and it is given such local names as the Passauer Wald, near the Bavarian border, and the Linzer and Greinwald. In medieval times, however, the ' imperial road ' linked Upper Austria and Bavaria *via* the Mühl valley and today the region is crossed by the railway from Linz to Budějovice in southern Bohemia. The nodal point of the eastern *Mühlviertel* is the small walled town of Freistadt, lying in the Feldaist depression, and dating from the 12th century. Most of the settlement in this region took place in late medieval times and is of the forest-clearing type. The magnificent baroque monastery of Melk, overlooking the Danube, dates from this period.

Linz, the capital of Upper Austria in the 15th century, is today a town of 195,978. It was founded as a defensive site by the Romans, but it developed in medieval times as a bridge town on the

Danube, where routes from Bohemia crossed the river on the way to the Salzkammurgut and Salzburg. Salt was the main commodity carried along these roads. Linz is today the administrative centre of Upper Austria and a river port of some importance, though it awaits the completion of the Rhine-Main-Danube canal. In recent years, Linz has become an important centre of heavy industry and of chemical production. Iron ore is derived from Styria and Sweden and coke from the Ruhr, while gas from the coke ovens is taken to a synthetic nitrogen plant, established under German stimulus before the last war. During the American occupation of Linz, further developments took place, especially with the construction of a hydro-electric power station at Ternberg, on the Enns above Steyr. More recent hydro-electric power developments have taken place on the Danube at Ybbs-Persenbeug. Here a modern steel mill produces hot strip from steel smelted in electric-arc furnaces. In the neighbourhood of Linz there are also a number of smaller scale industries, such as machine engineering, glass manufacture, textiles, woodworking, brewing and tobacco.

Lower Austria

The boundary between Upper and Lower Austria follows the Danube from the confluence of the Enns to a few miles above that with the Ybbs. Northwards, the province extends to the Czech frontier along the borders of south-eastern Bohemia and southern Moravia, touching southern Slovakia above Bratislava (Pressburg). To the south, Lower Austria includes the outer ranges of the Pre-Alps and the Wienerwald behind Vienna. This province lies in one of the great cross-roads of Europe, where the middle Danube valley route is joined by that from the upper Oder and Vistula valleys through the Moravian or March ' gate '. This special nodality has given Vienna its cosmopolitan significance for many centuries.

The south-eastern corner of the Bohemian massif which lies in Lower Austria is known as the *Waldviertel*, in contrast with the *Weinviertel* of the Danube valley below Krems. Granites, gneisses and schists give rise to a monotonous and largely wooded landscape, broken by impressive gorges such as that of the Thaya, a stream which in places forms the Czech-Austrian frontier. Occasionally, rounded uplands rise above the general level of the uplifted peneplain to heights of over 3,000 ft., such as the Tischberg (3,510 ft.), and the surface is frequently strewn with granitic blocks. Settlement is sparse and mainly in forest clearings.

To the south lies the *Weinviertel*, a region noted for its vineyards laid out on terraces above the Danube, enjoying shelter from cold northerly winter winds through protection by the *Waldviertel*. This strip of the Danube valley also produces wheat, maize and fodder crops, including sugar beet; the intensively cultivated loess-covered terraces contrasting with the water meadows on the alluvium of the valley floor. Krems, a town of 21,046 people, is the centre of the wine industry and is also a small manufacturing town. Between Krems and Tulln the region is given the local name of the Tullnerfeld. To the north, outcrops of Jurassic limestone give rise to local karst features and settlements are water-seeking, place names ending in -*brunn* being significant, such as Königsbrunn. A recent discovery in the east of this region has been petroleum, an extension of the field now worked for many years in the Marchfeld.

The eastern part of the Alpine Foreland which extends from the Danube to the Pre-Alps of Lower Austria lies between 650 and 1,200 ft. It forms a rolling, lightly wooded landscape, crossed by many streams but without recent moraines, as in the *Innviertel* of Upper Austria. Sheets of fluvioglacial gravel form the surface and these are cut into terraces by rivers such as the Ybbs and the Pielach, while loess frequently caps the gravels, especially immediately south of the Danube valley. Much of the Foreland is under cultivation, producing cereals and fodder crops and also orchard fruit. Dairy cattle form an important element in the economy and have to be stall fed in winter, Aschbach being an important market centre for dairy produce. The largest industrial town of the region is, however, St. Pölten, with a population of 40,112, with the only artificial silk factory in Austria, and also engineering and wood-working industries. Lignite is worked nearby.

To the south, the *Flysch* and Calcareous Alps lie along the borders of Lower Austria and Styria. They rise to over 6,000 ft. in the neighbourhood of the Semmering pass, the Rax reaching 6,582 ft. and the Schneeberg 6,812 ft. These peaks are divided by the Höllental, where reservoirs have been constructed to serve the city of Vienna. The region is one of jagged limestone peaks, with many karst features, and these present a steep face north-eastwards to the Vienna basin. The main break in the Alpine barrier is where the Semmering pass lies in a tectonic depression, between limestone ranges to the north and the gneissic and mica schist region to the south. The road over the pass dates from the 12th century and the railway, which reaches the summit level in a tunnel at 2,946 ft., was completed a century ago. A second tunnel was completed in 1952 and the line is now double tracked. Nearby, the village of Semmering has achieved international repute as a spa and winter sports centre.

The Vienna basin forms the last region of Lower Austria. It includes the Vienna and Wiener Neustadt ' bays ' and extends north of the Danube into the Marchfeld and the foot of the Little Carpathians. To the west of the Vienna ' bay ' lies the Wienerwald, a landscape of *Flysch* hills, rich in thermal springs, where forests of beech and fir formerly provided hunting grounds. Here vineyards occur on the sunny terraced slopes, such as the Kahlenberg north of Vienna. The hills form a gathering ground for much of Vienna's water supply. To the south, fault-guided springs break out, especially in the Helenatal, where lies the little spa of Baden, and this town as well as the neighbouring resort of Vöslau, are set at the foot of the flat-topped and gently sloping foothills of the Alps, rich in beechwoods but with vineyards in the forest clearings. Between Wiener Neustadt and the Bruck ' gate ' to the south, the Leithage-birge extend from south-west to north-east, thus continuing the line of the Little Carpathians across the Danube. The range has a core of crystalline rocks but is flanked by limestones. It culminates in the Sonnenberg, at 1,584 ft. The gentle slopes of these hills divide the Vienna basin from the Burgenland and the Pannonic basin of Hungary.

The centre of the Vienna ' bay ' is an open plain, sloping north-eastwards towards the Danube. It experiences a ' Pannonic ' climate, with mean monthly temperatures of 28·4° F. in January and 68° F. in July, while the rainfall is low and generally under 25 in. in annual total. To the south lies the Steinfeld, a gravel-covered plain, crossed by the Schwarza river and with a deep-seated water-table. This was originally a ' steppe-heath ' region, now partly reclaimed for arable farming and partly afforested with fir trees yielding resin. The chief town of the region is Wiener Neustadt, with a population of 30,500, the second town of Lower Austria. It developed as a market centre and a cathedral city, but today it is an important manufacturing town, with engineering, textile and paper industries.

To the north of the Danube below Vienna, the Marchfeld forms a low-lying region extending to the Czechoslovak frontier. Prior to the modern regulation of the Danube and March rivers, the region was liable to serious flooding, though the higher loess-covered terraces favour extensive arable farming; crops of wheat, maize, potatoes and sugar beet giving heavy yields. Like adjacent Czech Moravia, the landscape is open, the fields running in long parallel strips, with no hedges to break the monotony. To the north of the Marchfeld, borings for petroleum proved successful at Zisters-dorf as long ago as 1929, the field producing over 2·5 million metric tons of oil in 1964.   As a result of the prolonged Russian occupation of this zone, much of the oil found its way to eastern Europe as reparations.   The other centres of note, lie in the south of the Marchfeld, notably at Matzen and, since 1963, at Schonkirchen Tief and Voitsdorf.   Oil is sent by pipeline from Ingolstadt to modern refineries at Karlsruhe, in the Rhineland (Fig. 50).

Vienna

The capital of the modern Austrian Republic owes its world significance to its position, as it did in the days of the Habsburg Empire.   Here the barrier of the Alps and the Carpathians is broken through by the Danube, and the Vienna 'gate' lies where the upper Danube leaves the Alpine Foreland for the Hungarian plain

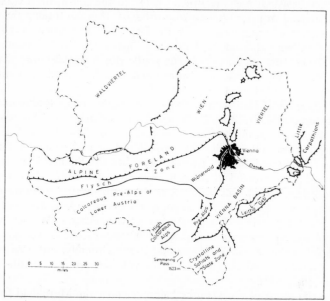

FIG. 58.   Vienna in its physiographic setting.

and the lower Danubian lands.   After the war this major east–west international highway was broken at Mauthausen, where the American and Russian Zones met, and through traffic on the Danube was largely paralysed for some ten years.   The Danube valley route is intersected from the north by the traditional 'amber' route which for many centuries has linked the Baltic coast (whence came the amber from the cliffs of Samland) and the Adriatic coast.

This route leads from southern Poland (formerly Austrian Galicia) and the upper Vistula and Oder valleys to Vienna *via* the March or Moravian ' gate ' and so over the Semmering pass to Venice and Trieste.

The imperial city of Vienna reached its zenith in the 18th century as the centre of Habsburg rule but its significance as a cosmopolitan focus of urban life increased in the mid-19th century with the coming of railway links with the Austrian Empire, especially with Bohemia and Moravia. At that time industries were developed, notably in Prague, Brunn (now Brno) and the Sudetenland, while the Austrian possession of Trieste provided an outlet to the open waters of the Mediterranean. The completion of the Orient Express route in 1886 meant that Vienna had through connections with Paris, Munich, Buda Pesth and Constantinople (now Istanbul). The improvement of the Danube waterway also attracted traffic to the river, especially in grain, timber and oil, though its outlet in the Black Sea and its winter freeze were insuperable handicaps. With the dismemberment of the Austrian Empire in 1919, Vienna became a city of unwieldy size when related to the largely Alpine state of which she was the federal capital. The decline in size of Vienna has continued since 1919, for its population in 1961 was only 1,627,566 compared with 1,874,100 in 1934 and 2,030,850 in 1910. Nevertheless the city retains over 23 per cent of the total population.

Vienna lies at the foot of the Wienerwald, where streams issuing from the *Flysch* hills have cut terraces in the detrital gravels. One of these, the Wien, gave its name to the town in the 9th century. The original Roman fortress was at Vindobona, on the Kahlenberg overlooking the Danube; while the ruins of the Roman city of Carnuntum and its amphitheatre lie east of Vienna. The city exemplifies very clearly the growth of an urban agglomeration around a central core or nucleus. The inner town or *Altstadt* lies on gravel terraces north of the Wien and includes the cathedral of St. Stephan, a splendid example of German Gothic style dating from 1258, with its tall spire and steeply pitched roof ornamented with brightly coloured tiles and now rebuilt after its partial destruction in the recent war. In this inner core are the great banking houses, formerly largely in Jewish hands, especially the Rothschilds. Here the streets are narrow and flanked by buildings several stories high. Beyond the *Altstadt* lies the thoroughfare known as the Ring and marking the limit of the medieval city. Along this boulevard are situated the great museums and the Vienna State Opera House, as well as the new Town Hall, the Parliament building, the University and the Palace of Justice. In this part of Vienna is the Hofburg, the town residence of the Habsburgs, whereas Schönbrunn, on the outskirts of the city, served as the Versailles of Vienna. To the north of the city and also beyond the Danube is the suburb of Floridsdorf, famous before the war for its blocks of working-class flats, and the industrial quarters. The 19th-century housing and

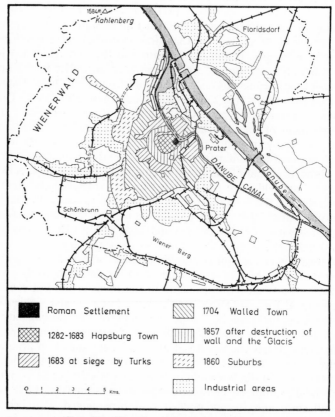

FIG. 59. The site and growth of Vienna.

factory developments took place on hitherto open ground outside the walls or *Gürtel* and known as the ' glacis '. Between the *Altstadt* and the Danube lies the park and fair ground of the Prater; the dividing feature being the former arm of the Danube, now known as the Danube canal.   On the outskirts of the town, villas formerly belonging to rich Viennese citizens, farmhouses and villages are scattered amidst fields, gardens and vineyards. To the west, the foothills of the Wienerwald form the 'lung' of the city and a modern road strikes off from Wiental to reach the heights of the Klosterneuberg, a much frequented viewpoint over the city.

Vienna (*Ger.* Wien) achieved the status of a city in the 12th century and it flourished on the strength of its long-distance connections with the Baltic ports, the Polish 'fair' towns of Cracow, and with Venice by means of the Semmering pass. By the following century Vienna had reached the limit of its defensive walls. The 16th century saw the union of Austria with Bohemia and Moravia but also the first siege by the Turks, the second coming in 1683. The walls thrown up then, on the Vauban star plan, were not destroyed until 1857, after which the town spread rapidly over the 'glacis' into the semi-rural countryside extending to the Wienerwald. The growth of Vienna to a city of over 2 million inhabitants (one-third of the total population of the country in 1919) gave it the status of a European metropolis, especially in view of its rich contribution to art and music as well as to international finance and banking. The 19th century also saw the growth of industrial Vienna, especially on the southern outskirts of the town and across the Danube, on land liable to flood prior to the regulation of the river. Vienna is world renowned for its luxury trades, especially clothing, the fur trade, porcelain and leather goods, but engineering, printing and the making of electrical apparatus are also to be found here. Extreme economic depression between the wars until the time of the *Anschluss*, coupled with the post-war division of the city into the four occupation zones, resulted in its modern decrease in size, though it remains one of the great outposts of Germanic life, a rôle it has fulfilled against south-eastern and eastern Europe for centuries.

Burgenland

Added to Austria by the Treaty of Trianon in 1919, the Burgenland forms a strip of the Pannonic basin which lies between Styria, the Vienna basin and the Hungarian frontier. Today it is Austria's advanced post against the Iron Curtain. The province has a mixed population, comprising German-speaking, Magyar and Croat elements. The landscape is monotonous and steppe-like, except in the north where the Alps send out a spur towards the Little Carpathians known as the Leitha-Gebirge, which rises to 1,350 ft. This faulted crystalline block which trends south-west–north-east dominates the large expanse of water known as the Neusiedler See which lies to the south-east. To the east of the lake, the wide fringe of ill-drained marshland as well as the large number of peat bogs and small lakes indicate the former extent of an arm of the Pliocene Sea. To the north lies the steppe region of the *Parndorfer Heide*. In this province of Burgenland is found the most continental type of climate experienced in Austria, with a precipitation on the low ground of less than 20 in. and a mean monthly temperature range from 28° F. to over 67° F. The soils are largely derived from Pliocene gravels and the typical method of obtaining water is by means of the beam and bucket well so often seen on the Hungarian Plain. Apart from viticulture and orchard fruit production on the sunny south-east-facing terraces of the Leitha-Gebirge, the Burgenland is mainly given to stock rearing and extensive grain cultivation, especially wheat and maize. The province records the highest percentage of improved land of all Austria, *viz.* 67 per cent, and is a major source of foodstuffs for Vienna.

REFERENCES

The standard work of reference on Austria, although written nearly forty years ago, is the two-volume work of N. Krebs: *Die Ostalpen u. das heutige Österreich*, 1928, while a post-war reference is H. Gsteu: *Länderkunde Österreichs*, 1948 ed. L. Kober: *Der Geologische Aufbau Österreichs*, 1938, is also useful for structural details. Since the war, a number of papers have appeared in the *Geographical Review* and elsewhere by G. W. Hoffman, who has also edited *A Geography of Europe*, to which he has contributed the chapter on Central Europe (1961). There is much post-war material in both volumes of *L'Europe Centrale*, by P. George and J. Tricart (1954). An Austrian reference book, published in 1953, is by A. Becker and L. Helmer, entitled *Österreich, Landschaft, Wirtschaft, Bevölkerung*. The topographic maps covering the country remained for a long time the 1 : 200,000 hachured series, published prior to 1918 by the Austrian Army Staff. A modern series on a scale of 1 : 50,000 is now in progress and is published by the *Bundesamt für Eich-u. Vermessungswesen*, in Vienna. Unofficial maps, useful to tourists, are published by Freytag-Berndt, in Vienna, on scales varying from 1 : 600,000 (for the whole country) to 1 : 50,000 for each province (the latter in colour, with hill shading). Recent cartographic and statistical data are to be found in *Österreichs Landwirtschaft u. Bevölkerung* (1953), as well as in the *Verwaltungsatlas auf statistischer Grundlage* (1952), published by the *Druck und Kommissionsverlag der Österreichischen Staatsdruckerei*. Modern atlases relating to specific provinces are: the *Atlas von Niederösterreich*, 1951, published in four parts, and the *Salzburg Atlas*, 1955. The *Atlas der Republik Österreich*, 1963, is available as a series of single sheets in separate folders.

CHAPTER 9

CZECHOSLOVAKIA: PHYSICAL FEATURES AND HUMAN GEOGRAPHY

THE REPUBLIC of Czechoslovakia has a unique place in Central Europe both physically and politically. Its two major physical elements, the Hercynian massif of Bohemia and the Alpine arc of the western Carpathians, which lies in Slovakia, are linked by the lowland corridor of Moravia, thus justifying physically the inclusion of the state in Central Europe. Czechoslovakia has a totalitarian régime since the *coup d'état* of 1948. It constitutes a ' people's democratic republic ', the Czechs and Slovaks having equal rights under the new constitution. Created as a succession state in 1919 by the Treaty of St. Germain out of the dismembered Austro-Hungarian monarchy, shorn of its historic Bohemian frontier in 1938 and occupied by Germany from 1939 until 1945, it now lies behind the ' iron curtain ' which divides western from eastern Europe politically, and is oriented towards the Soviet Union, whence came the armies of liberation in 1945.

Czechoslovakia comprises historic Bohemia and Moravia (with Czech Silesia),[1] both formerly part of the Austrian Empire though with a predominantly Czech population, and Slovakia, once incorporated in Hungary but mainly inhabited by Slovaks. The eastern province of Carpathian Ruthenia (Podkarpatská Rus) has been assimilated into the Soviet Republic of the Ukraine since 1945, since its Ruthenian (Little Russia) population is akin in sentiment and religion with the neighbouring Greek Orthodox Ukrainians. Czechoslovakia has a more compact shape than before the war, extending for about 470 miles from west to east but with a varying north–south extent, reaching a maximum width of 180 miles in Bohemia. This province is an historic entity and also forms a physical and economic unit, with Prague (*Czech*, Praha) as its metropolis.

---

[1] These provincial divisions were abolished in 1949 and replaced by 19 administrative regions.

185

Bohemia coincides with a massif of Primary rocks, covered in the north-centre with younger formations, and is bounded by highlands which form a natural barrier region. These comprise the Ore Mountains (Krušne Hory, Erz-Gebirge) in the north-west, the Giant Mountains (Krkonoše Hory, Riesen-Gebirge) and the Sudetes in the north-east, the Moravian Heights in the south-east and the Bohemian Forest (Šumava, Böhmerwald) in the south-east. The Bohemian block is tilted northwards towards the upper Elbe basin (the *Polabí*), and the major tributaries of the Labe (Elbe) are the Vltava (Moldau) draining from the south, and the Berounka and the Ohře (Eger) from the west. The Labe (Elbe) rises on the southern slopes of the Giant Mountains before being joined by the Vltava at Mělník, north of Prague, where the combined rivers flow northwards to the Dresden ' gate '. Moravia and Czech Silesia form a passage land between the Bohemian block and the western Carpathians, as well as linking Vienna and the middle Danube valley with the industrial region of Upper Silesia. Czech Silesia is drained northwards by the Odra (Oder) towards Wrocłav (Breslau), in Poland, while Moravia corresponds with the basin of the Morava (March), a left-bank tributary of the Danube. The regional capital of Moravia is Brno (Brünn), while Moravska Ostrava (Mährisch-Ostrau) is the chief town of Czech Silesia. Communications between Bohemia and Moravia are fairly easy across the Moravian Heights. The population, like that of Bohemia, is now largely Czech, thousands of Germans having been expelled across the frontiers in 1945 and few Jews surviving the years of the German occupation. Deserted villages in the Sudetenland bear witness to the flight to the West. To the east lies the Slovak Carpathian province of Czechoslovakia. Here the ' alpine ' environment supports a low density of population compared with Bohemia and Moravia (Fig. 67). It is a land of peasants cultivators and pastoralists, with a low standard of living, by nature conservative in outlook and still maintaining traditional modes of life and costume. Whereas the Czechs have hitherto adhered either to the Protestant faith (over a million), the Roman Catholic (950,000) or the Hussite Reformed Church (820,000), the Slovaks remain either Roman Catholics or they are members of the Greek Orthodox Church (50,000). Since the 1939–45 War, Czechoslovakia has stressed increasingly her affinity with Slavonic Europe and her pre-war tolerance of minorities has disappeared, though there were estimated to be 50,000 Jews in 1955. At first, reconstruction work was made difficult by lack of skilled labour, as the result of the wholesale expulsion of the Sudeten and other Germans, the number of such workers being reduced by nearly

25 per cent.   State planning and the nationalization of a number of industries are basic features of the present régime, while trade is increasingly with the Soviet Union.   The relatively high standard of living characteristic of the Czech people in recent years, resulting from the development of a well-balanced economy, forms a striking contrast with the impoverishment of the greater part of Slavonic Europe.   Highly organized cash crop farming *vis-à-vis* subsistence agriculture, combined with the systematic exploitation of natural resources such as coal, timber and metals, forming the basis of well-developed manufacturing industries, in contrast with the backwardness of the lower Danubian lands, enables Czechoslovakia to play an important rôle in the economic development of this part of Europe.

Structure and Physiographic Features

Czechoslovakia may be divided into three major contrasted regions: the Bohemian massif in the west, the Odra-Morava corridor in the centre, and the Carpathian arc in the east.   The Bohemian massif is one of the largest of the Hercynian regions of Europe, consisting of a Primary crustal block, folded and metamorphosed in both early and late Palæozoic times.   The Carpathians are the ' alpine ' element in Czechoslovakia, having experienced Oligocene-Miocene folding and uplift with accompanying vulcanism.   The Odra-Morava corridor is developed on sedimentary rocks of all ages, and, except for the Carboniferous areas, it has not been markedly affected by folding.   Crystalline rocks predominate in Bohemia, where gneiss, schists, granite and diorite are widespread.   After the period of Carbo-Permian folding, the region experienced prolonged denudation, sediments of Cretaceous and Eocene age being laid down over wide areas, especially in the north-centre.   Under the impact of the Alpine thrusting and folding movements, the peneplaned massif experienced re-uplift, tilting towards the north, combined with block faulting, fracturing and the ejection of vulcanic material, notably in the highland margins.   The Odra-Morava corridor includes rocks ranging from Devonian, through Carboniferous (including the Coal Measures of the frontier region of Silesia), to Cretaceous and Eocene.   In the Carpathians the structure is highly complex.   The core of the system is the crystalline ' window ' of the High Tatra, forming the highest range of the whole system, as in the Swiss and French Alps.   Although igneous rocks also occur in the Low Tatra, the Western Beskyds consist, for the most part, of highly folded sedimentary rocks, mainly Secondary, and ranging from Triassic to Oligocene.   Limestones predominate over wide areas, as in the Slovak Ore Mountains,

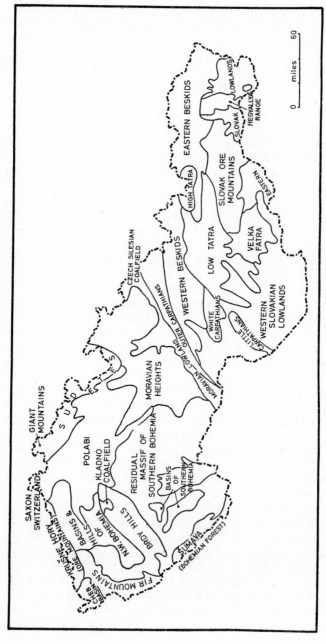

Fig. 60.   Czechoslovakia: physiographic regions.

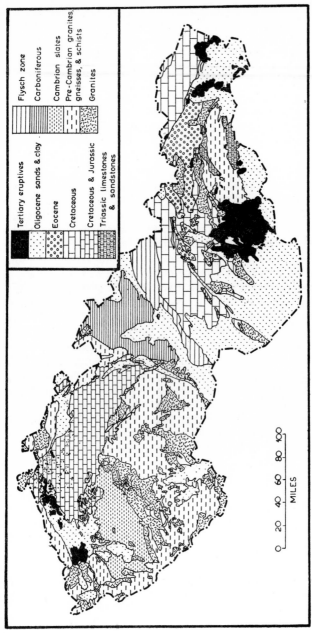

Fig. 61. Czechoslovakia: geology.

but igneous rocks have been intruded into them, especially in the region of the Hungarian frontier, as in the Matra massif and the Hegyallya range (Fig. 71). There is an outer zone of foothill country developed on *Flysch* (Tertiary conglomerate). Glaciation affected the highest parts of the Carpathians (the High Tatra), as well as the highlands on the Bohemian frontier, such as the Bohemian Forest and the Giant Mountains. Streams are deeply incised into the Bohemian massif as the result of rejuvenation, and are usually bordered by river terraces. Fluvioglacial and glacial drift deposits occur in the highlands. Along the Labe valley there are extensive tracts of loess, notably in the *Polabí*. These regions will be described in more detail later.

Czechoslovakia lies on a continental water-parting between drainage to the North and Baltic Seas and to the Black Sea. The divide first follows the southern highland rim of Bohemia, then crosses between the Morava and Odra drainage, keeping close to the Polish frontier along the Carpathians in Slovakia, except in the High Tatra, where the headwaters of the Vistula rise on the southern slopes, within a short distance of the Váh (Waag) tributary of the Danube. The Czechoslovak rivers have a spring maximum flow after the melting of the winter snow, and a summer minimum, except the Danube, which, fed by Alpine snow-melt and summer rain, has a marked summer maximum. In Slovakia, the Váh has the most regular régime, where there is a new development of hydro-electric power and more is now ' planned ' in the Carpathians. In Bohemia the Vltava is navigable for 500-ton barges from Prague to Mělník, and the Labe from Kostelnec to the German frontier (Russian zone). The Vltava is also utilized for hydro-electric power, the two barrages being at Orlik and Slapy, above Prague. The Czechoslovak stretch of the Danube forms part of that navigable waterway system, and the Váh tributary is navigable for 500-ton barges from Komarno to Sered.

Climate

Czechoslovakia experiences a Central European type of climate, modified by altitude in the Bohemian Highlands, and even more in the western Carpathians. Winters are long, cold and rather dry, with light snowfall, while summers are hot and accompanied by frequent thunderstorms. Prague has a mean January temperature of 30° F. and a mean July temperature of 66° F., while 39 per cent of the mean annual precipitation of 19 in. falls in the three summer months. The winter weather depends on the prevalence of either occasional mild spells associated with westerly or south-westerly air masses of Atlantic origin or, as is more often the rule, cold periods resulting from the dominance of northerly or north-easterly Polar Continental air.   In summer, westerly winds bring mild conditions and rain, while easterly air currents give rise to high temperatures on the lowlands, with convectional rainfall.   There is a lack of records for the mountainous regions, but actual temperatures are reduced at the approximate rate of 1° F. for every 270 ft. of ascent. The distribution of precipitation reflects exposure and elevation. The regions of heaviest total fall, with considerable winter snowfall, are, therefore, the Giant Mountains, the Bohemian Forest and the High Tatra (Fig. 62). Conversely, the regions of lowest precipitation are in western Bohemia, in the rain shadow of the western highland rim, and in southern Moravia in the less of the eastern Alps, for in both these regions the amount is less than 23 in. a year.   There is a continental summer maximum of precipitation everywhere, with a mid-winter minimum.   In eastern districts, depressions from the Adriatic result in a secondary maximum in October.

The Original Plant Cover

Few traces remain of the original woodland and grassland, and the present landscape is a reflection of the complex interplay of natural and man-made elements.   The Hungarian *puszta* or steppe grassland, with occasional oak woods (steppe-heath association), survives only on the borders of the Pannonic Basin, in the southern Moravian lowlands and plains of Slovakia.   Elsewhere, where the land has not been improved for farming, extensive tracts are under forest and woodland, but this is largely the result of systematic afforestation, except in the Carpathians.   Bohemia and Moravia each have 30 per cent of their total area under forest but in Slovakia the percentage rises to 34.   In Bohemia, 86 per cent of the forest is coniferous, notably in the highland rim, while in Moravia and Czech Silesia the figures fall to 62 per cent, and in Slovakia to only 31 per cent.   In the Carpathians, in spite of proximity to the eastern limit of the beech in Europe, deciduous woodland prevails on the lower mountain slopes, accounting for 69 per cent of the total forests. On the other hand, broad-leaved trees account for only 38 per cent of the forested area in Moravia and 14 per cent in Bohemia.   In the Hercynian region of Bohemia, only the Sudetes and the Bohemian Forest rise above the tree-line into the realm of glacial relict flora and alpine pasture.   The Pannonic plains have been largely cleared for pasture and cultivation, in the same way as the loess-covered plains of the *Polabí*.   Here the land is cultivated in long, parallel strips, with a marked absence of enclosure.   In the western

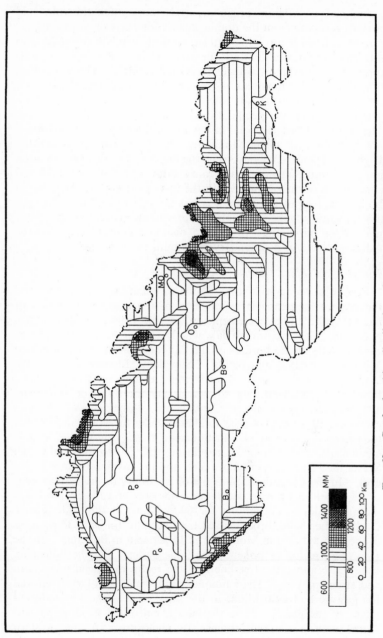

Fig. 62.   Czechoslovakia: distribution of mean annual precipitation.

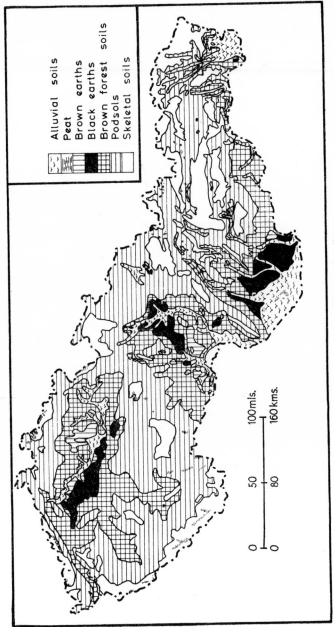

Alluvial soils
Peat
Brown earths
Black earths
Brown forest soils
Podsols
Skeletal soils

100 mls.
160 kms.

50
80

0
0

Fig. 63. Czechoslovakia: chief soil types.

Carpathians vegetation occurs in zones according to elevation : spruce forest extends from the cleared lowlands and intermontane basins up to 4,400 ft., above which there is a zone of *Pinus pumilio* up to 5,400 ft., followed by an alpine zone. To the east, beech woods predominate on the lower slopes, as in the Romanian Carpathians, and alpine pastures and sub-alpine scrub replace the *Pinus pumilio* zone. Much of the forest has been cleared from the southern valleys and lowlands, in favour of strip cultivation and pasture (Fig. 72).

Soils

In Czechoslovakia, soil character is in part related to the climate but the nature of the parent rock is the chief determinant (Fig. 63). Of the various kinds of soil which may be recognized, the black earths, akin to the Russian *chernozem*, are the product of a continental climate, with low precipitation (less than 20 in. annually), and an original steppe-heath vegetation. Such soils are found locally in the *Polabí* plains of northern Bohemia and also in the Moravian lowlands, where they are mainly utilized for wheat, flax and sugar beet growing. The Central European brown earths are similar, though lower in humus content, hence the lighter colour. They are found in regions of slightly higher precipitation (20–25 in. a year) and they are often utilized for cereal cultivation. A local variant is the *rendzina* type of soil derived from limestones, dark brown in colour and often under wheat or the vine. River alluvial soils are associated with meadow land. In some ill-drained lowland and upland areas, peaty soils have accumulated but the common highland type of soil is the grey, leached and acid *podsol* (Russian, ash soil). These are typical of forested regions with little undergrowth or accumulation of decaying leaves to provide humus, as with deciduous woodlands. In southern Slovakia, saline soils appear on the borders of the Hungarian *puszta* or grass steppe.

Land Utilization and Agriculture

Local variations in physical features, especially climate and soil as well as in economic conditions are strikingly reflected in a state characterized by so many diverse features. In the lowlands, the deepest and most tractable soils are generally under sugar beet, wheat and barley, with maize appearing in southern Slovakia. At levels above 1,000 ft., rye and oats are grown, with some wheat, but above 2,000 ft. rye and potatoes are alone possible, the improved land being otherwise under meadow and hill pasture. The proportion of land under cultivation and forest is shown in the table opposite based on percentages for 1928.

	Bohemia (%)	Moravia-Silesia (%)	Slovakia (%)	Czechoslovakia (%)
Agricultural land .	63	64	56	61
Forests	30	30	34	31
Other uses including waste	7	6	10	8

The intensity of agricultural output declines from the lowland sugar beet areas to the extensive pastoral regions, and rural population density decreases in proportion. Most of the land which is under crops in Bohemia is to be found in the Labe plains (*Polabí*) and in the Ohře valley. In Moravia it is found in the south and centre, while the lowlands of southern Slovakia are also highly cultivated. Moravia has a very high proportion of its farm land under crops (80 per cent), in contrast with 75 per cent in Bohemia and only 65 per cent in Slovakia. In the intensively farmed sugar beet areas, 84 per cent of the land is under crops, 72 per cent in the cereal regions, 66 per cent in the cereal and potato regions, and 50 per cent in the pastoral areas. As arable land, like gardens and vineyards, demands the greatest output of labour and capital, its proportion to total area is a measure of the agricultural standard of the region. Pasture land accounts for only 15 per cent of the farm land (including pre-war Ruthenia). It is least important in Moravia, where the percentage is 10, but in Slovakia it increases to 21. Forest land and wood exist where the land is unsuitable for agriculture, on account of steep slopes, poor soil or inaccessibility. The tables on page 193 indicate the main types of land use, and also crop production in 1948 and 1953 (planned), as well as the figures for 1964 for comparison.

The arable land (estimated as covering 42 per cent of the country in 1962) is mainly under cereals, *viz.* wheat, rye, barley and oats and also potatoes and sugar beet. The area under wheat increased between the wars at the expense of rye, the most widely grown cereal. Wheat averages one-sixth of the arable land, increasing to one-third on the plains of southern Slovakia. Yields have also increased in recent years with improved methods of farming technique, increased use of fertiliser and a decrease in the cultivated area since 1948. Rye is the great cereal crop of the less fertile soils and of the uplands, extending into the grain and potato regions as well as into those areas given mainly to grazing. Western and southern Bohemia produce a surplus of rye. It is used for brewing in Bohemia and Moravia as well as for bread making, especially in Slovakia, in the

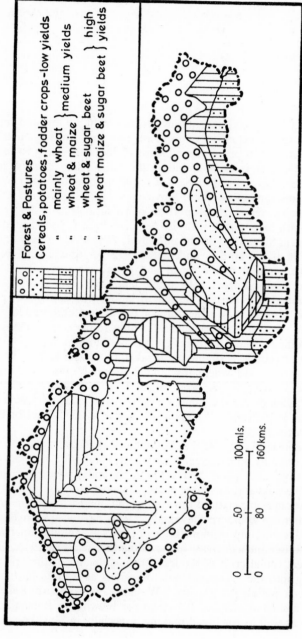

Fig. 64.   Czechoslovakia: types of land use.

LAND UTILIZATION

(1,000s of hectares)

	Average 1934–8	1948	1958	1965
Arable land	5,602	5,297	5,119	5,089
Permanent grassland . . ⎫	1,124	1,100	1,083	1,780
Hill pasture . . . . . ⎬	895	927	861	
Vineyards	20	20	22	—
Hop Gardens	12	7	8	—
Total improved land . . .	7,653	7,351	7,093	—
Forest	3,999	4,066	4,348	4,439
Water	46	53	52	—
Unclassified	99	98	57	—

AGRICULTURAL PRODUCTION

(1,000 metric tons)

	1948	1953 (Planned)		1960 (Planned)	1964 (Planned)
Wheat . .	1,441	1,558	Bread grains .	2,970	2,699
Rye . . .	1,173	1,000	Fodder grains .	3,910	2,563
Barley . .	1,085	1,266	Maize. . .	880	7,656
Oats . . .	1,017	1,137	Potatoes .	10,450	7,474
Maize . . .	—	—			
Potatoes . .	8,002	9,755			
Sugar beet .	4,719	5,540			

impoverished mountain valleys. The acreage under oats remains fairly constant. The crop is typical of poor soils and highland regions, especially in the Moravian uplands. Sugar beet and potatoes account for an eighth of the arable land. The latter are found, like oats, on the poorer soils and in the highlands, where they form the staple food of the peasants, as in Slovakia. The yields are highest on the plains of the *Polabí*, and in central and southern Moravia. After the break-up of the Austrian and Hungarian estates in 1919, the acreage under sugar beet increased rapidly until 1935. The Czech sugar beet industry has felt severe competition from sugar cane. The sugar beet crop is concentrated on the best soils, where the area sown may exceed 20 per cent. It is an intensive crop, making heavy demands on seasonal labour, but giving high cash returns to the grower, together with extra fodder in the form of beet tops, choppings and molasses. While the export trade declined before the war, there was a post-war increase owing to the great world shortage and restrictions in trade. Some fodder beet is also grown, especially in the dairying districts. Maize is produced for its grain only in southern Moravia and Slovakia, but the yields have declined and home supplies are insufficient. Tobacco, a state monopoly, was on the increase before the war, especially in southern Slovakia. Hops have been grown for centuries in Bohemia and Moravia but their cultivation is now limited to the best soils of Bohemia, a few acres in Moravia, with slight production in Slovakia. Orchard fruit growing is part of general farm practice, and plums, apples, pears, cherries and walnuts are commonly grown. Fruit trees are scattered over arable land, pastures and meadows, while they also line the country roads, appearing usually in most gardens, except in parts of Slovakia. Plums are sold as fresh fruit, for preserving, and also for distilling into brandy (*slivovica*). Viticulture was fostered by the kings of Bohemia and the monastic houses of the Middle Ages, burgundy being introduced from France in the 14th century. Today, most of the vineyards are in Slovakia, though the vintages of Mělnik, in Bohemia, are well known.

The cattle reared in Czechslovakia are mainly a cross breed between the native and Swiss stocks, except in Slovakia where the Austrian *Pinzgau* breed is reared. Cattle rearing is most important in southern and north-eastern Bohemia and also in north-eastern Moravia. The small farms which replaced the large landed estates rear more dairy cows per unit of agricultural land than hitherto, with an increase in milk production in consequence. While the Bohemian dairy farmer is mainly concerned with the production of liquid milk and butter, especially for urban markets, the Slovakian farmer, with poor access to urban markets, concentrates on butter and soft cheese. There had been some development of co-operative dairy farming in southern Moravia before the last war. The production of veal for the general home market is important in all parts of the state. Pigs are reared, especially to supply fresh pork, cured bacon and hams, for which Prague is especially noted. Sheep rearing is now only important in Slovakia, where the mountain pastures provide suitable grazing. Sheepskins are used locally for clothing, but the output of wool is insufficient for home needs. The peasants often keep goats instead of dairy cows. Poultry breeding is more intensive in the beet regions than in the grazing and potato areas, and is more important in the districts of Bohemia than elsewhere.

By the end of 1959, 84 per cent of all farm land had become collectivized, 19 per cent of the farms being state-owned. By 1965, the 7,135 collective farms accounted for 4·3 million hectares of farm land, but, in spite of the mechanization which has taken place, agricultural production, which it was planned to increase by 21 per cent during the third Five Year Plan, was less in 1965 than in 1961.   In fact, grain had to be imported from Canada (42 per cent) and the U.S.S.R. (38 per cent) in 1964.

Minerals, Motive Power and Raw Materials

Czechoslovakia includes within the state borders considerable resources of minerals and raw materials for industry. The chief source of motive power is coal, both bituminous and lignitic. Except on the Vltava and in southern Moravia, there is little development of hydro-electric power, though it is now being developed in the Carpathian regions of Slovakia. The thermal stations supplying Prague and industrial towns such as Brno and Ostrava burn coal or lignite. The output of minerals is given for comparative purposes in the following table, only planned figures being available.

MINERAL PRODUCTION

(Million tons)

	1925–33 (Average)	1945	1964
Coal	13·4	11·7	28·2
Lignite	18·6	15·3	71·5
Iron ore	1·3	0·2	2·8
Copper and lead . . .	0·03	—	·7
Rock salt	0·14	—	·16
Crude oil	0·01	—	—
Uranium	0·21 kg.	—	—

There has been a rapid recovery in coal production under the third Five Year Plan, the output of over 28 million tons in 1964 comparing with the peak year of 1929, when 22 million tons were produced. In that year, the Czech Silesian field accounted for 75 per cent of the total output, with the Kladno field contributing 12 per cent, Plzeň 6 per cent and others 7 per cent. Lignite is worked chiefly in north-west Bohemia (77 per cent), with Falknov

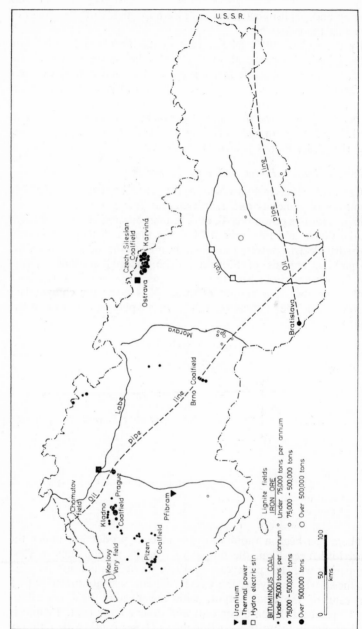

FIG. 65.   Czechoslovakia: sources of fuel, power and iron ore.

(a) Panorama of Prague, showing the Hradčany and Charles bridge over the Vltava river.

17. ELEMENTS IN THE LANDSCAPES OF CZECHOSLOVAKIA—I

(b) View of the recently completed Slapy dam on the Vltava river above Prague.

(a) Industrial landscape at Ostrava, Czech Silesia, showing thermal station and new iron and steel plant.

18. ELEMENTS IN THE LANDSCAPES OF CZECHOSLOVAKIA—2

(b) Gottwaldov (formerly Zlin) an industrial town in the Carpathian foothills of Moravia, specializing in footwear (Bata).

contributing 19 per cent, Slovakia 3 per cent and southern Moravia 1 per cent. Slovakia has long been mainly responsible for the output of iron ore, 30 per cent of the total coming from the Slovak Ore Mountains in 1929. Very little of the ore is reduced in Slovakia but is mainly transported to the blast furnaces of Ostrava, Brno, etc. Slovakia also produces some copper and lead ore, as well as rock salt. Uranium, long exploited at Jachymov, in north-west Bohemia, is now obtained mainly from Příbram.

INDUSTRIAL PRODUCTION
(Million metric tons)

	1953 (First Five Year Plan)	1957 (Second Five Year Plan)	1964 Third Five Year Plan
Coal	20·8	24·4	28·2
Coke	8·0	7·4	9·4
Lignite	32·2	48·7	71·5
Iron Ore	1·4	2·8	2·8
Pig iron	2·7	3·6	5·7
Raw steel	3·5	5·2	8·4
Rolled steel . . .	2·7	3·4	5·6
Electricity	11·2 kWh.	17·7 kWh.	31·9 kWh.

Czechoslovakia has a very wide range of raw materials at her disposal in addition to the minerals mentioned already. Timber is a valuable resource in the highland regions of Bohemia, the Moravian uplands and the Slovak Carpathians. Most of the timber (which covered 4·4 million ha. in 1958) is softwood but in Slovakia beech is also exploited. Many Czech industries use timber and its by-products, notably the furniture trade, the chemical industries (matches), paper, cellulose and artificial silk, in addition to forestry products such as charcoal, tar, asphalt and resin. The textile industry has to rely mainly on imported raw materials, such as cotton, wool, hemp, jute, raw and spun silk and rayon. The local production of flax and wool, which provided the basis of the former domestic industries, has helped, together with water power, to locate the modern mills, especially in the Sudetes. Furs, leather, rubber, etc., have also to be imported. Local sands have long been used in the traditional glass industry, notably at Jablonec in the Sudetes. Kaolin, quarried locally, forms the basis of the porcelain industry around Karlovy Vary (Karlsbad). Lime and cement industries are located near large limestone quarries at Teplice-Šanov, north of Brno, and also west of Prague. Industries working up agricultural produce include the extraction of sugar from sugar beet, especially important in northern Bohemia; the distillation of spirit from potatoes; brewing from hops and barley; flour milling; and tobacco production, especially at Plzeň and Prague.

Industry and Manufacture

In 1964, 2·4 million people were employed in nationalized industries. The chief centres of industrial activity in the former province of Bohemia are in the north-west and north-east frontier regions, in central Bohemia (in the Labe valley), and in the western part of the province on the Kladno coalfield, in the Plzeň region and in Greater Prague. In Moravia-Silesia, the industrial areas are on

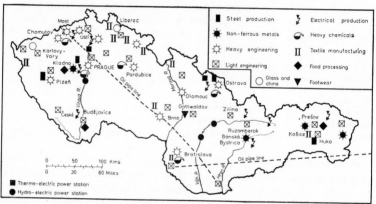

FIG. 66. Czechoslovakia: distribution of major manufacturing industries.

the Czech Silesian coalfield and also along the Dyje or Thaya valley, as well as in Brno, with access to hydro-electric power. In Slovakia, industries are established in the south-west in Bratislava, and in the central mountain valleys. The coalfields of Bohemia and Silesia produce coke and briquettes, and these form the basis of the iron and steel and heavy engineering industries of Děčin-Chomutov, the Prague region, and Plzeň, with its great Skoda works today nationalized but originally owned by the French armament firm of Schneider Creusot. In Moravia, a subsidiary steel works was established by this firm during the last war at Brno, where there is a long tradition of steel making, as in Moravska-Ostrava and at Bratislava on the Danube.

Raw steel production increased to 6·8 million tons in 1960, with 10·5 million tons as the target under the present plan. A new integrated steel plant has been built at Košice and is planned to produce 3·8 million tons of steel per annum. Recent developments include the completion of an oil pipeline from Brody, in the western Ukraine, to Bratislava in 1962 and another line came into operation at Zalnzi, near Most, in north-west Bohemia, in 1965.

Local examples of small-scale specialization are the production of cutlery and of buttons in the Sluknov district of Slovakia, spades and mattocks near Košice, and tacks and nails in the Brody district of central Bohemia. Musical instruments are made in the valleys of the Krušně Hory, while Liberec is noted for its pianos. The pottery and glass trades are characteristic of the frontier regions of Bohemia; the production of all types of glass ranging from plate to optical glass, jewellery and cut glass. Before the war, competition with Japan was severe, especially in the Indian and Far Eastern markets. Today, Czech goods are again appearing for sale in Britain and western Europe, where they compete successfully on account of lower production costs; hence their comparatively low prices.

The textile industries are mainly located in the highland valleys of the Krušně Hory and the Sudetes, and also in northern Moravia Here the original advantages were local wool, flax, water power and skilled rural labour for which there was otherwise little demand. The industries of the Sudetenland suffered severely during the depression of the early 1930's, especially in competition with Germany. After the war, the problem was that of an acute labour shortage as the result of the wholesale expulsion of the German population, many displaced persons becoming employed in refugee settlements in Bavaria and the Rhineland, where their skill could be used in the establishment of new factories. The large cities such as Prague, Brno and Bratislava retain their clothing, leather and paper trades. Timber mills are found on a large scale in Slovakia, especially in the valleys of the Low Tatra, with smaller establishments in Bohemia. The production of bentwood chairs from beechwood has long been a Czech speciality. Zlin, now Gottwaldov, in eastern Moravia, is a town of nationalized industries, the pre-war centre of mass-produced boots and shoes, associated with the firm of Bata, and of allied trades, such as rubber and leather goods, and also plastics.

Transport and Foreign Trade

In Czechoslovakia, the railways carry most of the freight traffic, waterways being of minor importance. The main items conveyed are coal, a third of the total tonnage, the rest consisting chiefly of timber and sugar beet. Waterways are handicapped by their physical unsuitability to carry heavy traffic, by the climatic conditions imposed by winter freezing, spring flooding, and summer low water. Only the Vltava and the Labe are useful to Bohemia as links with the German Elbe waterway system, providing before the war a North Sea outlet for this land-locked country. It is now planned to connect the Danubian port of Bratislava with Szczecin (Stettin), at the mouth of the Oder, a waterway which would lie entirely east of the Iron Curtain. Czechoslovakia, with one mile of railway to 65 sq. miles of area, is thus placed eighth among the countries of Europe according to the density of the rail net. Bohemia and Moravia-Silesia possess 71 per cent of the whole system (a legacy from the days of the Austro-Hungarian Empire), Slovakia having a poor system of rail communications, although new lines were built into the Carpathian valleys between the wars. Motor transport was also greatly extended, while Prague was linked by air with the capitals of Europe.

As far as foreign trade was concerned, the new state benefited from the prosperous years of the 1920's, to suffer a severe set-back during the world depression of the 1930's. The future will show how Czechoslovakia of today will adapt herself to her Central European position, pivoting between East and West, but tending to be drawn increasingly into the political and economic orbit of Slavonic Eastern Europe and the Soviet Union. Today, over one-third of the foreign trade is with the Soviet Union and another third with the satellite states of Eastern Europe.

Czechoslovakia has a reasonably well-balanced internal economy but she lacks a sufficiency of foodstuffs, especially wheat and flour, maize, edible fats, fruit, coffee, rye and vegetable oils. Similarly a wide variety of raw materials has to be imported, including in order of value cotton, wool, coal, raw hides and skins, tobacco, iron ore, mineral oil, etc. Imported finished goods include machinery, textile fabrics, silk, cotton and woollen yarns, chemicals, manufactured iron and steel, leather and rubber goods, and motor vehicles. To balance this list, Czechoslovakia exports foodstuffs, including sugar, malt and barley; raw materials, such as coal, timber, hops and cellulose, etc., together with a wide range of finished goods, of which cotton and woollen fabrics, iron and steel goods, glass ware, boots and shoes, woollen and cotton yarns, silk fabrics, clothing and porcelain lead in value.

Whereas before the war the chief countries from which Czechoslovakia imported goods were Germany, the U.S.A., Great Britain, France, Romania and Austria, since the war the Soviet Union and the People's Democracies, including China, have handled 65 per cent of the total foreign trade. This trade is now a state monopoly in the hands of eighteen import and export corporations.

Distribution of Population

Before the war, Czechoslovakia had a population of nearly 15 millions; in 1947, despite the restoration of the 1938 frontiers (though with the loss of Carpathian Ruthenia) the figure was reduced to little more than 12½ millions, but it is now 13·7 millions. The expulsion of thousands of Germans across the frontiers and the death and disappearance of nearly half the Jews account for the post-war decrease.

POPULATION OF CZECHOSLOVAKIA BY
NATIONALITIES 1964

	%
Czechs	65·4
Slovaks	28·5
Magyars	3·9
Germans	1·0
Poles	0·5
Ukrainians and Russians . .	0·4

The Czechs and Slovaks are nationally one, in spite of slight linguistic and considerable religious differences, and also in spite of a much higher standard of living enjoyed by the Czechs than the Slovaks, especially in the rural areas. The distribution of population closely reflects the varying economic resources and their development in the historic provinces. Bohemia had the highest density of population before the war and was economically the most advanced. Since the war, the density has been appreciably lowered by the expulsion of *Sudetendeutsch* from the frontier districts, as well as from the large towns, so that by 1947 the density figure for industrialized Czech Silesia and for Moravia was rather higher than for the former Sudetenlands. Slovakia supports only a low density of population on account of its inhospitable and largely forested and mountainous environment. The figures on page 206 bear out these points.

Both Bohemia and Moravia-Silesia have a fairly high proportion of urban population and the density of population is correspondingly high in and around the towns and in the mining and industrial areas of north-east and north-west Bohemia, as in Czech Silesia and southern Moravia. The only notable concentrations in Slovakia are in and around Bratislava, the Slovak port on the Danube, and in Košice, the regional capital of the eastern part of the province. Elsewhere the density is very low, especially in the northern Carpathians. Between the wars, there was a rapid growth of population in the capital city of Prague (Praha), which doubled in size, its

POPULATION OF CZECHOSLOVAKIA
(Millions)

	Area (million sq. km.)	Population			
		Total			Density (per sq. km.)
		1930	1947	1957	1961
Bohemia	52	7·1	5·6⎫	9·5	113
Moravia and Silesia .	26	3·5	3·1⎬		113
Slovakia	48	3·3	3·3	3·9	70
[Ruthenia	33	0·7]	—	—	—
Total (excluding Ruthenia)	126	13·9	12·0	13·4	107

population not quite reaching one million in 1938 (950,000). In 1965 it had a population of 1,020,000. The industrial towns, such as Brno (327,000), Bratislava (266,000) and Ostrava (259,000) have also grown rapidly, the same as smaller centres, such as Ústí (70,000) and Liberec (69,000). The lignite coalfield south-east of the Krušně Hory has also attracted miners in recent years. The rural areas have, on the other hand, experienced depopulation, partly by pre-war emigration to France, the U.S.A., Canada, the Argentine and Germany. Bohemia thus lost over 67,000 people between 1922 and 1933, Moravia-Silesia 39,800, Slovakia 138,924, and Ruthenia 15,235, totalling 261,065. To a minor degree this exodus was formerly offset by a small number of returning immigrants who, having made enough money abroad, usually in the New World, returned to their home town or village in their old age. After the Munich Agreement in 1938, an unknown number of anti-Nazi Germans, together with Jews, left the Sudetenland and many Czech towns, where they had formed large minority groups, never to return. After the end of the war in 1945, Czechoslovakia ordered the mass expulsion of all Germans within the state, irrespective of political belief or of value to the state as miner, industrial or farm worker. Since the establishment of the Communist régime in 1948, the tendency has been for Czechoslovakia to emphasize increasingly her Slavonic orientation and to develop her nationalized industries and her collectivized agriculture on the conventional lines of a satellite state in the Soviet *bloc* of Eastern Europe. Czechoslovakia

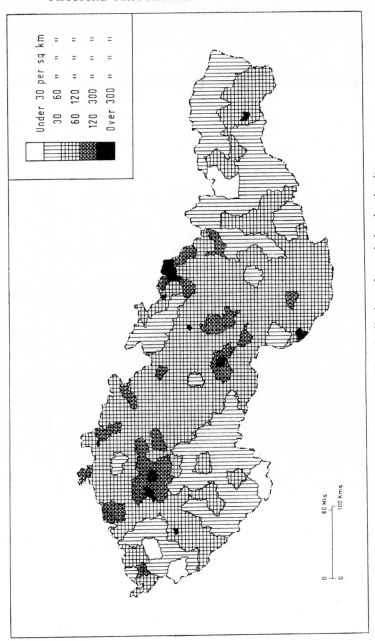

FIG. 67. Czechoslovakia: distribution of population by density.

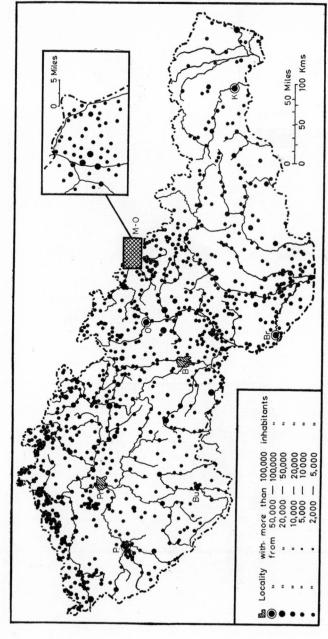

FIG. 68. Czechoslovakia: distribution of agglomerated settlement.

is the most prosperous state in Eastern Europe today, partly on account of her industrial tradition and hard-working population, and, for a Communist state, the standard of living is quite high but by no means luxurious.   The country has recently been described as ' the Belgium of the East ' and it is certainly the most industrialized state beyond the ' Iron Curtain '.

CHAPTER 10

THE HISTORIC PROVINCES OF BOHEMIA, MORAVIA-SILESIA AND SLOVAKIA

ALTHOUGH THE FOUR provincial divisions set up when the Republic of Czechoslovakia was instituted in 1919 were abolished by the Communist régime in 1949, when 19 administrative regions were established, it is convenient to retain them for purposes of regional description. Bohemia, Moravia and Czech Silesia also have historic significance as provinces of the former Austrian Empire, while Slovakia represented the northern rim of the Hungarian Empire gained by Czechoslovakia in 1919.

BOHEMIA

The most westerly historic province of this Slavonic state is also the historic and economic heartland of the Republic. Diamond-shaped, Bohemia retained its historic frontier with the Germanic world for nearly a thousand years, that is, until the German advance into the Sudetenland in 1938. The capital city of Prague (Praha) is the focal point of the former province, as of the state, in spite of its excentric position in relation to the rest of the Republic. It has one of the most striking sites of any European capital on the banks of the deeply incised Vltava (Moldau) river, originally fordable at this point (*Praha* means a sill). The town developed on the lowland on the right bank of the Vltava, inside a large incised meander, a river cliff on the left bank leading up to the castle terrace crowned by the *Hradčany*; with the *Vyšerad*, a second eminence, forming high ground to the south of the town. The *Hradčany*, the traditional residence of the kings of Bohemia since the later Middle Ages, together with the Gothic cathedral of St. Vitus, both within the original walls of the fortress in typical Slavonic or *Kremlin* style, bear comparison with the *Walwal* fortress of Cracow. This part of the town, serving today as the residence of the President of Czechoslovakia and as the administrative core of the capital, is linked with the commercial section of Prague by means of the medieval bridge across the Charles river, with its imposing line of statues. The medieval market town on the eastern side of the Vltava has spread over the river terraces and up the tributary valleys, so that modern Prague is surrounded by a straggling belt of suburbs, interspersed with small garden cities. The medieval ghetto, with its Golden Street and synagogue, now restored, is near the *Hradčany*. Thus modern Prague, with a population of 1,020,000, is an urban unit with a diversity of functions characteristic of most European

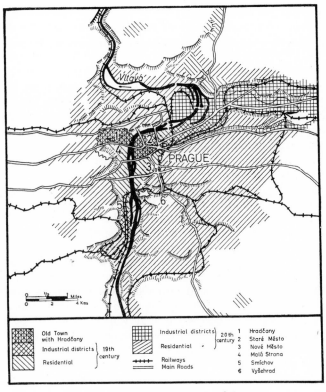

Old Town with Hradčany	Industrial districts	20th century	1 Hradčany
Industrial districts } 19th century	Residential	}	2 Staré Město
			3 Nové Město
Residential	Railways		4 Malá Strana
	Main Roads		5 Smíchov
			6 Vyšehrad

FIG. 69.   The site and growth of Prague.

capital cities, concerned with administration and learning, commerce and industry.

Other large Bohemian towns are manufacturing centres, such as Plzeň (Pilsen), with a population of 138,000, with its huge iron and steel works, once the property of the Skoda armaments firm and now a centre of the nationalized steel industry. It also has a world-famous brewery. České Budějovice (Budweis) in southern Bohemia, with its graphite and associated lead pencil industry, has a population of 63,900.   Smaller industrial towns are Kladno, on the coalfield of that name, supplying fuel to the thermal stations serving Prague, and Liberec (Reichenberg) in the industrial Sudetenland. The spa towns of north-west Bohemia, such as Karlovy-Vary (Karlsbad) and Marianské-Lazny (Marienbad), are world famous. The lignite field of the same region also supports a dense population, including the towns of Chomutov, Most and Teplice-Sanov.

Bohemia is in essence part of Hercynian Europe. The massif exemplifies the same degree of structural complexity as, for example, the *Massif Central* in France, with which it is comparable in area. Relics of Caledonian folding are preserved in the Brody Hills, a ridge of Cambrian slates rising to 2,571 ft., with upstanding quartzites, trending north-east–south-west and lying to the south-west of Prague. Folded and uplifted in Carbo-Permian times with accompanying local metamorphism, the massif consists of a core of gneissic and granitic rocks, mainly mantled by forest. Crystalline basement rocks underlie the broken and dissected southern uplifted peneplain (the *Rumpfläche* of the German geographers) and also the elevated mountain rim. Resisting pressure from the Alpine earth movements in Miocene times, the massif was uplifted, fractured and tilted with accompanying vulcanism. These features are especially pronounced in the region of the thermal springs and radio-active ores in the north-west around Karlovy-Vary and Jachymov (Joachimstal). The coalfields also experienced extensive faulting, thus adding to the difficulty of mining. The highland rim of Bohemia was much uplifted, faulted and divided into individual ranges, especially in the Sudetes, the drainage being rejuvenated, so that streams flow across the massif in narrow, incised valleys, bordered by river terraces and providing sites for water power. Drainage is consequent upon the tilting of the block northwards and it converges on the Labe (Elbe), the main tributaries of which are the Vltava from the south, joining the Labe at Mělník below Prague; the Ohře and the Berounka coming in from the west. The Labe has an anomalous course, rising on the southern slopes of the Sudetes before crossing the *Polabí*, a broken and dissected lowland developed mainly on Cretaceous and Eocene rocks. The river finally leaves Czechoslovakia between Litoměřice and Ústí by means of a gorge cut in Cretaceous sandstone. This region is known to the Czechs as Středohoří and to the Germans as ' Saxon Switzerland '; the fantastic erosion of the red rocks into buttes and canyon-like forms, frequently forest-covered, is paralleled in the Česky Raj or ' Bohemian Paradise ', near Jicin.

Inner Bohemia is clearly a remarkable physical unit, in spite of

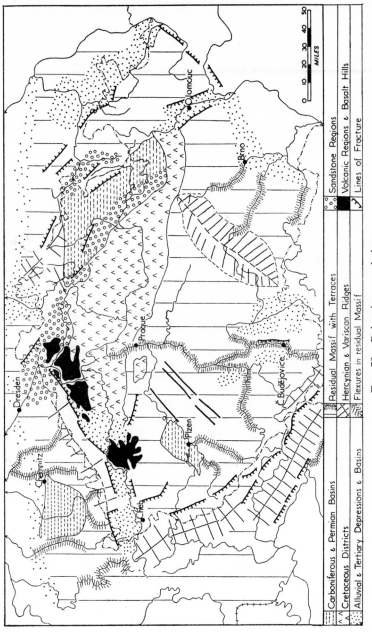

FIG. 70. Bohemia: morphology.

its physical diversity.   It is defined by the highland framework of
the Ore Mountains (*Czech*, Krušné Hory; *German*, Erz-Gebirge)
to the north-west, along the frontier with Saxony.   This highly
dissected and therefore easily penetrated range trends from north-
east to south-west and culminates in Klinovec (3,732 ft.), but has a
general elevation of over 2,000 ft.   East of the gorge cut by the
Labe *en route* to Dresden, the Sudetes form the frontier with East
Germany and Polish Silesia.   The general trend of the range is from
north-west to south-east but it is broken into a series of individual
ranges such as the Giant Mountains (*Czech*, Krkonoše Hory;
German, Riesen-Gebirge) and the Eagle Mountains (*Czech*, Orliche
Hory; *German*, Adler-Gebirge).   The Giant Mountains culminate
in the Schneekoppe (5,330 ft.), a glaciated mountain mass, resembling the Feldberg in the Black Forest.   Similarly, the Bohemian
Forest, on the borders of Austria, rises to comparable heights in
the Javor Mountain (*German*, Arber), a rounded, granitic massif
rising to 4,371 ft., with occasional glacial lakes of the *Kar* type,
surrounded by unbroken stands of fir forest.   The Bohemian Forest
(*Czech*, Šumava; *German*, Böhmerwald) forms an unbroken range,
parallel to the Bavarian Forest and to the Danube valley between
Linz and Regensburg.   It is divided from the Fir Mountains (*Czech*,
Český Les; *German*, Fichtel-Gebirge) by the Fürth-Cheb (Eger)
gap.   This tangle of highlands is a major hydrographic divide,
throwing off streams to the upper Main, Naab and Saale on the
German side of the frontier and to the Ohře (Eger) in western
Bohemia.   To the south-east of Bohemia, the Moravian Heights
(Českomoravská) form relatively subdued upland country, trending
from north-east to south-west and with a general height of 2,000
ft. but culminating in Javořice (2,505 ft.).   In the north of Bohemia,
where the crystalline basement rocks are covered by younger and
sedimentary formations, coalfields occur, as at Kladno and Plzeň,
and lignite is quarried at Chomutov.   The plains of the *Polabí*,
drained by the upper Labe on leaving the Sudetes, are partly covered
by drift deposits, notably loess; hence the soil fertility of these ' black
earth ' lowlands, in contrast with the podsolized soils of most of
the rest of Bohemia.   There are also narrow strips of alluvial
material bordering the streams and these are frequently cut into
terraces, while there is glacial and fluvioglacial drift in the mountain
valleys of the Sudetes and Bohemian Forest.   These highland
regions contain a variety of minerals, some of which are now virtually
worked out, such as silver-lead and copper in the Ore Mountains,
originally sufficient to attract German miners into the mountains
at the time of the Reformation.   Iron ore, graphite, rock salt and

china clay are of some importance today, as is the pitchblende of Přibram, associated with radio-active springs. In the highlands, semi-precious stones have long been worked on a small scale, such as garnets, for which Bohemia is noted, and also agates and jasper.

The climate of Bohemia is cool temperate continental in type but conditions vary locally according to differences in elevation, slope and exposure, etc. In the highlands there is heavy winter snowfall, often lasting for over 45 days, but the lowlands of Bohemia are in the lee of the Bohemian Forest, the Ore Mountains and the Sudetes, and, as the prevalent wind is westerly, they receive under 27 in., whereas the Ore Mountains record a mean annual precipitation of over 80 in. There is a typical continental summer maximum and a winter minimum precipitation. When Polar Continental air masses prevail, associated in winter with dry, bright and calm weather and also with east or north-east winds coming off the east European high-pressure area, temperatures below freezing point occur. In summer, high-pressure conditions result in high temperatures and heavy thunderstorm rain, whereas when depressions bring Tropical Maritime air from the Atlantic with westerly or southwesterly winds, relatively mild, rainy weather is characteristic at all seasons.

Bohemia is characterized by a sharply contrasted pattern of soils and land use. Much of the plateau has a thin soil covering and the surface is often ill-drained, as the result of the considerable rainfall occurring on the impervious granitic and gneissic rocks. Much of the plateau is wooded or under marsh or grassland. Stock rearing is the main activity, together with forestry. The northern plains of the *Polabí* provide a marked contrast, for they are intensively cultivated on a strip pattern and relatively high yields are the rule, including that of industrial crops such as sugar beet, flax and hops. Polyculture prevails here, and there is a high density of rural settlement, mainly in agglomerated villages. In Bohemia there has long been an even balance between agriculture and industry. Under the Austrian Empire, industries were developed on the coalfields, notably the Skoda works at Plzeň, and in the mountain borders of Bohemia especially in the Sudetenlands, using water power, local timber, wool and mineral ores, and also drawing on rural labour, much of which was German-speaking. Under the Czech government, a variety of industries was encouraged, some based on agricultural products, such as brewing, sugar refining and linen manufacture. China clay was available for the production of both fine porcelain and cheap pottery, and local sands could be used for the making of glass, as well as graphite for pencils. Textile industries are especially widespread in the valleys of the Sudetes, notably at Liberec (Reichenberg), and, in these remote sites, glass ware of a variety of types is produced, as at Jablonec. The coalfields of Kladno and Plzeň form the basis of local heavy industries and of thermal electricity, in the production of which lignite has also been used for a long time. The Elbe formerly provided a navigable waterway to and from the North Sea at Hamburg, for it is navigable for 750-ft. barges as far as Ústí (Aussig), while smaller barges and river craft continue as far as Prague *via* the Vltava (Moldau). The capital city of Prague is the hub of the state railway system, and from it radiate modern main roads, as well as air routes to Eastern Europe.

MORAVIA

Moravia (*German*, Mähren) was, like Bohemia, an historic kingdom, and its importance lay in its corridor position between Bohemia and Slovakia, bordering Austria and the Danube valley in the south, with Polish Silesia to the north. The Czech province of Silesia was incorporated in Moravia in 1927. The lowland, known as the Moravian or March Gate, is clearly defined by the Moravian Heights to the west and the White Carpathians to the east. In the south, the Austrian frontier follows the Dyje (Thaya) valley and then turns along the lower Morava (March) valley to the Danube above Bratislava (Pressburg). In the north, the Moravian corridor is constricted by the approach of the Carpathian foothills to the Sudetes. The province is drained mainly by the Morava (March) and its tributaries, including the Jihlava and the Dyje. In the north, the Odra (Oder), rising in the south-eastern Sudetes, drains across Czech Silesia *en route* to Poland. The region has been a highway of movement for centuries between east-central Europe, i.e. Poland and Austrian Galicia and Vienna. It lies on the ancient amber route between Samland, on the Baltic coast of former East Prussia, thence *via* the Vistula valley and Cracow to Brno (Brünn) and Vienna.

The former province of Moravia is characterized by a landscape of open, rolling country, developed mainly on Secondary and Tertiary rocks, partly covered by drift deposits, including loess. In north-west Moravia-Silesia, Coal Measures extend towards the Polish frontier. This region, with its coal mining and its associated iron and steel industries in and around Moravská Ostrava, includes also the industrial town of Brno (Brünn) now a city of over 300,000, and the modern Carpathian valley town of Gottwaldov (formerly

Zlin) with 54,200 people. Most of Moravia is otherwise agricultural. The soils are enriched by extensive deposits of windborne loess, which breaks down into a rich loam. Wheat is grown on these soils, and the cultivation of other cereals, sugar beet and potatoes, fruit and vines in favourable areas such as the Carpathian foot-hills, is important. Cattle and sheep rearing are carried on, especially on the upland pastures. Large farms are typical; the absence of enclosure and the prevalence of long strips of cultivation, reminiscent of the former open field system of Central Europe, enhancing the monotony of these rolling landscapes. Moravia is second to Bohemia as a producer of cash crops on modern Central European lines, wheat and sugar beet being the leading products. Industry is developed in such towns as Brno (Brünn), which formerly had a considerable German population. It is a centre of heavy industry, with a branch of the nationalized Skoda works, and also a university town. Olomouc (formerly Olmutz), in the upper Morava valley, and a group of towns in Czech Silesia, of which Moravská Ostrava is the centre, are also concerned with heavy industry, on the basis of Silesian coal.

SLOVAKIA

Today the most easterly of the former provinces of Czechoslovakia since the incorporation of Carpathian Ruthenia in the U.S.S.R., and formerly part of the Austro-Hungarian Empire, Slovakia lacks the historic individuality of Bohemia and Moravia. Physically, how-ever, it corresponds with the western Carpathians and the lowlands to the south which fringe the Pannonic basin of Hungary. The northern mountainous frontier, following in part the High Tatra, divides Slovakia from Poland very effectively, but, to the south, the Carpathian foothills give way gradually to the Hungarian plains, and here much intermingling of Magyar and Slovak was formerly characteristic, the Magyars being the land-owning aristo-cracy and the Slovaks the peasant labourers. The western spurs of the Carpathians, known as the Little and White Carpathians, border Moravia, and to the east the mountain system is continued in Ruthenia (Podkarpatská Rus), now incorporated in the Ukraine. The chief town of Slovakia is Bratislava (*German*, Pressburg), a river port on Danube (*Czech*, Dunaj), with a population of 260,000 in 1963. It originated as a fortress site on a bluff overlooking the river, where the Little Carpathians end against the Danube. It is concerned with the transhipment of foodstuffs, especially wheat, and also oil and timber transported by barge up the Danube, with

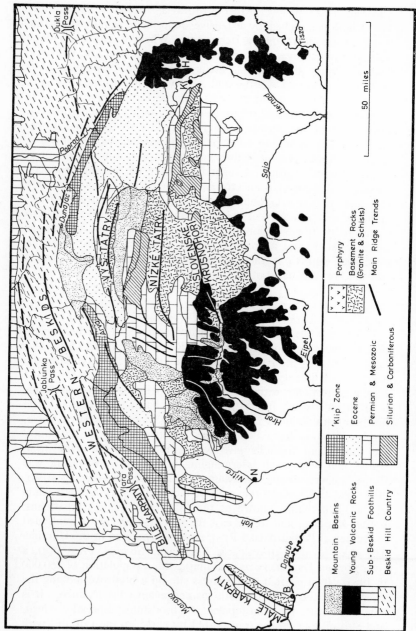

Fig. 71. Morphology of th...

coal and various manufactured goods making up the return traffic. Other important towns are Košice (*Magyar*, Kassa; *German*, Kaschau), on the Hernád river in eastern Slovakia, with its cathedral in Byzantine style, and the market town of Prešov (*German*, Eperies), higher up the valley. Apart from small mining centres, the health resorts and winter sports centres of the High Tatra, the population is mainly rural and grouped in small villages.

The Carpathians form a mountain system which is Alpine in type, although the general elevation is lower than that of the Alps and snow lies only in patches in summer on the highest peaks. The Carpathian arc, which originated in Oligocene-Miocene times, curves through Ruthenia into Central Romania, in sympathy with the Hercynian Bihor (Bihar) massif, in Transylvania. Known sometimes as the Western Beskids, the western Carpathians are complex in structure and comprise several distinct parts. The High Tatra (Vysoky Tatry), forming the Polish frontier, are alpine as regards land forms. The Low Tatra (Nizké Tatra) lie in the centre of the system at a much lower elevation, and the Slovak Ore Mountains (Slovenské Krušnéhoři) form the most southerly ranges. Other local ranges of importance are the Little Carpathians (Malé Karpaty), trending south-west–north-east from the Danube at Bratislava, and the White Carpathians (Bilé Karpaty), parallel to the same range and dividing the Morava drainage from that to the Váh (Waag). The Prešovské Hory (Slanské Pohorie) and the Hegyallya ranges, trending north-south, form a distinctive region to the east of the Hernád valley. The highest peaks of the Carpathians are found in the High Tatra (Mt. Gerlachovká, 7,989 ft., Rysy, 7,509 ft.), where a 'window' of highly resistant granites, gneisses and schists has given rise to rugged mountainous scenery, with pyramidal peaks and arête ridges, where the effect of mountain glaciation is apparent. Snow lies well into the summer on these peaks. Glacial lakes occur, such as Štrbské Pleso and Popradské Pleso. The Low Tatra have a general elevation of 4,000 ft., rising to 6,135 ft. in Mt. Dumbier. They, in common with the greater part of the western Beskids, except the High Tatra, comprise highly folded sedimentary rocks, with the addition of local intruded rocks and volcanics. The Slovakian Ore Mountains are formed mainly of Carboniferous limestone and Mesozoic rocks, and they have long been associated with the mining of iron ore and copper. The Prešovské Hory and the Hegyallya ranges are volcanic, like the Velka Fatra and the Mátra massif to the south of the Carpathians. Local features of interest are the caves and grottoes at Demänová, with their stalactites and stalagmites; the ice cave at Dobšiná;

and the cold geyser at Herlany, north-east of Košice. Between the main mountain ranges are structural basins, floored by Eocene rocks, with cultivable soils, especially where enriched by vulcanic downwash and loess.

The Carpathians form an impressive barrier between the upper Vistula basin and the historic routeway which lies across it *via* Cracow and the Danube basin. The long river trenches between the ranges provide ways of penetration into the mountain system, notably *via* the Váh, Hron and Hernád valleys, opening southwards to the Hungarian Plain. The Poprad, one of the headstreams of the Vistula, rises within a few miles of the Váh, flowing to the Danube, on the southern slopes of the High Tatra. The northern mountain rim is breached by several passes, of which the

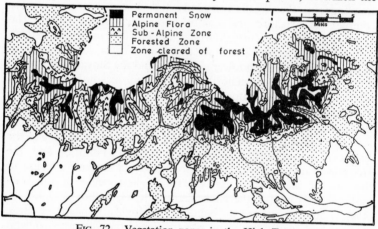

FIG. 72.   Vegetation zones in the High Tatra.

Jablunkovsky (Jablunka) in the west, the Muszyna gap (Poprad valley), and the Dukla pass in the east, are most important. The Carpathians, with their east-central European ' mountain ' type of climate, receive heavy precipitation, with winter snow and a summer rainfall maximum. Except for the High Tatra, which extend into the realm of bare rock where alpine flora grow in pockets of soil, the mountain slopes are mostly heavily timbered; coniferous forest, including spruce, silver fir and larch, being predominant. The valleys and basins have long been cleared for pasture, cultivation and settlement. Mining has in places increased the rate of deforestation, on account of the use of charcoal for the smelting of the ore. Charcoal burning is still carried on in the forests. Apart from the mining of iron, manganese and copper ore, in the Slovak Ore Mountains, opals were formerly mined in the Prešovké Hory, but competition with Australian opals caused the French company to close down over forty years ago.

Slovakia lags behind the rest of Czechoslovakia in the utilization of its resources and has a low standard of living, so that its economy bears comparison with eastern and south-eastern Europe rather than with central Europe. The forestry industry is not well organized, mining methods are primitive, and most of the population live a life of meagre subsistence farming. Slovak peasant villages are scattered through the mountainous valleys. Strip cultivation is carried on for the cultivation of potatoes, rye and, in places, maize, with a patch of flax and chicory. Sheep and cattle are reared extensively, but there is very little utilization of the summer mountain pasture, as in the Alps. Systems of farming are primitive and traditional, hand reaping being general, with the use of oxen as draught animals. The farmhouses are usually timber structures, with thatched roofs; the more prosperous having a garden with fruit trees. Many dwellings turn inwards, presenting a wall of wood and stone to the street. Water supplies are usually derived from shallow wells, worked on the beam and bucket principle, as on the Hungarian *Alföld*. The peasants spin and weave wool and flax for their own use, but there is little development of craft industries as in the more prosperous mountainous regions of central Europe, although the peasants are often skilled at embroidery. Before the 1939–45 war, in spite of liberation from Magyar landowners and the resulting division of their large estates among the peasants, emigration to the United States was a regular drain, though some Slovaks returned eventually to buy land in their own village. The rich grain lands of the southern Slovak lowlands, with their former Magyar population majority, together with the vineyards of the Tribecké Heights around Topolčiansky, form a striking contrast with the forested slopes of the Carpathians. Between the wars, the Czechoslovak government began to develop the High Tatra as a health and winter sports resort. Railways were built from Moravia into the valleys of the Western Beskids, and motor roads were constructed. The modern hotels and sanatoria of Štrbské Pleso and Tatranská Lomnica contrast sharply with the primitive Slovak villages nearby, dominated by the Roman Catholic or Greek Orthodox church. Here the peasants have preserved their traditional dress and customs. There is not much development of hydro-electric power in the Slovak Carpathians, although under the present Communist régime industrial development on this basis is planned in the Váh valley, where before the last war industries were non-existent. Iron ore was quarried to be reduced in the blast furnaces of Czech Silesia and Moravia. Bratislava is Czechoslovakia's river port on the Danube and water connection with the upper Odra (Oder) is planned. Komarno is a river port of minor significance, where the Váh and Nitra join the Danube. The town of Nitra, with its thousand-year-old church, together with the small cathedral town of Košice and also Prešov (Eperies), have local industries. The two latter towns are on the north–south railway from southern Poland (Cracow-Tarnów) to Hungary (Buda-Pesth) and Košice is also on the line which runs through the Hernad valley to the Váh, thus linking Carpathian Slovakia with Moravia. Since 1953, some development of industry has taken place here, an iron and steel plant at Huko, near Košice, processing local ores.

REFERENCES

The Atlas of the Czechoslovak Republic (*Atlas republiky Československé*), Prague, 1936, with explanatory text in English and French, is the best pre-war source of material, as well as being a fine piece of cartography, since reproduced in modern form. Mrs. Steers (*née* Wanklyn): *Czechoslovakia* (1953) is a political and social study. There are useful chapters on Czechoslovakia in D. Warriner: *Economics of Peasant Farming*, 1939, and in H. G. Wanklyn: *The Marchlands of Eastern Europe*, 1941. E. de Martonne: *Europe Centrale*, Vol. IV, Part II, in the *Géographie Universelle* series, and F. Machatschek: *Landeskunde der Sudeten u. West-Karpatenländer*, are useful pre-war references. The chapter in George et Tricart: *L'Europe Centrale*, Vol. 2, is especially concerned with topical economic developments. The Czech geographer, Dr. J. Moscheles, has written on the ' Natural Regions of Czechoslovakia ', in the *Geographical Review*, Vol. 14, 1924, and on the ' Economic Regions of Greater Prague ', *ibid.*, Vol. 27, 1937. M. Blažek: *Ökonomische Geographie der Tschechoslovakischen Republik*, 1959, transl. H. Langer is a major modern reference; R. H. Osborne: *East-Central Europe*, 1967, Chap. 5. The topographical maps covering the country on a scale of 1 : 200,000 are the Czech edition of the Austrian Staff maps.

CHAPTER 11

GERMANY : PHYSICAL GEOGRAPHY

IN DESCRIBING the physical features of Germany, the political division of the country into the East and West Republics is ignored, for this divide is artificial and has no bearing on the relief, structure and drainage, nor on the climate and plant life, since these features apply to a wide and diversified belt of Central Europe extending from the Rhine basin to the Oder-Neisse line and beyond.

STRUCTURE AND RELIEF

Germany is a kind of structural microcosm of Europe, for all the great morphological and relief elements are included within its boundaries, with the exception of the Fenno-Scandian Shield. In the Middle Rhine Highlands, the Caledonian trend is represented by deep-seated folding, occurring at the surface in the Hohes Fenn in the Eifel, where Cambrian rocks are exposed. However, the great tectonic movements which are reflected in the present-day land forms and relief are the Carbo-Permian (Hercynian) folding, the Saxonian (in the northern uplands) and the Alpine (Oligocene-Miocene).

Carbo-Permian Folding. The Hercynian folding, which involved the crumpling and local metamorphism of rocks older than the Permian, was responsible for the late Primary fold ranges which extended from the Ardenne *via* the Harz and Thuringian Forest to the Erz-Gebirge, from the Rhenish Palatinate (Hardt) to the Fichtel-Gebirge, and from the Black Forest to the Böhmerwald. The structure of these massifs varies widely, Devonian sandstones and slates predominating in the Middle Rhine Highlands, granites and gneiss in the Black Forest and Bohemian Massif. In addition, the Carboniferous rocks were involved in these folding movements, so that today the Coal Measures of the Ruhr and the Saar basins are preserved in a series of synclines divided by saddles (Fig. 108). Subsequent to the folding and uplift of these massifs, they were reduced to peneplains; the even sky lines of the Hoch Eifel, Hunsrück and Taunus bearing witness to this. In the Black Forest, Odenwald

223

and Spessart, these surfaces were largely buried by the subsequent deposition of Permian and Triassic rocks which were laid down unconformably on the basement gneisses, schists and granites.   As

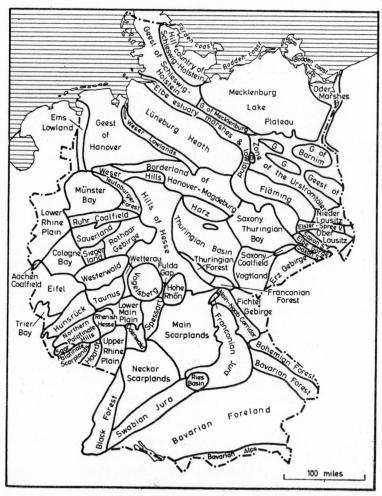

FIG. 73. Germany: morphological regions.

the result of subsequent erosion, these fossil peneplains have been exposed, especially in the southern Black Forest and Odenwald.

Saxonian Folding. This period of folding, as its name implies, is peculiar to north Germany and it continued from Jurassic to

Miocene times. It affected especially the foreland of the Harz and the Weser Uplands. The general trend of the sedimentary rocks involved is from north-west to south-east, and, as the result of subsequent erosion, these hills now form a series of blocks, such as the Wiehen- and Weser-Gebirge, divided by the gap of the Weser above Minden and known as the Porta Westfalica. To the west of these limestone hills is the crescentic line of the Teutoburgerwald, formed also of Mesozoic rocks.

Oligocene-Miocene Folding. The great Tertiary orogenesis which saw the uplift and folding of the Triassic and Jurassic rocks of the Bavarian Alps had many repercussions on the relief to the north. In particular the Primary massifs yielded to the pressure from the south by block uplift and tilting, as well as by local faulting and fracturing. Occasionally, isolated massifs such as the Harz, bounded by faults, formed *horsts*, but most of the Primary massifs have asymmetrical slopes, especially where the Vosges-Black Forest, Hardt-Odenwald blocks were severed by the progressive foundering which produced the Rhine rift valley or *Graben*. These Hercynian uplands present a series of eroded and faulted scarps towards the trench of the Rhine. Many of the faults, which trend from north-east to south-west, are buried beneath the fluvioglacial and alluvial deposits which cover the floor of the rift valley. The Ruhr coalfield, like the Saar, was also heavily faulted and great thrust planes serve greatly to complicate mining operations. Vulcanicity also accompanied the Tertiary earth movements, and relics of these volcanic eruptions give a distinctive type of scenery to the Hohe Rhön and Vogelsberg, as well as to the Eifel, with its crater lakes (*Maare*). The basalts of the Sieben-Gebirge, where ' the castled crag of Drachenfels frowns o'er the wide and winding Rhine ', form a rugged margin to the right bank of the Rhine near Andernach, and the dissected plug of the Kaiserstuhl, in the upper Rhine valley near Freiburg, is also a local landmark. In the Hegau, a region between the Black Forest and the lake of Constance, there is a line of isolated volcanic plugs. Another result of the Miocene thrusting was the tilting of the Jurassic scarplands of Swabia and Franconia, so that these uplands present a steep but fretted scarp westwards and north-westwards towards the Neckar and Main valleys, divided by the tectonic basin of the Ries, where there was also local vulcanism. The long dip slope of the Swabian Alb is towards the Danube valley and that of the Franconian Alb towards the Naab and Pegnitz. As the result of subsequent erosion of these tilted surfaces, the Neckar and Main basins exhibit a variety of scarp and vale features, the scarps reaching their greatest extent in the Jurassic limestones but also appearing in the eroded Keuper sandstones of the Franconian Heights and Steigerwald.

As the result of the earth movements responsible for the Alps, a major structural trough or geosyncline developed between the Alps and the Plateau Jura. Here great thicknesses of sand and gravel were laid down by streams draining northwards from the Alps and these deposits became compacted to form *Molasse*. This Miocene formation occasionally forms east–west ridges in the Bavarian Foreland and the Allgäu, but it is covered by subsequent glacial and Recent drift deposits. The Rhine rift valley was the scene of progressive deposition in a region of continued subsidence. The diversion of the Rhine below Basle and the cutting of the Rhine gorge are post-Pliocene features, to which the rejuvenated valleys of the Neckar, Mosel and Lahn are also related, as is the diversion of drainage from the upper Danube to the upper Rhine. In the north-west, the Rhine, together with the Meuse (*Dutch*, Maas), laid down great sheets of gravel in the form of river deltas along the edge of the Pliocene sea.

Quaternary Glaciation and Recent Features. Germany was affected by the advance of the continental ice sheets from Scandinavia and the Baltic in the north, by the Alpine mountain glaciation in the south and by local ice caps in the Black Forest, Böhmerwald and Sudetes. The maximum advance of the ice which left its imprint on the present-day landscape is that of the second or Riss-Saale phase. This ice sheet advanced southwards to the line of the lower Rhine and the Ruhr. It was halted by the rising ground of the *Mittelgebirge* in central Germany, but in the Alpine Foreland it crossed the upper Rhine, diverting its course near the site of Schaffhausen and advancing across the Danube to the foot of the Swabian Jura. To the east, the ice lay across the Foreland, advancing in three great lobes towards the Danube (Fig. 8). As the ice sheets retreated and the ice caps of the high Hercynian massifs melted, sheets of glacial drift remained, to be reassorted by river action. This forms the Older Drift of north-western Germany. In places it forms low morainic hills, as in the region of the Dutch frontier. In the Alpine Foreland, great crescentic lines of terminal moraines form a striking feature of the landscape from the lake of Constance to the Inn valley. In north-west Germany, long stretches of marshy depression mark stages in the retreat of the ice towards the Baltic. These *Urstromtäler* or melt-water channels extend from the lower Rhine, Ems, Weser and Elbe but there are a number of east–west valley trenches, some of which have been utilized by canals, such as the *Mittelland*. Most of the glacial drift west of the Elbe has been reassorted by subsequent river action and covered by fluvio-glacial outwash from the Würm-Vistula ice sheet.

The Würm-Vistula ice did not advance beyond a line crescentic to the Baltic and extending from Schleswig-Holstein to the middle Elbe valley and thence eastwards across the upper Oder into Poland. In the Alpine region, the Würm ice halted north-west of lake Constance and well to the south of the Riss moraines. In the Baltic lowlands much of the ice remained static and, as it melted, sheets of ground moraine remained. Towards the Baltic, however, impressive terminal moraines marked the various stages of the retreating ice, known variously as the Brandenburg, Frankfurt and Pomeranian. The most impressive of these glaciated landscapes is the region of the Mecklenburg lake plateau. Material washed out by melting ice-water and re-deposited by river action forms the *Geest* areas of sterile sands and gravels which stretch from the Lüneburg Heath across the upper Elbe into the Fläming and across the Elster into Nieder-Lausitz. In some districts, the streams escaping from the ice sheet deposited outwash deltaic material known as *Sander*, consisting of alternating bands of sand and gravel.[1] Great melt-water channels extend across the plain beyond the Elbe, notably along the Spree-Havel valleys in the Berlin region, as well as along the Oder and Neisse. In the south, elongated drumlin ridges occur north-west of lake Constance, as they do in the northern plain towards the Baltic coast.

An important inter-glacial and post-glacial feature of Germany is the loess. This æolian deposit lies in considerable thicknesses on the level surfaces of the northern sub-Hercynian zone and also on the high terraces of the upper Rhine and Danube, where it has been preserved from erosion. It reaches a depth of several feet on the slopes of the Kaiserstuhl and is significant in the Wetterau, Rheingau and in the Bergisches Höhe. It is also preserved locally on terraces in the Neckar valley and on the Main terraces around Würzburg. This deposit, laid down beyond the limits of the Younger Drift, breaks down into a rich soil resembling *chernozem* or black earth.

In post-glacial or Recent times, various changes have taken place in the surface features of the landscape. They include the silting of lakes and the development of boggy tracts of high and low moor. In the Alpine region, lake deltas have been formed and glacially eroded valleys rejuvenated by post-glacial stream erosion. Along the North Sea and Baltic coast, a number of changes have taken place as the result of eustatic movements, including the formation

[1] P. George and J. Tricart: *L'Europe Centrale*, Vol. 1, p. 79.

of the East Frisian islands and the *Watten*; the estuaries of the Ems, Weser and Elbe; the deep inlets such as the Flensburg *förde*; and the broad bays and *Haffe* of the Baltic. Here, along a tideless coast, great shingle spits have been built up by the action of onshore winds and the drift of coastal currents; the coast from Peenemunde to the mouth of the Oder (Das Haff) being one such area and the broken coast of the island of Rügen another. Further depositional features are the sand dunes which extend along the outer side of the Frisian islands and along the Baltic coast, where they attain considerable heights. The North Sea coast is low-lying and formerly marshy, fringed offshore by mud flats or *Watten* which are exposed at low tide. Their channels are constantly shifting but the estuaries of the Weser and Elbe are kept clear by strong tidal scour combined with constant dredging.

CLIMATE

Germany lies in a transitional position, where maritime influences gradually decrease eastwards to be replaced by those of the continental land mass. In winter, Germany experiences two contrasted types of weather, the one arising from the predominance of mild, moist, unstable air of Tropical Maritime origin and the other from cold, dry, stable Polar Continental air masses. In summer, the weather depends on the extent to which cool, Maritime air streams break up the general ' continental ' heat, accompanied frequently by thunderstorm rainfall. The extent of the modification of winter cold by the penetration of tropical air masses is illustrated by the 32° F. mean January isotherm which swings south-westwards from Lübeck across the middle Elbe to skirt the foot of the middle Rhine highlands and the Black Forest to Basle. To the east of this line, all stations record temperatures below freezing point in January; Berlin, for example, averaging 30° F. Thus a zone of uniform cold extends from the Baltic to the Alps for a north–south distance of over 500 miles, with regional differences of only about 4° F. The lowest temperatures occur in the highlands of central Germany and in Bavaria, where mean January temperatures of 17° F. occur. The North Sea coastlands, the Rhineland and Mosel valleys are usually above freezing point, so that, not only are the ports of Hamburg and Bremen seldom seriously handicapped by ice, but the Rhine is normally open to navigation all the year. Hamburg, on the Elbe, records an average of 30 days per annum with ice. Mainz records 15 days on the Rhine and the Bodensee (lake Constance) 16 days. In East Germany, snow lies long but never deeply on account of the low total winter precipitation. The Kiel canal is affected by ice on an average of 10 days per annum but the length of the winter freeze increases south-eastwards, the Elbe being frozen for 30 days at Magdeburg and the Oder for 43 days at Frankfurt. Frost may be expected on more than half the days of the year everywhere and on 75 per cent of the days in the year in the east. Spring and autumn are prolonged in the west but are considerably contracted in the east; temperatures rising to 43° F. in the North Sea coastlands by early April.

Temperature. Four contrasted climatic zones may be recognized in Germany. The North Sea coastlands experience a fairly low mean annual range of temperature, from a monthly mean of 35° F. in January to a mean of 60° F. in July; Hamburg recording a range of 31° F. Cloud and rain may occur at all seasons, though there is an autumn maximum. From the Rhine to the Elbe a modified continental type of climate exists, with temperatures ranging from 30° F. in January to 60° F. in July and with frequent bright skies and considerable sunshine. Precipitation totals are generally lower than in the north-west and there is a summer maximum and spring minimum. The mean annual range of temperature for Magdeburg is 34° F. In the continental east, beyond the Elbe, winters are increasingly severe but summers are warm; a mean range of 28° F. in January to 68° F. in July being representative. There is less precipitation on the lowlands in the east than in the west; the rainfall occurring in heavy downpours and mainly in summer, for there is a pronounced winter minimum. The cloud cover is less than in the maritime west and reaches its maximum in the afternoon, especially in summer when convectional thunderstorm rain may occur. The Alpine zone of Bavaria and the Foreland has a climate representative of the Alps as a whole, with mean temperature ranges from 11° F. in January to 35° F. in July, considerable winter snow, sufficient to block the Alpine passes into Austria, and a summer maximum of rainfall. The bright sunny weather typical of the Zugspitze region in winter contrasts with the frequent cloudiness in summer. Under anticyclonic conditions, a blanket of cloud may form over the Foreland and in deep Alpine valleys caused by temperature inversion, and this water vapour will disperse and rise slowly in the form of banks of cloud as the day proceeds.

Pressure and Winds. The main tracks of depressions lie from south-west to north-east across the southern North Sea in winter but they migrate northwards in summer. In winter, when winds are mainly from the south-west or west, a ' spine ' of high pressure lies over alpine Europe. Local factors play an important part in wind direction at all times of the year, especially in Alpine valleys and the Hercynian uplands. The *Föhn* brings warm, dry air to the Bavarian Foreland in spring, so that snow may melt rapidly, and katabatic winds are frequent in the valleys opening on to the Rhine; the *Wispertal* in the Taunus sometimes bringing fog and frost to the upper Rhine gorge in spring and so damaging fruit blossom. A similar wind occurs in the *Höllental*, in the Black Forest, behind Freiburg. The Rhine valley itself serves to canalize winds, for the prevalent direction at Cologne is from the south-east following the alignment of the gorge, and, in the Mosel valley, the chief direction at Trier is from the south-west.

Rainfall. The distribution of mean annual rainfall reflects the interplay of the passage of depressions and relief. Whereas the North Sea coastlands experience 28 in. mean annual precipitation and Hanover 24 in., the total amount increases in the Rhine highlands and in southern Germany; the Black Forest averaging 55 in., the Harz 60 in., the upper Bavarian Foreland between 60 and 80 in., and the Alps over 80 in. (Fig. 4). The Alpine valleys lie frequently in the rain shadow of the highlands and so usually experience under 30 in. Except for the North Sea coastlands and the Lübeck bay region, where an autumn maximum and a spring minimum are experienced, most of Germany has a summer maximum of precipitation, for the high-pressure conditions which prevail over the ' continental ' east and over the Alps in winter serve to fend off depression rainfall and only light showers occur, often as snow. Hamburg records 30 days of snow per annum, Bayreuth 50, Munich 41, the Brocken 61. In the uplands above 1,500 ft., snow may fall as late as April, and again in October. The summer months are characterized by convectional thunderstorms, and these heavy downpours, though of generally short duration, may seriously damage the hay crop, as well as standing crops of cereals, including maize in southern Germany, as well as orchard fruit and vines.

NATURAL VEGETATION

The original pattern of woodland, heath, marsh and meadow has been greatly modified by centuries of clearance for cultivation and settlement.[1] The *horrida silva* of Tacitus experienced its major onslaught in the *Rodungszeit* of the 9th and 10th centuries in western Germany, the ' forest clearing ' type of settlement appearing rather

[1] H. C. Darby: ' The Clearing of the Woodland in Europe '. Contribution to *Man's Rôle in Changing the Face of the Earth*, ed. by W. L. Thomas, Jr., 1956.

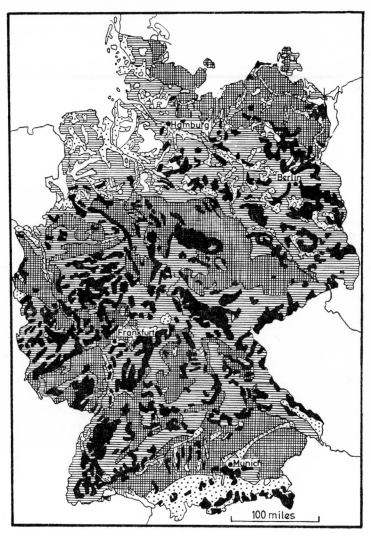

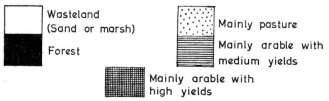

Fig. 74. Germany: chief types of land use.

later east of the Elbe, in the lands occupied by the Slavs. Today, much of the forest land is the result of systematic planting, especially in the Black Forest and in Bavaria. Nevertheless, in spite of the extensive clearance of the original forest cover, some 27 per cent of pre-war Germany was under forest and woodland and 67 per cent of this was coniferous, including the indigenous pines, silver fir, spruce, larch and yew.

Forest. The present area of woodland includes numerous spruce and pine plantations, as well as some tracts of state-owned forest reserves.[1] The most widespread deciduous tree in western Germany appears originally to have been beech (*Fagus silvatica*) which covered the greater part of the middle Rhine highlands, the Spessart and the Jurassic uplands of southern Germany (Fig. 5). It is well adapted to moist, well-drained soils, especially those with a high calcareous element, and is associated with equable, maritime conditions. The tree is susceptible to late spring frost and thins out beyond the Oder-Neisse line. Its occurrence is similarly restricted to the lower slopes of the Hercynian highlands and the Bavarian Alps, for it dies out above 2,000 ft. in the Harz and above 4,500 ft. in Upper Bavaria, where it is replaced by spruce. Fine stands of beech remain in the Taunus, on the lower slopes of the Hunsrück, in the Odenwald, Spessart and Black Forest, where the wood has long been in demand for clock carving. Along the sheltered coastlands of the Baltic, from Flensburg to Lübeck, beech also forms fine woodlands. Other deciduous trees include the lime or linden tree, often found on poor, dry soils, and more particularly oak, which is often associated with either birch on the heaths of north Germany or with beech and hornbeam. The oak seldom occurs as pure stands and the trees with which it is mingled, as well as the variety of oak, depend largely upon local soil conditions. As damp oakwood (*Quercus robur*), it forms an element in the oak-birch-heath associ-ation of the *Geest*, where hardpan (*Ortstein*) may occur in the sub-soil. The dry or durmast oak (*Quercus sessiliflora*) forms semi-natural woodland in combination with beech and hornbeam, notably on the loess lands of the sub-Hercynian zone, extending from the Belgian frontier through Westphalia to the Börde and Leipzig embayment. Other deciduous trees native to Germany are alder, willow and poplar, all swamp-loving trees which flourish on damp soils along river banks, especially in the *Ried* districts of the upper Rhine flood-plain. Where the drainage is better than on the peat or heavy clay soils of alluvial tracts, oak, ash, elm and hornbeam intermingle. Hedges, a relatively modern feature of the rural land-

[1] F. Heske: *German Forestry*, 1938.

(a) Ceský Ráj (the Bohemian Paradise) landscape, showing weathering of Cretaceous sandstone in northern Bohemia.

19. ELEMENTS IN THE LANDSCAPES OF CZECHOSLOVAKIA—3

(b) Pastoral landscape in the High Tatra, showing glaciated mountain scenery in background.

(a) Hay harvest at Pfronten, Allgäu Alps.

20. RURAL LIFE IN THE GERMAN FEDERAL REPUBLIC

(b) Pastoral scene in the Black Forest near St. Peter.

(c) Forest clearing street village (*Waldhufendorf*) in the Taunus.

scape (*Heckenlandschaft*), occur in Germany only in the region of the North Sea coastlands and in parts of Westphalia. Elsewhere, the arable land is laid out in strips or blocks without enclosure.

Coniferous forests formed 67 per cent of the wooded area of pre-war Germany. Scots pine (*Pinus silvestris*) covered 45 per cent of the total area under woodland, often as plantations, though the species is found in most parts of Germany, especially east of the Elbe in Brandenburg and the Berlin region (*Spreewald*). In the Black Forest and the Bavarian Alps, Scots pine ascends to 4,000–5,000 ft., for it thrives on poor, acid soils and can tolerate prolonged frost and snow. It forms a thin and uneven canopy, in complete contrast with beech, so that light can penetrate, enabling an undergrowth of juniper, bilberry, heather, mosses and lichen to develop. Spruce (*Picea abies*) is also widespread on the poor soils and steep slopes of southern and central Germany, where it often forms fine plantations. Spruce is tolerant of winter cold and frost but not of summer drought. In the Black Forest and in the Bavarian Forest, as well as in the Thuringian Forest and the Erz-Gebirge, spruce intermingles with beech and silver fir, eventually replacing these trees and extending up to the tree-line, except where larch and mountain pine exceed it in elevation. In the Black Forest, the Feldberg (4,905 ft.) rises just above the limit of spruce into the sub-alpine zone, as does the Arber on the Bohemian frontier. With a general rise in mean annual temperature from north to south, the upper limit of spruce ascends steadily to nearly 5,000 ft. in the Black Forest and to 7,000 ft. in the Alps. Spruce forests form thick stands of monotonous appearance, for the trees cast deep shade and permit no undergrowth. Other conifers include silver fir (*Abies alba*), a native of central and southern Germany. This tree needs warmth and shelter and is often mingled with beech on the rich, moist soils of the lower mountain slopes, as on the western side of the Black Forest, the Thüringerwald where it ascends to 2,600 ft., and the Bavarian Alps where it dies out above 5,000 ft. Other needle-leaved trees include deciduous larch (*Larix decidua*), which is frequently intermingled with spruce and Arolla pine in the forest zone covering the slopes of the Bavarian Alps between 1,500 and 6,500 ft. In some districts, larch forms pure stands almost up to the limit of tree growth. It forms little shade and is intolerant of other trees. Its light green foliage forms a striking contrast in spring against a background of dark-hued spruce wood. The dwarf conifer, *Pinus montana*, is a native of the Black Forest, the Bavarian Alps and the Böhmerwald. It adopts a creeping habit and may form impenetrable thickets (*Krummholz*) above the limit of standing timber as high as 7,250 ft. in the Bavarian Alps.

C.E.—I

It also occurs on boggy soils and has been planted to fix dunes along the Baltic coast. The Arolla pine occurs in the Bavarian Alps up to 6,100 ft., mixed with larch or mountain pine. Yew (*Taxus baccata*) occurs mostly in forest reserves.

Scrub and Heath. These types of vegetation are tolerant of both considerable drought and cold. They are found in association with mosses and lichens on poor, podsolized soils, such as the *Geest* of the north German lowland. Here extensive stretches of heath (*Calluna vulgaris*) intermingle with birch, poplar and aspen. In the boggy districts of the North Sea coast, the cranberry appears. Heather moor and scrub vegetation also appear above the tree limit in the middle Rhine highlands, as in the *Hohes Fenn* (the *Hautes Fagnes* of Belgium) and on the summit of the Harz.

Fen, Marsh, Bog and Moor. There are two types of swamp vegetation in Germany. Fenland or *Flachmoor* develops on calcareous peat soil, where alder forms the climax vegetation. On silt soils, the chief members of the plant association are willow, poplar, ash and alder, as are found in the *Ried* districts of the upper Rhine plain and the upper Danube valley (*Donauried*); these woods form *Auenwald*. If drained, these areas form good grazing land, as on the alluvial flood-plain of the Rhine between Baden and Alsace. Bogs occur along the North Sea coast, in the *Marschen* of Oldenburg, and on the acid peats of the Bavarian Foreland, where sphagnum moss and cotton grass flourish. There is a marked contrast between the *Flachmoor* regions, with their permanent high watertable and their alder and reed swamps, and the *Hochmoor* or raised bog. These 'high moors' are convex in profile, with a dry raised centre, where heather, bilberry and cranberry flourish but where trees fail to grow except for stunted pines, and a depressed margin, where reeds, birches, willow and pine trees grow. There are numerous valley bogs or regions of *Moos*, where poor, acid soils occur, as in the *Donaumoos*. On exposed summits, blanket bogs may form in regions of constant humidity and perched water-tables developed on impervious rocks, such as that of the *Hohes Fenn* in the Eifel.

Salt Marshes. The belt of *Watten* along the North Sea coast, uncovered at low tide and lying between the East Frisian Islands and the mainland, favours the development of halophytic vegetation on marine silts. These salt-loving plants have succulent leaves or stems, such as marsh samphire, and also include eelgrass (*Zostera*). Many of the coastal marshes have long been reclaimed and now form rich grazing land.

Sand Dunes. The main belt of dunes is along the North Sea coast, the East and North Frisian Islands and the Baltic. On some of the islands, such as Sylt, they rise to 125 ft. and consist of bare blown sand, forming 'white' dunes, in contrast with the 'grey' dunes which have developed a covering of sand sedge, mosses, lichens and sea holly (*Eryngium maritimum*). Along the Baltic coast and elsewhere, dunes have been fixed by planting marram grass, the creeping stems and penetrating roots of which hold the sand.

Grasslands. The present-day distribution of permanent grassland appears to bear little relation to the natural vegetation, for most meadow and pasture land has been won from reclaimed marshland or by forest clearance. Along the North Sea coast, fine polder land occurs, reclaimed from salt marshes, while other areas of grazing exist where the forest has been cleared in the Alpine valleys and Hercynian uplands and on the Bavarian Foreland. Only the alpine pastures above the tree limit are natural and these are covered by snow for at least half the year. Some natural grassland characterizes the sub-Hercynian zone between the Elbe and the Oder valleys and appears to have been partly associated with the rather dry zone of loess soils.[1]

SOILS

Germany includes within her borders a wide range of soils, including all types found in humid cool temperate latitudes. In summarizing their chief features, it is convenient to base the description on the Russian system, in which climate and vegetation are the conditioning factors rather than parent rock. However, in view of the geological variety of Germany and the diversified relief, the significance of local factors may completely override wider climatic and ecological considerations.

Podsols. These leached, grey ash-coloured soils are rather widespread, both on the *Geest* of the northern lowlands and on the high moors and forested uplands of the west and south. In the north, with its humid lowland climate, acid raw humus forms readily and, as the result of percolation and the leaching of soluble salts and their re-deposition in the sub-soil, a layer of iron pan may form, known as *Ortstein*. This hardpan impedes soil drainage and so increases its acidity. In consequence, these areas form natural heathland and, although they are difficult to improve for crop farming, they have been successfully planted with Scots pine, as in the Lüneburg Heath. In southern Germany, *podsols* occur on the light sandy

---

[1] N. Krebs: *Atlas des Deutschen Lebensraumes in Mitteleuropa*, map of natural vegetation by K. Hueck.

areas, for example on the *Bunter* sandstone of the north-eastern Black Forest, and also on the Keuper sandstones of Franconia.

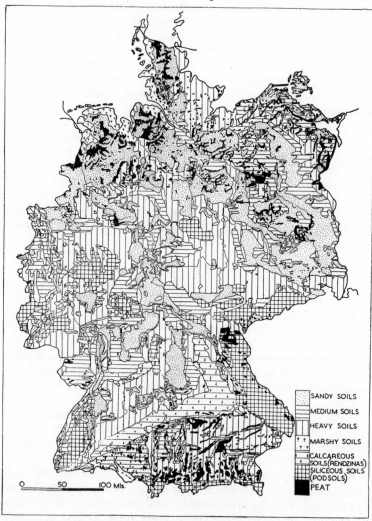

FIG. 75. Germany: chief soil types.

There are also some *podsols* on the leached sands of the Rhine valley. On the upland moors and heaths, skeletal soils occur and, above the tree limit on mountain slopes, raw humus develops under conditions of persistent high humidity and low mean annual temperatures.

Brown Forest Soils. East of the Elbe, these soils show varying degrees of podsolization, but this feature is least marked on the Younger Drift or boulder clay which forms good arable land south of the Baltic coastlands. In contrast, the more permeable sands and gravels of the *Urstromtäler* are more podsolized and best maintained under pasture rather than crop land. The Bavarian Foreland shows similar features, for the drift includes stretches of acid peat, ground moraine and gravel terraces. The districts with deciduous woodland, such as occur on the lower slopes of the massifs bordering the Rhine valley, also have brown forest soils.

Chernozems. These 'black earth' soils are widely scattered over Germany. They are especially associated with the loess terrains of the sub-Hercynian zone, the Thuringian basin (*Goldene Aue*), the Wetterau and the Rhenish Palatinate. Strips of loess also occur on the *Haupterrassen* of the upper Rhine plain, the Neckar valley, the Danube in the region of the *Dungau* and the Main valley around Würzburg. In parts of Swabia and Franconia, especially where *Muschelkalk* outcrops as in the Baar east of the Black Forest, similar soils are found and are intensively cultivated. In the Jurassic limestone uplands of southern Germany, as well as in the Göttingen region, a modified 'black earth' soil is developed, known as a *Rendzina*. These stiff, shallow soils, containing fragments of limestone, are dry on account of the deep water-table and are generally under upland pasture. Given an assured water supply, as from springs, they are highly tractable.

Alluvial Meadow Soils. These are found where the water-table is high and they are developed on clay or silt. The black A horizon is rich in humus and rests upon retentive clays which form the sub-soil or B horizon. They underlie the *Ried* areas of the Rhine valley and the Danube (*Donauried*) and they are also widespread along the lower Rhine valley between Cologne and the Dutch frontier as well as on the reclaimed marshes of the north German lowland and the Bavarian Foreland.

Salt Marsh Soils. These form a wide belt along the southern shores of the North Sea from the Dollart to the Danish frontier. They flank the estuaries of the Ems, Weser and Elbe, and they also occur on the East and North Frisian islands. When drained they form excellent grazing land, especially for Frisian cattle.

REFERENCES

The standard pre-war work on Germany was that of G. Braun: *Deutschland*, 2nd ed., 1936. There is a useful general section in R. E. Dickinson: *Germany*, 1953, entitled Part I, ' The Lands '. W. Köppen and R. Geiger: *Handbuch der Klimatologie*, provides useful climatic data. A. F. W. Schimper: *Pflanzengeographie*, 1936 ed., deals in detail with vegetation; while H. Stremme: *Die Böden des Deutschen Reiches*, 1936, gives a full account of soils. F. Heske: *German Forestry*, 1938, is useful reading. Atlas references include: N. Krebs: *Atlas des Deutschen Lebensraumes in Mitteleuropa*, 1937–, with climatic, vegetation and soil maps on a scale of 1 : 3 million; G. Hellmann: *Klima-Atlas von Deutschland*; and the *Deutscher Landwirtschaftsatlas*, 1934. Geological base maps were produced in the Lepsius series between 1894 and 1897 on a scale of 1 : 500,000, but a new series, known as the Geologische Übersichtskarte von Deutschland, on a scale of 1 : 200,000, was in progress between the wars. A useful reference map on a scale of 1 : 2 million, compiled by W. Schriel, in 1930, is now being superseded by a new series of regional geological maps, on a scale of 1 : 500,000, beginning with *Bavaria* in 1954 and now covering the major part of the German Federal Republic. An atlas, of which some sheets have appeared, is *Die Bundesrepublik in Karten*. A useful morphological map is that of H. Waldbaur: *Landformen im Mittleren Europa. Morphographische Karte mit Reliefenergie*, on a scale of 1 : 2 million, 1958.

CHAPTER 12

GERMANY: HUMAN GEOGRAPHY:
PART I. GENERAL

LAND USE

THE PATTERN of land utilization in Germany presents a veritable mosaic, in spite of the widespread prevalence of mixed farming. Germany is not so well endowed with rich arable soils as is, for example, France, and much farm labour is needed to maintain a high output. In fact, German agriculture has been described as the Achilles' heel of the Common Market. Yet, prior to 1939, Germany produced four-fifths of her needs of foodstuffs. There are few areas of specialized cash crop farming and these are mainly on the loess lands of the Börde with their great grain and sugar beet farms, and the upper Rhine valley with its polyculture. Few areas specialize in stock farming, though in the Bavarian Foreland there is a predominance of pastoral activities towards the Alps; while the rich grazing lands of East Friesland specialize in rearing dairy cattle. The German peasantry has experienced over a century and a half of freedom, the abolition of serfdom coming in 1807, but the consolidation of holdings did not take place until the mid-19th century. The land is still mainly cultivated on the strip system or in great blocks of arable, where the rotation of crops is practised. About three-fifths of the German countryside is improved, a high proportion in view of the fact that 27 per cent of the pre-war area was forested. About 9 million people work on the land, about a quarter of the total gainfully employed population, and most of these are peasants, living often by little more than subsistence farming, based on small-holdings with the sale of surplus produce in the nearby market town.

Woodland and Forest

Germany is rich in reserves of softwood timber and there are also considerable resources of hardwoods, especially beech and oak. About 70 per cent of the forested areas consist of coniferous woodland and these are to be found especially in the Hercynian uplands of the Black Forest (where in some areas 80 per cent of the land is under forest), the Rothaar-Gebirge, Harz, Spessart and Oden-wald. A high proportion of the Allgäu is also wooded, especially

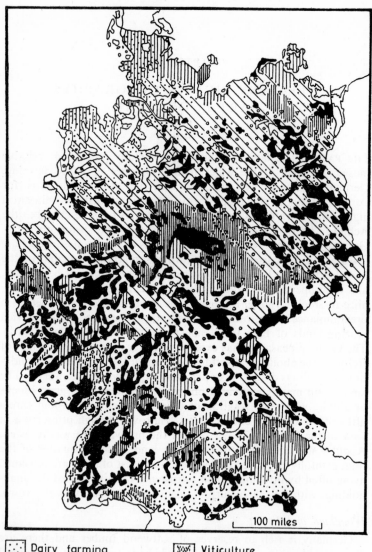

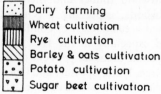

Dairy farming
Wheat cultivation
Rye cultivation
Barley & oats cultivation
Potato cultivation
Sugar beet cultivation

Viticulture
Orchard fruit & market gardening
Tobacco
Hops
Forest

100 miles

FIG. 76. Germany: chief land use regions.

the morainic hills, and so are the scarps of Swabia and Franconia and the heaths of Brandenburg (*Spreewald*). There are strips of deciduous woodland in the *Ried* districts of the upper Rhine plain (Hanauerwald), and the Teutoburgerwald presents a wooded slope towards the plain of Westphalia. In fact, the main treeless regions are the rich arable lands of the loess zones and the Baltic ground moraine, while the amount of forest cover on the *Geest* depends on the extent of modern planting. The chief deciduous forests are in

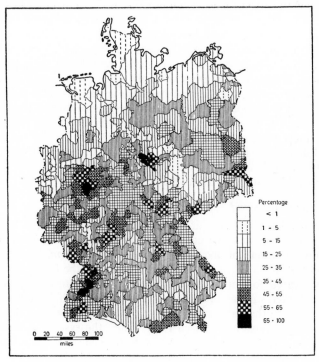

FIG. 77. Germany: percentage of land under woodland.

the west, with its relatively mild winters and long summers. Here beech and oak are widespread, especially on the lower hill slopes of the Taunus, Hunsrück and Spessart. The coniferous forests are extensive but spruce and silver fir characterize the mountain slopes of the Black Forest, Bavaria, the Fichtel-Gebirge and Thuringia, whereas the Scots pine prevails in the north German plain and on the sandy soils of Franconia. In the Baltic region, much afforestation of sand dunes, as well as of heath, has been carried out by the planting of mountain and Jack pine. In boggy districts, the Sitka spruce is found, and in the limestone uplands, black pine plantations have been made successfully. The standard of forest management in Germany is very high, especially where the forests are the property of the communes, and so it was on the private estates, especially in East Germany before the war.

Heath and Moorland

Today, the area of land which remains as heath or moor has been reduced to 7 per cent of the total. In particular, the heaths associated with the *Geest* have been largely reclaimed by breaking the underlying hardpan, burning the heath and applying potash, then sowing rye. Many such areas are now covered by vast pine plantations. Similarly, few areas of high moor remain undrained in the northern plain, for the peat has been cut and removed and the underlying sandy loam, when given a dressing of lime, forms tractable soil. On the summits of the Harz, the Feldberg and the Arber such tracts remain above the limit of tree growth, as they do in the Hohes Fenn in the Eifel. In the Bavarian Foreland, tracts of infertile moorland also occur on some of the glacial outwash gravels and peat bogs, as in the *Donaumoos*.

Permanent Grassland

There are only a few areas maintained as permanent grazing land. These include the coastal polders of the North Sea region, the alluvial tracts of the river valleys and *Urstromtäler*, and the humid soils of the *Ried*. In the upland regions, the forest has been partly cleared for hill pasture and here there is an abundance of surface water so that the meadow grasses are lush, giving a rich hay crop. In the Bavarian Alps, both the valley floor and the high mountain pastures are utilized for grazing; the system of seasonal migration to the *Almen* of Bavaria being general in late spring. There are certain regions of improved grassland and stock specialization; the Allgäu being noted for its dairy cattle, in the same way as parts of the Börde in Hanover and the North Sea polders. Oldenburg is noted for its horses and so were the Baltic coastlands, where horse rearing, especially for the Prussian cavalry, was a specialized activity on the *Junker* estates. The Lüneburg Heath and Saxony are the main areas of sheep rearing, though the limestone uplands of Swabia and Franconia also carry a number of flocks. Until 1939, there was a general increase in dairy and stock farming, with the continued growth of urban markets and the fall in the world price of grain. In consequence fodder crops had to be imported.

In the 1930's, this tendency was a reflection of the drive for national
sufficiency in meat, butter and other animal fats, but much of the
improved production came from stock reared on arable farms,
especially in the Börde, where sugar beet production is integrated
with stock farming and pig rearing.   Since the post-war division

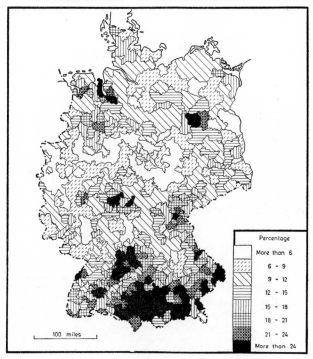

FIG. 78.   Germany: percentage of improved land under grass.

of Germany into West and East Republics, the Ruhr industrial
towns have lost a major source of meat and dairy produce in the
grazing lands beyond the Elbe and the food shortage was very
pronounced immediately after the war, especially in view of the
flood of refugees from the East.

Arable Land

The chief areas of arable farming are widely scattered but, today,
they represent over 50 per cent of the farmed area.   The most
important crop-producing regions, where highly intensive, large-
scale farming is carried on, are the loess lands of north-central
Germany.   These include the region at the foot of the Ardenne-Eifel

block, the Cologne embayment, the Paderborn-Soest strip in Westphalia, the Börde country of Hanover, Brunswick and Magdeburg,
the Thuringian basin and the Leipzig ' bay '.   Other areas of arable
farming on loess are to be found in the Wetterau, the Rheingau, the
Bergisches Land, the terraces of the upper Rhine, Neckar and

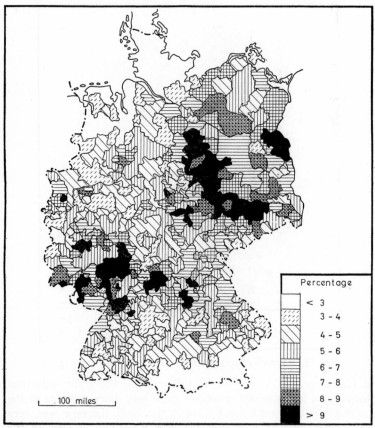

Fɪɢ. 79.   Germany: percentage of improved land under arable.

middle Main valleys, together with the Dungau section of the upper
Danube valley, and the Kaiserstuhl.   In the northern loess lands,
the dark brown or black soils, deep, well drained and easily tilled,
produce high yields of winter wheat, sugar beet, clover and potatoes.
These are regions of mechanized cash crop farming where there is
heavy expenditure on chemical fertilizer to maintain productivity.

Elsewhere, the loess soils are mainly under grain and fodder crops, including rotation grasses, such as clover, lucerne and sainfoin, and fruit trees are often scattered through the fields.   In the upper Rhineland, the loess-covered terraces are given over to polyculture; wheat, maize, tobacco and hops being cultivated in association with orchard fruits.   In specially favoured districts such as the Kaiserstuhl, where the loess overlies Tertiary basalt, the vine occurs, as

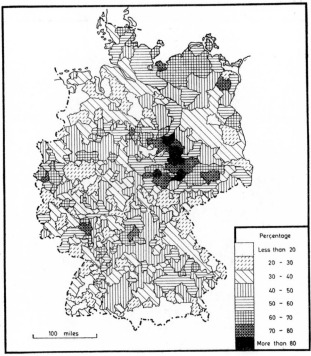

Fig. 80.   Germany: percentage of arable land under cereals.

it does on the terraces at the foot of the Black Forest and in the region of the *Bergstrasse*.

Cereals.   About 60 per cent of the arable land is given over to cereal production, for which the loess soils and the dry Baltic coastlands are well suited.   Rye still predominates over the other grain crops, followed by oats, winter wheat and spring barley.   Maize appears on the terraces of the Mosel valley, in the upper Rhineland and in the Bavarian Foreland.   In the north, rye is rotated with oats and potatoes or with barley and potatoes, especially on the small farms of the acid sandy tracts of Oldenburg, Mecklenburg and the Fläming.   Some is fed to livestock but much is made into black bread.   Oats are found especially in the damp, raw climatic zone of north-west Germany and along the Baltic coast.   In central and southern Germany, they are rotated with wheat.   Most of the crop, which has decreased in recent years on account of the decrease in horse rearing, is fed to livestock on the farm.   The production of wheat is hampered by the cool, damp climate of the

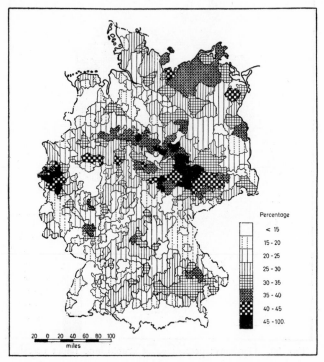

Percentage

	< 15
	15 - 20
	20 - 25
	25 - 30
	30 - 35
	35 - 40
	40 - 45
	45 - 100.

20   0   20   40   60   80   100
miles

FIG. 81.   Germany: percentage of arable land under rye.

north and by the patchy distribution of suitably rich and level areas. It grows on the boulder clay soils of the Baltic slope, where the mean annual rainfall is under 25 in., but it produces the highest yields on the deep, well-drained soils of the Börde, where the rainfall is fairly low.   Elsewhere it forms an important element in the crop rotation in the Wetterau, the Rhenish Palatinate, the Bauland of the Main valley, and the upper Rhine and Danube valleys.   Germany produced insufficient wheat for her own needs before the war and grain was imported from the New World *via* Hamburg, Bremen and Rotterdam.   Today, the Federal Republic has not enough wheat to feed its greatly increased demands and in the Democratic Republic the fall in the standard of living has been accompanied by marked changes in farming techniques and production.

Potatoes.   Germany is a major producer of potatoes, both for

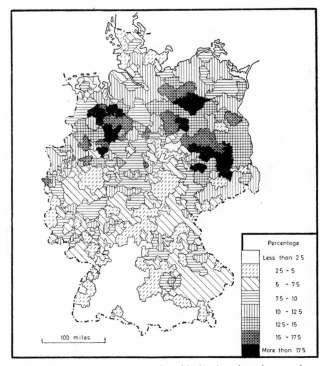

Percentage
Less than 2·5
2·5 – 5
5 – 7·5
7·5 – 10
10 – 12·5
12·5 – 15
15 – 17·5
More than 17·5

100 miles

FIG. 82.   Germany: percentage of arable land under wheat and oats.

human consumption and as fodder for pigs.   In the northern lowland, the expansion of the crop acreage has been made possible through the application of heavy dressings of chemical fertilizer, especially potash salts from Stassfurt.   Potatoes are widely grown in the upper Elbe lowland and in the Leipzig embayment, where the acreage amounts to over 9 per cent of the total.   In southern Germany, potatoes are a major item in the crop rotation in the Kaiserslautern depression, the Rheingau and Rhine rift valley.   They are also grown as a subsistence crop on the upland farms of western

Germany, in the Kaiserstuhl region, in the Kraichgau (where they are rotated with tobacco and fodder crops), and in Upper Bavaria.

Sugar Beet. This remunerative dual-purpose root crop was introduced into Germany during the Napoleonic Wars at the time of the Continental Blockade, and Germany was a pioneer in the extraction of sugar from beet. The soils and climate which suit wheat also favour high yields of sugar beet, so that these crops are

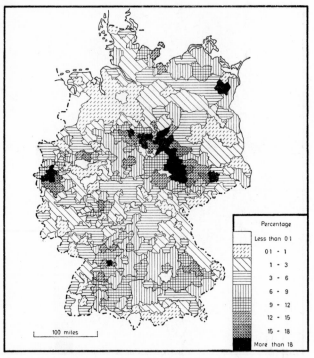

Percentage

Less than 0 1

0 1 - 1

1 - 3

3 - 6

6 - 9

9 - 12

12 - 15

15 - 18

More than 18

100 miles

FIG. 83. Germany: percentage of arable land under potatoes.

the main elements in the rotation of the farms of the Magdeburg Börde, the Cologne-Aachen region and the Rhenish Palatinate. Some beet is also grown successfully in the dry climatic zone of Mecklenburg, as well as on the rich soils of the Kraichgau and the Neckar terraces.

The Vine. The cultivation of the vine spread from the region of the lake of Constance into the upper Rhine and Mosel valleys in Roman times, but the main encouragement to viticulture came with the establishment of the monastic houses through western Germany in medieval times. The successful production of vintage wines depends upon the laborious tending of vineyards laid out on artificial terraces on the sunny slopes of the Mosel valley, the Rheingau and the Rhine gorge above Koblenz. Vines are also grown on terraces below the castle which crowns the bluff overlooking the Main at Würzburg, and again on the slopes of the Kaiserstuhl and in the *Bergstrasse* region. In parts of Württemburg the vineyards are not

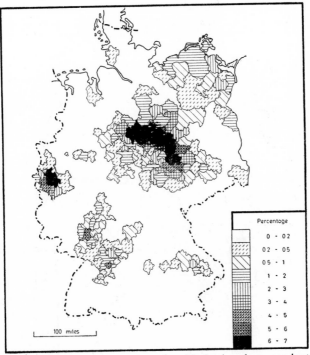

Fig. 84. Germany: percentage of arable land under sugar beet.

terraced but the quality is not so high as in the Bernkastel and Cochem districts of the Mosel valley or the Rüdesheim vineyards of the Rhine gorge. Elsewhere, in each year there is the risk of inclement weather and the spread of disease, and the sheltered slopes such as the Rheingau, facing south, are most favoured, and here hock is produced. From the neighbourhood of Worms, in the Rhenish Palatinate, comes the renowned *Liebfraumilch* wine and, from the Mosel, *Riesling*.

Tobacco and Hops. These crops are mainly restricted to south-western and southern Germany, where they fit into the general system of polyculture. The crops are grown on smallholdings and are found in the upper Rhine valley, along the *Bergstrasse* (cigar leaf tobacco) and on the terraces of the Mosel and of the Main near Würzburg. The area under tobacco has greatly decreased in recent years on account of foreign competition.

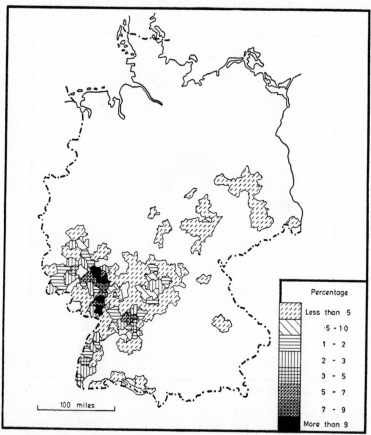

FIG. 85. Germany: percentage of arable land under viticulture.

Orchard Fruit and Market Gardening. The warm, sunny climate of the upper Rhinelands, the Mosel, the Neckar and the Main valley around Bamberg are suited to orchard fruit production and in these areas fruit trees are often found bordering the roadside and interspersed through the crop land. The *Hellweg* zone of Westphalia around Paderborn and Soest is also important. The production of market garden crops and of crops grown under glass is generally related to proximity to urban markets, as in the Cologne 'bay' region and the Ruhr-Westphalian industrial zone. Below Hamburg, market garden crops are produced on the reclaimed

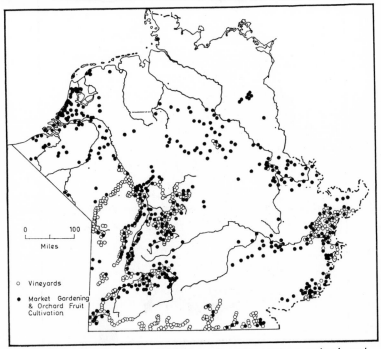

FIG. 86. Central Europe: distribution of market gardens, orchards and viticulture.

marshlands of the *Vierlanden,* while Berlin derives its supplies from Werden. Certain areas are noted for specialities, Mainz and Brunswick for asparagus, Rhenish Hesse for sweet cherries, the Neckar valley for apricots. Much of the fruit and market garden produce is consumed locally but Mainz and Frankfurt-am-Main are centres of fruit canning and preserving.

Wasteland

Most of the unimproved lowland lies near the Dutch frontier (the Bourtanger Moor) and in the Lüneburg Heath. In the Bavarian Alps and Allgäu the percentage of wasteland is over 20. It is least in the upper Rhineland, the Rheingau and Wetterau, the Cologne-Bonn ' embayment ' and on the loess soils of the Saxony Börde. In the Ville region, great stretches of derelict land are being created,

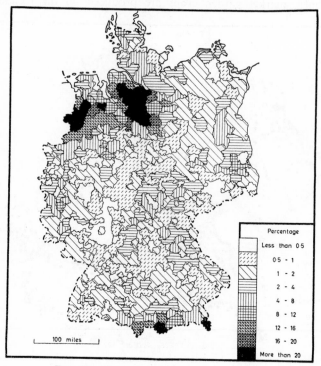

FIG. 87.   Germany: percentage of wasteland.

as elsewhere in Germany, by the excavation of lignite in vast open pits, though reclamation schemes are now compulsory. In the older mining districts like the Ruhr, land has gone out of use through the waterlogging of soil by pumping from the mines and subsidence is also a problem.

POPULATION DISTRIBUTION

Taking East and West Germany together, the total population of the two Republics, *viz.* 75 million (1963), is greater than that of any other European country outside Soviet Russia. Before the war, the total population was 69·6 million (1939), so that, as the result of the movement of 12 million refugees and Displaced Persons from beyond the ' Iron Curtain ', the total is little less than before the war, in spite of huge losses through aerial bombardment and casualties amongst the armed forces. The overall density of population is quite high, namely 380 to the square mile, though

FIG. 88. Germany: chief cities, navigable waterways and canals.

the areas of high density are patchily distributed, being at their greatest in the district of Nord Rhein-Westfalen and in the numerous urban centres not on the Ruhr coalfield. Berlin has a total population of 3·3 million, while Hamburg once again exceeds 1·8 million. Two-thirds of the German urban population live in towns with more than 100,000 inhabitants and 25 per cent in towns of over 20,000. There are also many large villages and small towns, with between 2,000 and 5,000 inhabitants, where industry and trade are more important than agricultural pursuits. The intensity of urbanization is a modern feature, dating mainly from the creation of the German Empire in 1871, and it postdates the completion of the main railway network, which, after that of Belgium, provides the closest mesh in Europe. It coincides with the rise of the great coal-mining, iron and steel and chemical industries of the Ruhr-

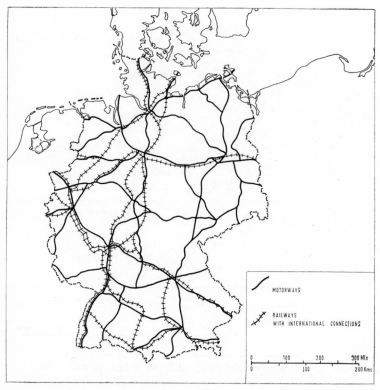

FIG. 89. German motorways and railways with international connections

Rhine region, and these industrial resources, given Germany's reserves of man-power, made possible the launching of two world wars in the present century.

Population Density Distribution

The areas of highest population density are in the Ruhr industrial region and along the greatest internal 'axis of circulation', the Rhine valley. Other great nodes are Berlin and the North Sea ports of Hamburg and Bremen, together with Munich (*German*, München), the regional capital of Upper Bavaria. The Saarland reacquired since 1957 is a peripheral area of high population density, with over 1,100 to the square mile. Other rural-cum-industrial areas lie in the sub-Hercynian zone extending from Aachen through Cologne to the Börde, the Leipzig 'bay' and Nieder Lausitz. Patches of high density in the loess zones of the upper Rhineland and south Germany, including the Wetterau, Rheingau, Breisgau and the region around lake Constance. In contrast, there are the areas of low density, with under 50 persons to the square mile, on the heaths, moors and marshes of the north German lowland, as well as on the forested Hercynian uplands, such as the Hunsrück, Rothaar-Gebirge and Böhmerwald, together with the scarplands of Swabia and Franconia.

West Germany and the Rhineland. In the upper Rhine valley there is an even division between urban and rural population, Baden recording 49 per cent as rural. This is a region of prosperous agriculture, with smallholdings and intensive cultivation, as in the Breisgau around Freiburg and the *Bergstrasse* between Heidelberg and Darmstadt, and in these areas the density is over 250 to the square mile. The regional centre and market town of Freiburg now exceeds 150,000 and, along the main route northwards, lies the route centre and planned town of Karlsruhe, with over 241,000, and Darmstadt, with over 130,000. At the confluence of the Neckar and the Rhine, Mannheim-Ludwigshafen, with its great chemical plants, represents a conurbation, today largely rebuilt, of over 320,000. In contrast with the high density of population in the Rhine rift valley, the bordering Hercynian uplands have a relatively low population density, though this applies mainly to the forested Bunter sandstone plateaus, with their deep-seated water-table. The granitic and gneissic areas, on the other hand, have quite high densities for upland regions, largely because of the use of water power and timber in local industries such as wood carving and clock making, as at Furtwangen, St. Georgen and Triberg in the Black Forest. There are also health resorts, such as St. Blasien and the planned town of Freudenstadt founded by the Moravians in the 17th century and now rebuilt in the same style. In the Odenwald, most of the larger villages, such as Neckarsteinach, are along the Neckar gorge, but Michelstadt is a medieval survival within the forest.

In the Middle Rhine Highlands, the striking contrast is between the sparsely populated uplands and the number of villages and small

towns along the valleys which break up the massif into separate
blocks, and also occurring in the marginal lowlands. South of
the Hunsrück there is a thickly settled region which lies on the
route from Mainz to the Saar and here Kaiserslautern is the chief
centre. Across the Rhine from Mainz, the Rheingau, with its
numerous villages and small centres of modern industry such as
Höchst and Rüsselsheim, also includes the spa town of Wiesbaden,
hardly changed by the war. Both the Hunsrück and Eifel are
regions of marked rural depopulation in favour of the Saar, Cologne
and the Ruhr. The steep southern slopes of the Taunus are mostly
forested but towards Limburg there is a rich zone of arable farming
on Pliocene-derived loamy soils. Limburg, a medieval castle town
commanding the Lahn valley, has retained many of its half-timbered
houses. Along the Mosel valley, villages are strung out on the
terrace fragments amidst the vineyards of the Moselberge and Vor-
Eifel. Some of these, such as Cochem and Bernkastel, are famous
centres of wine production, though the city of Trier, with its sandstone Porta Nigra and other Roman relics, is the main centre of
the industry. It is a cathedral and market town of over 90,000
people. In the volcanic Eifel, there is much working of the basalt
quarries for road metal but the surrounding region, apart from the
monastic foundation of Maria Laach by the Laacher-See, is rather
desolate. In contrast, there is the thickly settled Neuwied basin
behind Koblenz, and along the Rhine gorge there is an almost continuous string of villages, mainly but not entirely on the western side
of the Rhine, aligned parallel to the river, mostly of medieval origin
as the castle ruins above them suggest, but today centres of viticulture and tourism. Bingen, Rüdesheim and Bacharach, together
with Oberwesel and St. Goar, provide examples. The uplands to
the north-east of the Rhine gorge, namely the Westerwald, Siegerland, Sauerland and Rothaar-Gebirge, have lost much of their
population to the Rhineland and Ruhr, but the Sieg valley retains
its ancient iron industry around Siegen, and the Sauerland serves
as a recreational area for the Ruhr towns.

Below the town of Bonn, the site of the federal capital, begins
the Cologne embayment, including the Ville lignite field. Here
small villages are being engulfed by the spread of lignite quarrying
and there are several industrial sites, such as Knapsack, concerned with briquetting. The hub of this region is the ancient city
of Cologne, with a present population of over 835,000, its medieval
streets destroyed but its cathedral preserved to dominate the river
front adjacent to the great railway station. Downstream are the
ancient Roman settlements of the lower Rhine valley, namely

Jülich, Emmerich, Kleve and Wesel, centres of a rich agricultural and pastoral region.

The Saarland. With a total population of over a million in 1963, the high average density attained here results from the restricted area in relation to its recent industrial development. The mining and industrial towns are aligned along an L-shaped area, over which there is an average density of over 1,100 to the square mile. The chief centres are Saarbrücken, with over 132,000, the capital of the *Land*; Neunkirchen, and Völklingen, each with over 40,000. There are also several small industrial towns in the lower Saar valley, such as Merzig. Most of these mining centres, with their tip heaps and pit-head gear, lie within sight of the wooded slopes of the Hunsrück, for coal-mining and heavy industry have been superimposed on a rural landscape.

The Ruhr-Rhine Industrial Region. This agglomeration of over 10 million people, with an average density of 3,500 to the square mile, extends from Wesel on the Rhine to Hamm in the north, and from Mönchen-Gladbach west of the Rhine to Düsseldorf in the south; while the Wüpper valley also comes within the orbit of the Ruhr industrial region. The rapid spread of coal-mining and steel and chemical production has completely engulfed pre-industrial population centres such as Duisburg, the rebuilt river port at the confluence of the Rhine and the Ruhr; though Düsseldorf, the capital of the *Land*, retains some of its cultural character, dating from the 18th century. There appear to be three main belts of industrial towns on the exposed Coal Measures.[1] There are the towns of the Ruhr valley, on the site of the ancient *Hellweg*, namely Duisburg-Ruhrort, Essen, Bochum and Dortmund, which expanded with the early exploitation of the exposed Coal Measures. To the north are the urban products of the German industrial revolution: Hamborn, Oberhausen, Gelsenkirchen, Wanne Eickel and Herne. To the north again are the newer centres of coal-mining, such as Gladbeck and Recklinghausen. Detached from the coalfield, but closely related to it, are the steel and textile towns of Remscheid, Solingen and Wuppertal; while on the western side of the lower Rhine there are the textile centres of Mönchen-Gladbach, Rheydt and Krefeld.

Aachen, a town of over 174,000, owes its modern growth to its importance as a traffic node and to its small coalfield. It is also the centre of a rich agricultural region stretching from the Belgian frontier to Cologne.

Central Germany. Here the contrasts in population density are

[1] Peter Hall: *The World Cities*, 1966.

between the rich loess-covered lowlands, such as the Börde, and the forested uplands, with their occasional small industrial centres; while the *Mittelgebirge* includes at its foot minor coalfields, such as

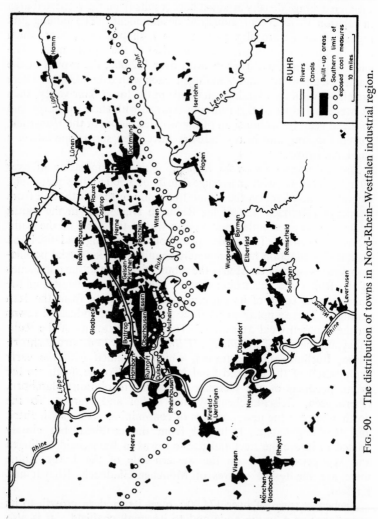

FIG. 90. The distribution of towns in Nord-Rhein–Westfalen industrial region.

that of Saxony and the highly important lignite field of the Leipzig 'bay'; as well as centres of salt working, such as Stassfurt; iron ore extraction, as at Salzgitter; and petroleum drilling, as in Hanover.

The loess zone of which the Börde forms an integral part extends from the Cologne region across the Münster ' bay ' to the Hanover-Brunswick-Magdeburg region, and so to Leipzig and Nieder Lausitz. Here the population density varies from 400 to 800 per square mile. The main loess belt in Westphalia lies in the region of the *Hellweg*, along which lie Soest and Paderborn, walled towns which date from the time of Charlemagne. The cathedral and university city of Münster lies to the north, on the Dortmund-Ems canal, and is an important route centre. Beyond Minden and the Weser Hills are the market towns of Hildesheim and Halberstadt, both ancient cathedral and castle towns. In the Hanover-Brunswick region the population density averages between 200 and 300 per square mile and here modern industry has been added to medieval regional centres and market towns such as Hanover, with over 567,000 inhabitants, and Brunswick, with 242,686. In the 1930's this region, remote from the eastern and western frontiers, developed a steel industry as well as great chemical plants, as at Merseburg-Leuna. To the east lie the potash and lignite workings of Saxony, around Stassfurt and Halle, while to the south is the industrial region based on the Saxony coalfield. Chemnitz, now Karl-Marx-Stadt, has a population of over 280,000 and is the chief centre of coal-mining and woollen textiles; while Zwickau, with over 84,000, is a mining centre. The great cities of the Leipzig embayment are Leipzig, with over 588,000, an historic centre of commerce, with its annual trade fair now revived; Halle, with 278,049; and, to the north, Magdeburg on the Elbe, with over 267,000, where the *Mittelland* canal joins the Elbe. Dresden, a city of 499,014, lies on the Elbe, a few miles below the Czech frontier, and is slowly declining.

Between the Börde and the upper Rhine, Main and Neckar valleys there extends a complex region of uplands, basins and depressions, some of which are thickly settled. There is a sharp contrast between the forested hills of Hesse and the basins of the Fulda, Werra and upper Weser. This is a region of small towns, such as the university centre of Göttingen, the spa of Bad Pyrmont and the monastic site of Fulda. Kassel, once a regional capital, lost much of its importance through wholesale destruction, but it has now been rebuilt as a ' new town '. The small towns of Marburg and Giessen, in the upper Lahn valley, are on the route from Kassel to the rich agricultural district of the Wetterau.

A region of varied population density occurs in the Thuringian basin, on account of the varied outcrops of sandstones, limestones and marls and the soils of differing fertility associated with them. This basin lies on routes from northern Germany to the Rhineland, and towns such as Eisenach were of strategic importance in medieval

times.   Erfurt is a cathedral town, with a population of over 166,000;
while Weimar and Jena grew to importance as small centres of
industry, especially optical glass manufacture (Zeiss works).   To
the south-west, the Thuringian Forest forms a by no means thinly
peopled upland, for its valleys have long been noted for their mineral
workings; centres such as Schmalkalden and Sonneberg being
famous for firearms and cutlery, while Eisenach produces the
traditional glass, porcelain and toys for which Thuringia is renowned.
To the north of the Thuringian basin, beyond the thickly settled
agricultural region of the *Goldene Aue*, rises the Harz massif, mainly
forested but with a high density of population on the periphery.
In medieval times the Harz was known for its silver and copper
mines and St. Andreasberg and Clausthal have seen some recent
revival.   Goslar and Wernigerode are towns at the foot of the
Harz.   To the east lies the Erz-Gebirge, on the Czech frontier, and
here medieval German miners penetrated into the mountains to
found Annaberg and Freiberg.   Uranium and cobalt working have
brought new life to these small centres.

Northern Germany.   North of the Börde zone the density of
population is below the average for Germany and is between 50 and
100 per square mile.   It is low on the heaths and moors, and on the
Geest of Schleswig-Holstein there are no towns.   Lüneburg, a town
on a Chalk eminence above the *Geest*, records 58,000; Celle, 58,000;
and Stendal, 31,000.   In the marshlands, the largest ' fen colony '
is Papenburg, with 15,600; while Oldenburg is a thriving market
centre of 9,300, deriving its thermal power from peat cut nearby.
The main foci of population are the North Sea ports which lie on
the great river estuaries draining to the North Sea from the mouth of
the Ems to the Elbe.   Emden, a town of 44,000, lies where the
Dortmund-Ems canal reaches the coast near the Dutch frontier.
Hamburg, the second city of Germany, together with its outport of
Cuxhaven, once a Hanseatic city, developed as a great trans-atlantic
terminal and railway port in the late 19th century, as did Bremen
and its outport Bremerhaven.   The shipbuilding industries of these
great ports have been revived, as are the associated industries of
marine engineering.   These ports are dealt with in detail elsewhere.
East of the Elbe, the remaining coastal ports are Kiel and Lübeck,
the latter founded in 1143 and later a leading member of the medieval
Hanseatic League.   The cutting of the Elbe-Trave canal in 1900
was an attempt to revive the trade of the town after the cutting of the
Kiel ship canal.   It now suffers on account of its position in relation
to the frontier between West and East Germany.   Behind Lübeck
the countryside is thinly settled, except for the town of Brandenburg,

with 64,000 inhabitants. Berlin, divided into Eastern and Western sectors, with its declining population of 3·2 million, dominates this inhospitable region. To the east lies Frankfurt-am-Oder and, upstream, the new ' planned ' town of Eisenhüttenstadt; while, in Nieder Lausitz, Kottbus and Görlitz are older centres of population in a region of new ' planned ' industrial development.

Southern Germany. Here the population density map is very varied according to the diversity of the physical environment. The overall density is low, under 200 to the square mile, and great cities such as Munich and Augsburg are surrounded by thinly populated agricultural land. At the foot of the Bavarian and Allgäu Alps, there are small tourist centres with local industries, like Mittenwald, Garmisch-Partenkirchen and Oberammergau, as well as the ancient monastic foundation of Füssen on the Lech valley route to the Fern pass. There are small towns on the Foreland, such as Kempten on the Roman road from Constance to Augsburg, and Kaufbeuren. Augsburg, the great ' fair ' town on the Lech valley route, a cathedral city and centre of modern industry (Messerschmidt works), has now been largely rebuilt, including the Renaissance craftsmen's housing estate known as the *Fuggerei*, after the Fugger family of merchants who founded it. The great city of southern Germany is, however, Munich, which now totals over a million in population. It is a major nodal centre, with modern industries, and it has become a flourishing commercial city, serving Upper Bavaria.

Towards the Danube, the density of rural population increases, especially in the rich grain-growing district of the Dungau. There are several historic bridge towns on the Danube, including Passau on the Austrian frontier, Regensburg (Ratisbon), Donauwörth and Ulm. To the north, the Swabian and Franconian Jura form limestone uplands which support a meagre density of population. Settlement is water-seeking, especially where springs break out at the foot of the scarp. The walled town of Nördlingen, in the Ries basin, is an interesting survival on the route from Würzburg and the Main valley to Upper Bavaria. In the diversified country to the north-west, the chief towns are located in either the Neckar or the Main valleys. Stuttgart, with over 634,000 inhabitants, is a rebuilt town, and a major centre of motor-car engineering (Mercedes-Benz) and of electronics. Heilbronn, the upper limit of barge navigation on the Neckar, is an ancient health resort and centre of salt working. In the Main basin, Bamberg lies where the Regnitz joins the Main. Würzburg is the regional capital. Its well-preserved medieval castle looks down on to the rebuilt town, where little but the bishop's palace survives of this former centre of

German baroque. Along the Pegnitz tributary of the Main lies the medieval city of Nürnberg, remarkably restored and continuing its traditional wood-working industries. It is an important nodal centre and railway junction for traffic continuing into Czechoslovakia. To the east, the forested slopes of the Fichtel-Gebirge, like the Böhmerwald to the south-east, offer little inducement to settlement. Bayreuth, with its Wagner festival, is an isolated resort and small baroque town of 61,000.

RURAL SETTLEMENT

In a part of Europe where, before the war, half the total population lived in the countryside, the forms of rural settlement and the field systems of the German peasantry are of special interest.[1] In many parts of Germany, the medieval form of the village or hamlet has survived until today, though the system of landholding has changed, especially with the consolidation of strips in the early 19th century. The hedgerow, as a mark of enclosure, is a rarity except in Westphalia, in the North Sea coastlands and in Schleswig-Holstein, and the open-field pattern of either long, narrow strips or compact parcels of arable land around the village or hamlet is to be found almost everywhere.

The type of rural settlement which evolved in the Romanized West depended both on physical circumstances and on social and economic factors. Throughout western Europe, areas of fertile loam soils, free of trees or lightly wooded, favoured the development of the compact, arable settlement or *Haufendorf*; whereas upland regions with abundant rainfall were better adapted to dispersed pastoral settlements, with either the single farmhouse (*Einzelhof*) or the cluster of farmhouses forming a hamlet.[2] Such settlements are typical of the Hercynian uplands such as the Black Forest, Spessart and Fichtel-Gebirge, with their abundant surface water to maintain pasture. There was also a third type of settlement, found especially in southern Germany, where a system of crop rotation was followed for a few years before the fields reverted to pasture, scrub or woodland, a type of economy known as *Egartenwirtschaft*.

The arable land in medieval Germany was of two contrasted types, both of which appear in the German countryside today. In one type, the land is laid out in long narrow strips (*Streifenflur*), a furlong in length, a system known as *Gewannflur*. These strips

---

[1] W. Christaller: *Die Ländliche Siedlungsweise im Deutschen Reich*, 1937.

[2] G. Pfeifer: 'The Quality of Peasant Living in Central Europe'. Contribution to *Man's Rôle in Changing the Face of the Earth*, 1956.

were cultivated with the aid of the heavy Saxon plough drawn by a team of oxen, and today oxen are still in common use as draught animals on farms in western Germany. A second type is known as *Blockflur*, in which the compact arable fields lie around the village. These farms are usually cultivated with a small plough or *Hakenpflug*, and they are concerned with mixed farming, the peasants producing grain and rearing cattle, sheep and pigs. In

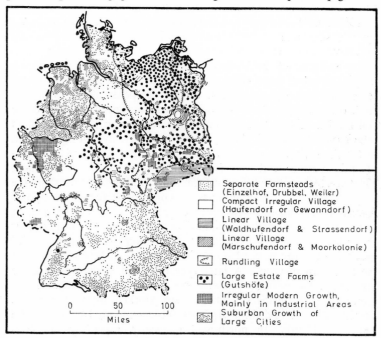

Separate Farmsteads
(Einzelhof, Drubbel, Weiler)

Compact Irregular Village
(Haufendorf or Gewanndorf)

Linear Village
(Waldhufendorf & Strassendorf)

Linear Village
(Marschufendorf & Moorkolonie)

Rundling Village

Large Estate Farms
(Gutshöfe)

Irregular Modern Growth,
Mainly in Industrial Areas

Suburban Growth of
Large Cities

0   50   100
Miles

FIG. 91. Germany: types of settlement.

Germany both the three- and the two-field systems persisted until the early 19th century, the first being found on the better soils and producing wheat and barley, while the second was mostly associated with rye cultivation on the poorer soils, notably the sandy *Geest* of the north German plain. In the 18th century, a four-course rotation became possible with the introduction of roots and fodder crops, and in the Rhineland the specialized production of maize, tobacco and potatoes, as well as of vines, orchards and hops, led to a system of polyculture and to much overdivision of the land, partly as the result of the system of inheritance.[1] This system is

[1] E. Juillard: *La Vie Rurale dans la Plaine de Basse Alsace*, 1953.

known as *Realerbteilung* or the division of holdings between all the sons, in contrast with the *Anerbenrechte* or undivided inheritance.[1] The *Bergstrasse*, with its string of villages at the foot of the Odenwald, is such an area.

The loess terrains of the sub-Hercynian zone, the upper Rhine valley, the Neckar valley and the Wetterau, as well as the upper Danube valley, have been occupied continuously from Neolithic times, but the main period of village settlement by the Alemannic and Frankish tribes was from the 5th to the 8th century, as indicated by the *-ing* and *-heim* place-name endings of the Rhineland and Bavarian Foreland and by the *-leben* of the Börde. Later place-name endings of subsidiary settlements are those of *-hofen*, *-dorf*, *-hausen* and *-weiler*. The typical farmstead of these regions is the *Dreisässenhaus*, a great stone structure with one roof, often of wooden shingles covering dwelling house and cattle stalls alike. After A.D. 800 came the *Rodungszeit*, with the main attack on the forested uplands, both in the Hercynian regions and in the Alpine valleys. The significant forest-clearing place-names of this period end in *-bach*, *-feld*, *-berg*, *-rodt* and *-brand*. The two-storeyed Black Forest farmhouse, with its vast overhanging hipped roof of thatch or shingles, is typical of these regions of later Alemannic settlement. In north Germany the earliest permanent settlements were on the reclaimed heaths, often on elevated sites above the surrounding marshland. These were known as *Esch* and they were usually worked on an in-field and out-field system, with rye as the main crop. A later type of heath settlement was the *Einzelhof* and in some places there arose the *Drubbel* or loose grouping of farmsteads. These were worked by free peasants known as *Kötter* and these 'squatter' settlements are frequent in the Lüneburg Heath. In north-west Germany, especially in Westphalia, there are many dispersed settlements, but these are the result of secondary dispersal and, in contrast, there are many instances of the abandoned village or *Wüstungsdorf*, especially in the Börde, where the high value of the arable land used for commercial crop production favoured the growth of large agglomerated villages rather than many small ones.

In Germany east of the Elbe, Germanic settlement is post-1200. In these 'colonial' lands, the German feudal system was superimposed on the primitive culture pattern of the Slavonic tribes who lived by stock rearing rather than by crop cultivation. Whereas the Slav lands were laid out on the block system, the German method was that of strip cultivation (*Gewannflur*). The new German vil-

[1] G. Pfeifer: 'The Quality of Peasant Living in Central Europe', *op. cit.*

lages were often planned by a *Lokator* and assumed one of a series of forms. The most general was the group of farm buildings strung out along a main road, known as a *Strassendorf*, and its variant the *Angerdorf*, in which an open green strip was left between the two rows of farm buildings providing the site of the church and of some common grazing land. An example is Skaup, north of Grossenhain, in Saxony. Where the forest lands were cleared, the *Waldhufendorf* appeared, often a series of dwellings along a track cut through the woodland, with strips running back from the farm-house, the grazing land extending between them and the forest. Such villages are particularly typical of regions originally inhabited by the Slavs, as in the forested Erz-Gebirge region of Saxony. A number of examples also survive in the Rhine Highlands, as at Kniebis in the northern Black Forest and at Oberrodt and Waldorf in the high Taunus (Plate 20(c)). In other regions of original Slavonic occupation, small villages known as *Rundling* survive, as in Branden-burg and Saxony. Here the farm buildings are arranged around a central point, as at Werbelin near Delitsch, in Saxony. Another type of rural settlement is the *Marschhufendorf*; where fenland has been reclaimed by dyking, as in the lower Weser and Elbe valleys and in the polder lands of East Friesland. The farmhouses are often on raised mounds known as *Terpen*, above the level of the former marshland, and they are usually built of brick and timber, with reed-thatched roofs.

Post-medieval settlement concerns mainly the ' colonial ' territory of the German Empire beyond the Elbe, for in the west the pattern was fixed by the end of the forest-clearing period. Especially under the Great Elector, many new settlements were made, both in the reclaimed melt-water channels (*Urstromtäler*) and in the marsh-lands (*Fehnkolonien*). An example of this period is Papenburg in Hanover, a settlement laid out along two roads which meet here at right angles, the arable strips forming a regular pattern running back from the farmhouses. The other dominant feature of eastern Germany which arose as part of the expansion of Prussia was the *Gutshöfe* or *Junker* estates, typical of the Baltic coastlands and of Mecklenburg, as well as of pre-war Pomerania and East Prussia. Since the establishment of the Communist régime in the German Democratic Republic, these estates of the Prussian nobility have been confiscated and the land broken up and distributed amongst the peasants. In West Germany, numerous new rural settlements have also been created, especially by refugees from the East, notably in the Odenwald and in Bavaria.

C.E.—K

URBAN SETTLEMENT

The rate of growth of German towns was phenomenal in the 70 years prior to 1939. It is estimated that the urban population increased by 250 per cent between 1870 and the beginning of the first world war, a figure only paralleled in the U.S.A. This urban growth represented partly an expansion from existing nuclei, as in the historic centres of trade and commerce, route centres and ports; and partly the growth of new industrial towns, especially in the Ruhr. Between the two world wars, other industrial sites arose especially in the middle Elbe basin, where Merseburg-Leuna became identified with the chemical industry, Salzgitter with the exploitation of low-grade iron ore, and Wolfsburg, near Brunswick, with the *Volkswagen* and later tanks and armoured cars. Since 1945, new towns have been created by Communist planners in East Germany, as at Eisenhüttenstadt on the Oder, and in the West new small industrial centres have arisen to accommodate displaced persons, such as Neu Gablonz, near Kaufbeuren, in the Allgäu.

It is estimated that Cologne lost 36 per cent of its population during the *Blitz* and Hamburg 17 per cent, while smaller cities where there was wholesale destruction include Frankfurt-am-Main with 22 per cent, Hanover with 23 per cent, Nürnberg with 25 per cent, Kiel with 28 per cent, and Mannheim with 24 per cent. The last two decades have seen the phenomenal rebuilding of these towns, so that most of them attain or even surpass their pre-war size in population, though overcrowding is rife. Apart from the return of bombed-out people to the rebuilt towns, there has also been a tremendous influx of refugees in search of industrial and commercial employment. At first Schleswig-Holstein, nearest to the Eastern Zone, and Saxony and Bavaria, nearest to the Sudetenlands and Bohemia, received the greatest numbers.[1] These refugees have since been largely re-settled in the Rhineland (Baden, with relatively little damage, Hesse and the Rhenish Palatinate receiving large numbers), while many have found work in the Ruhr and in Württemberg and Bavaria. These additional 12 million people from the East have settled largely in the towns, where they have formed an additional source of labour for rebuilding, etc., but many have also made homes in rural areas. On account of the housing problem, a feature of modern German life is the large number of urban workers who travel long distances from the country to their place of work, and these are known as *Arbeitspendler* (commuters).[2]

[1] P. George and J. Tricart: *L'Europe Centrale*, Vol. 2, pp. 338–41.
[2] *Economic Survey of Europe*, 1957, Chap. 7, p. 22.

Various attempts have been made to classify German towns.[1] Such attempts meet with some success where the medieval cities are concerned, for many have certain features in common, as has rural settlement, but, with notable exceptions, even before the war the large towns had quite outgrown their historic core and likewise the value of the site factors which led to their early settlement. In some instances, towns, such as Koblenz, originated at a river confluence, or on a defensive island site like Lübeck, which replaced the earlier Slav settlement in 1143, or at a valley exit site like Heidelberg, or on a well-drained alluvial fan, commanding routes between forest and plain, like Freiburg-im-Breisgau. Alternative types of site are exemplified by hill-slope sites, like Nürnberg; plateau-top sites, like Rothenburg ob der Tauber; valley sites, like Limberg on the Lahn; and local depression sites, like Nördlingen in the Ries basin. These cities were alike in their defensive character, though this feature is least marked in the ' free city ' of Freiburg, with the diminutive castle ruin on the hill overlooking the town. Whereas most towns lost their ancient and encumbering walls during the expansion which took place in the later 19th century, some ' fossilized ' towns, remote from main railway routes and modern centres of industry and trade, have retained their defensive ramparts and medieval gates, Nördlingen, Dinkelsbühl and Rothenburg being examples. In the city of Bremen, once a thriving member of the Hansa League, the late medieval core of the town, marked by the *Rathaus*, cathedral and Customs House, formed the heart of the old town. It is divided from the new by a semi-circular green belt with ornamental lake, laid out on the site of the medieval walls and moat. In fact, the general siting and distribution of German towns remained untouched until after the Thirty Years War (1618–48). In the latter part of the 17th century, certain towns in the Saar valley such as Saarlouis, and in the Rhineland such as Neu Breisach, were fortified on the lines of the star plan developed by the French engineer, Vauban. In the 18th century, towns were replanned on formal lines, under ducal or royal patronage such as Stuttgart, with its baroque castle and municipal buildings, few of which have survived the war; Dresden, another magnificent example of German baroque, now mostly obliterated by bombing and subsequent destruction by fire; Meissen, also in Saxony and world-famous for its porcelain production; Karlsruhe and Mannheim in the Rhineland.

[1] K. Olbricht: ' Die Entwicklung der deutschen Grossstädte ', *Geog. Anzeiger*, Vol. 35, 1934, etc., quoted at length by R. E. Dickinson in *Germany*, Chap. 7, pp. 176–89.

The late 19th century saw not only the expansion of the great historic cities and cathedral towns, such as Cologne, Bremen and Munich, beyond their out-dated walls, but the mushroom growth of Berlin and new industrial towns, especially in the Ruhr. Some of these were well planned, like Essen, with its garden city, in spite of its association with coal and steel. The mid-20th century has witnessed the wholesale destruction of the 'core areas' of most German towns, except Heidelberg and Wiesbaden. Most of the rebuilding has been on modern American lines, with steel, concrete

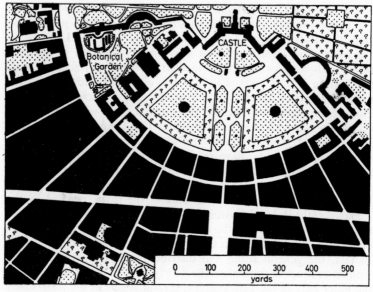

FIG. 92.   Plan of Karlsruhe.

and glass as the chief media, though there have been some remarkable pieces of restoration, as in Nürnberg, Frankfurt-am-Main and Augsburg. On the site of the congested streets of central Essen, new blocks like miniature skyscrapers have arisen to provide flats, offices and departmental stores, and the same pattern of building is repeated in Frankfurt, Cologne and Stuttgart, as well as in Munich. Berlin has also been transformed, the boundary between West Berlin and the Eastern sector being defined by the Berlin wall. To the west a town with a population of 2·1 million thrives on a free economy, though cut off from its natural hinterland by the fact that it is an *exclave* in East Germany. To the east has arisen a re-built town totalling 1·0 million inhabitants in 1963, with the Soviet embassy set amongst the new government buildings along the Unter den Linden. Here there is also 'full employment' but everywhere 'the pattern of drab Communist endeavour'.

HUMAN GEOGRAPHY: PART II. WEST AND EAST GERMANY

GERMANY PRESENTS today a sharply divided front as far as her human and political geography are concerned and the division between the Western and Eastern Republics is a grim reality, presenting a problem to which no immediate answer appears. Since 5 May 1955 the Federal Republic of Germany has been a sovereign, independent state, with its federal capital in Bonn, the seat of the modern parliament or *Bundeshaus*. West Germany is a member of the Council of Europe, of the Common Market, of N.A.T.O., and of the European Coal and Steel Community. East Germany, except for the *exclave* of West Berlin, presents a complete political contrast, for it is a ' Democratic Republic ', extending east of a line from Lübeck to the Harz and Thuringia across to the Oder-Neisse line, which today forms the frontier with Poland. East Germany is part of Communist-controlled eastern Europe and it has been completely reorganized on the basis of a planned socialist economy, whereas West Germany maintains a capitalist free economy, with a western outlook towards the Atlantic margin. In 1963, the total population of the German Federal Republic was 57·8 million, including 2·1 million in West Berlin, whereas that of East Germany has fallen to 17 million. Just half the population of West Germany is Protestant (Lutheran) and 21 per cent Catholic (mainly in the Rhineland, Westphalia and Bavaria); whereas East Germany, including a large part of former Prussia, records 80 per cent as Protestant and only 12 per cent as Catholic. During and since the war, the population of West Germany has increased by 25 per cent, in spite of war-time losses. It is estimated that over 12 million *Volksdeutsche* have fled from eastern Europe since the end of the war in 1945,[1] and the process continues. In East Germany, the total population has declined since 1949 on account of the wholesale movement westwards of refugees from former German territory beyond the Oder-Neisse line and from the Eastern Zone. In consequence, there is an abundance of labour of all types in the West but man-power is at a premium in the East, especially where skilled workers are concerned. The percentage of the total population employed in industry in the West rose from 42 per cent in 1936 to 45 per cent in

[1] R. E. H. Mellor: ' Refugee Industries in Western Germany ', *Geography*, Vol. 40, 1955, pp. 191–2.

1955; while the number thus employed in the East is now 49 per cent, a figure which shows a decline when compared with the pre-war figure of 51 per cent.[1] In both zones there has been a phenomenal rebirth of industry, combined with rebuilding and the equipment of plants with modern machinery. Whereas the 'miracle' in the

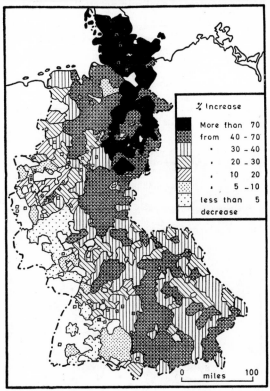

% Increase

More than 70
from 40 - 70
" 30 - 40
" 20 - 30
" 10 20
" 5 - 10
less than 5
decrease

0 miles 100

FIG. 93. Population changes in the German Federal Republic, 1939–46.

West was greatly aided by American capital and today by membership of the European Coal and Steel Community, the East had been handicapped by a shortage of capital and labour, ruthless dismantling of plant immediately after the war, to a degree unparalleled in the West, and the adverse rate of exchange with the West after the revaluation of the mark in 1948. Since the dismantling of plant ceased in 1949, followed by the first Five Year Plan in 1950 and the

[1] Economic Commission for Europe Report: *Structural Adaptation in East and West Germany*, 1957.

second in 1955, the economy of East Germany has been subject to 'planning'. Today the two units, once broadly complementary, are now (in theory) more competitive. West Germany possesses the chief source of bituminous coking coal in central Europe in the Ruhr and has some iron ore reserves, together with petroleum; while the pre-war centres of coal-mining, steel manufacture, engineer-

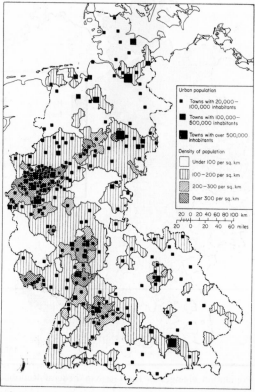

FIG. 94. Population changes in the German Federal Republic, 1946-50.

ing, chemical production, china and glass have been revived to a highly prosperous level. West Germany has adequate supplies of iron and steel, including now a surplus of processed steel and engineering products for export, as well as a sufficiency of synthetic rubber, asbestos, oils, fats and sulphur. The West is short of paper cellulose and clothing. Before the 1939-45 War, the West produced most of the hard coal, petroleum and iron ore but the East had much larger supplies of brown coal and potash, as well as the Saxony centres of wool, clothing, knitwear, optical glass and photographic materials, together with the Thuringian musical instrument and toy factories. Berlin was the chief centre of electrical engineering in pre-war Germany and today the industry has been resurrected in the Eastern sector. Whereas West Germany has coal and coke, steel and heavy industries, as well as capital goods for reconstruction and export, East Germany has brown coal, fewer capital goods and far more consumer goods depending on imported raw materials, with an absence of foreign markets outside the Soviet *bloc*.

WEST GERMANY

With a total population of over 57 million (1963), West Germany includes two cities with a population of over a million people, the Western sector of Berlin recording 2·1 million and Hamburg 1·8 million. The chief city of southern Germany and Bavaria, namely Munich (München), totals over 1·1 million, while Cologne now records over 835,000 (compared with 768,000 in 1938). The great industrial cities of the Ruhr-Rhine industrial region, namely Essen, Düsseldorf and Dortmund, all exceed 500,000, as do such regional capitals as Frankfurt-am-Main, Stuttgart and Hanover. Only 25 per cent of the total population is employed in agriculture and the contrast between the modern city life of Germany, where industry is frequently concentrated, and the traditional peasant way of living, which survives in the adjacent countryside, is frequently striking. Apart from the long-established centres of craft industry and trade, West Germany's manufacturing industries, based on steam power and coking coal, are a product of the 19th century. Today, the increasing use of thermal power and oil is resulting in a certain decentralization of industry, also stimulated by the establishment of small manufacturing concerns by refugees in rural areas, especially in Bavaria and the Rhineland.

The present industrial pattern of West Germany is the outcome of the 19th-century economy which was temporarily shattered by the two world wars of the present century. Pre-war Germany was a 'community of iron and steel'. Indeed, after the victory of Prussia over France in 1870–1, there was a precocious concentration on coal-mining and heavy industry, at first benefiting from access to the recently acquired Lorraine minette iron mines following the introduction of the 'basic' process in 1879, and later using increasing quantities of scrap and high-grade Swedish hæmatite, especially after the opening of the Dortmund-Ems canal in 1899, which served both to cheapen the cost of Swedish ore imported *via* the German North Sea ports and the local movement of Ruhr coke. The completion of the *Mittelland* canal in 1938 made possible the cheap movement of Ruhr coal and coke by inland waterways as far as the Elbe at Magdeburg, while it facilitated the industrial development of the Merseburg-Leuna and Salzgitter region of central Germany, just before the outbreak of the 1939–45 War. Today, 4·7 per cent of the active population is engaged in extractive industries, mainly coal-mining (including lignite), a figure only exceeded in the world by Great Britain. The main reserves of coal in Europe are here, totalling 43,000 million tons, to which the 900 million tons of the Saar have recently been added. The output of coal in West Germany exceeded 142 million metric tons in 1963, compared with 138·5 million tons in 1938. Of this total, the Ruhr produces over 90 per cent, the rest now coming from the Saar, Aachen and Lower Saxony fields.

Before the 1914–18 War, vertical integration was a marked feature of German industrial organization; the ownership of the mines, coking plant, blast furnaces, steel works, mineral lines, barge fleets and engineering works being in the hands of cartels. In fact, the means of production were largely concentrated into the hands of a few great families, notably those of Krupp at Essen, Louis Baare (*Bochumer Verein*), Thyssen and Hugo Stinnes. The main railway systems serving the Ruhr-Westphalian industrial zone were owned and operated by the State. Under the National Socialist régime of the 1930's, the organization of industries into great *Konzerne* reached its maximum. During the 1939–45 War, these giant enterprises assumed a technocratic structure,[1] vast undertakings such as the Hermann Göring steel works having controlling interests in the former Austrian *Alpine Montangesellschaft* steel plant in Styria, as well as in the Leuna-Merseburg industrial complex. After the *Anschluss* with Austria in 1937, the *Vereinigte Stahlwerke* produced 37·5 per cent of the pig iron, 43 per cent of the steel and 30 per cent of the rolled steel output of Germany, Austria and the Saar. This corporation also controlled much of the coal production of the Ruhr, where Gelsenkirchen accounted for nearly 15 per cent of the total coal output of Germany and 21 per cent of the coke. In addition, over 10 per cent of the coal reserves of the Ruhr were under the corporation's control. Barge fleets were owned on the Rhine as well as on the Dortmund-Ems canal and the *Mittelland* canal network. During the 1939–45 War, the *Vereinigte Stahlwerke*

[1] P. George and J. Tricart: *L'Europe Centrale*, Vol. 2, 1954.

had a monopoly of the output of steel tubes (40 per cent) and steel bars (29 per cent).

In similar fashion, the chemical industry of pre-war Germany was monopolized by *I.G. Farben*. The production of soda, calcium carbonate, caustic potash and heavy acids was closely integrated, especially in such major centres of the chemical industry as Mannheim-Ludwigshafen on the upper Rhine, and at Leverkusen on the Rhine between Cologne and Düsseldorf. This trust also monopolized the production of synthetic rubber (*Buna*), cellophane, wax, synthetic lubricants, dyestuffs and nickel. The production of electrical goods was almost entirely in the hands of Siemens-Schuckert (Berlin) and *A.E.G.*, the former specializing in the production of telephones, radio apparatus and cables, and the latter in electric light bulbs (Osram). At the height of the war, 11 per cent of the national wealth was in the hands of some 77 industrial groups, the five main banks owning between 5 and 9 per cent of the national capital.

In 1945 the Potsdam agreement aimed at decentralizing the pre-war and war-time German economy and, whereas this policy was ruthlessly carried out by the Russians in the Eastern Zone, in the West, apart from some early dismantling and the destruction of shipyards at Hamburg and Bremen, there have been two decades of reconstruction and recovery, and once again the coal, coke and steel output of the Ruhr dominates the industrial picture. Moreover, since West Germany entered the Atlantic Pact, the construction of ships, especially oil tankers, has begun again at Hamburg and Bremen. Since 1955 the *Lufthansa* has operated regular air services between Frankfurt-am-Main, Düsseldorf, Munich and London Airport, with additional flights from Hamburg, Hanover and Berlin.

The post-war industrial recovery of West Germany and her return as a keen competitor in the world market for her industrial products has been greatly aided by her abundant supplies of fuel and raw materials, by her technical skill and by the mobility of her large supplies of labour, as well as by the energy and drive of her population, to which foreign aid, especially from the U.S.A., has been added. Since the end of the war, the West has had an extra labour supply of 2·7 million workers and, of these, 1·2 million have gone into metal processing, 0·7 million into basic and light industries, and over 100,000 into food industries. In particular, there has been a great increase in the output of electrical engineering goods, to offset the loss of the East Berlin industry, and also of vehicles, notably at the *Volkswagen* works at Wolfsburg near Brunswick, machinery of all kinds, precision articles (including optical apparatus and photographic equipment) and ' Jena ' glass (at Mainz). The basic industries of rubber processing, chemicals, oil refining and crude oil extraction have also greatly expanded. The industries in which the increased output is below the average increase include coal and steel, metal ore extraction, non-ferrous metal production and ship-building, industries which were relatively slow to recover on account of war-time devastation and the destruction of plant by bombing, especially in the Ruhr. Today the situation is changing rapidly and in 1964 West Germany was producing 4·2 million metric tons of raw steel a month and the annual output of steel had expanded to 22 million ingot tons. West Germany, together with the regained Saar territory, accounts for 51 per cent of the total aggregate of coal and steel produced by the Coal and Steel Community.

Mineral and Extractive Industries

The high proportion of the working population which is engaged in mining in West Germany, namely 4·7 per cent, is largely accounted for by the huge reserves of the Ruhr, where relatively easy conditions of working, combined with the introduction of new equipment and modern mining techniques, make this coalfield the most important in western Europe. In addition, West Germany has extensive reserves of lignite in the Ville region between Bonn and Cologne, and also some reserves of iron ore, non-ferrous metals, potash, rock salt and petroleum.

Bituminous Coal

The Ruhr-Westphalian Coalfield. The Coal Measures which outcrop along the Ruhr valley extend northwards towards the Emscher valley and subsequently dip under a covering of Cretaceous and younger rocks in the direction of Münster. A description of the physical features and of the development of the field is given elsewhere (pp. 353–8). The seams are easily worked and the shafts vary in depth from 900 ft. in the south to over 3,000 ft. in the concealed coalfield of the Münster basin. The field is noted for its wide range of types of coal, including some 57 seams which yield coking coal, 55 which produce gas-flame coal and 10 which give anthracite.[1] Today, production is in the hands of large companies, and small colliery villages around large modern pits are the rule. The chief centres of coal production, though of decreasing production, remain in the Essen basin (over 11 million tons of coal in 1949), Bochum

[1] P. Kukuk: *Geologie des Niederrheinisch-westfälischen Steinkohlengebietes,* 1938.

(over 9 million tons), Gelsenkirchen (7 million tons) and Oberhausen
(4 million tons).   Once again the coal and steel town of Essen, the
home of the Krupp family, has arisen aligned along the narrow
valley of the Ruhr and again dominates the industrial life of the
region.   Since its war-time destruction by bombing, the centre of

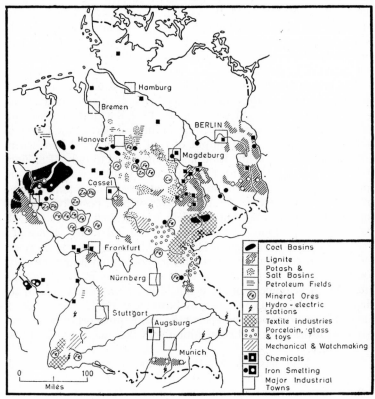

FIG. 95.   Germany: distribution of major mineral and power resources,
industries and manufacturing towns.

the town has been entirely rebuilt and in 1963 Essen recorded a
population of over 728,000.   The business centre consists of massive
modern steel, glass and concrete blocks, some of which approach
the height of skyscrapers, conforming in style with the general
pattern of severe 'functional' structures to be found in most rebuilt
German towns.   Dortmund, with a population of over 652,000 in

1963, is the second urban centre of the Ruhr. The other large clusters of urban and industrial population include the resurrected river port of Duisburg, with its great new bridge at the confluence of the Ruhr and the Rhine, a town with a population of over 497,000, and the main centre for the handling of Ruhr coal and coke. Detached from the Ruhr coalfield but integrated with its development is the textile conurbation of Wuppertal, where an overhead railway following the main street links the towns of Elberfeld and Barmen, which together form an industrial complex of over 421,000. The smaller centres of industry which depend on Ruhr coal and coke are the largely rebuilt steel city of Solingen, the textile centres of Krefeld and Mönchen-Gladbach on the left bank of the Rhine, together with the mining towns on the coalfield of Gelsenkirchen and Oberhausen.

The Saar Coalfield.   Since 1 January, 1957, the ' lost ' territory of the Saar coalfield has again become an integral part of the German industrial economy.   The output of coal is very small here when compared with that of the Ruhr and it amounted to only 17 million tons in 1956, compared with 14 million tons in 1938, while 4 million tons of coke were produced in 1955, compared with 3 million tons in 1938.   There are considerable reserves of coal, possibly amounting to 900 million tons, but the field has suffered on account of its marginal position between France and Germany; hence its chequered political history (it has reverted to Germany twice since 1935).   Saar coal is not very suitable for coking but it finds a ready local market in the chemical and glass industries of Saarbrücken, etc.   The development of the coalfield has been closely related to that of the Ruhr and to the nearby Lorraine ironfield.   The lack of navigable waterways has hampered the cheap transport of coal compared with the Ruhr and competition with that major coalfield has been severe.

The Saarland has retained its German language, culture and sentiment in spite of its political vicissitudes.   It now has a total population of 1,019,100, compared with 849,454 in 1939, a figure increased by war-time and post-war refugees.   The density of population of over 1,100 to the square mile reflects the urbanization of the population crowded into the small area of the coalfield. Saarbrücken, with a population of 132,000, is the capital of the *Land* and the town retains many of the features of the pre-war mining, steel and chemical manufacturing town, while new factories have arisen on the southern bank of the Saar.   The two other towns on the coalfield are Neunkirchen and Völklingen, each with over 40,000 people.   The rest of the population of over a million is found mostly in small colliery villages superimposed on a hitherto rural landscape. The total number of miners in the Saar is nearly 40,000, a tenth that of the Ruhr.[1]

As the result of the plebiscite held in 1956, France abandoned her claim to the Saar coalfield, apart from her retention of the Warndt mines, west of the Saar river. To offset the ' loss ' of the Saar, France put up over half the cost of the scheme to canalize the Moselle from Koblenz to Thionville, although 126 miles of this river are in German territory and 24 miles in Luxembourg. The main desire for this improvement to the meandering Moselle came from the Lorraine iron and steel industrialists, for the canalization of some 170 miles of waterway for barges of up to 1,500 tons has cheapened the cost of transporting Ruhr coke to the Lorraine blast furnaces. The scheme has taken over seven years to complete and has involved the construction of nine locks and barrages in Germany and one on the Luxembourg border.

Other Bituminous Coalfields. West Germany has two other very minor centres of bituminous coal production, both structurally related to the Ruhr. They are the Aachen field, which, prior to the reversion of the Saar, accounted for 6 per cent of the total production of West Germany. The Lower Saxony field produced 2 per cent prior to 1966. The Oberkirchen and Ibbenbüren field (lying north-west of the Teutoburgerwald and approaching exhaustion) account for the remainder.

Lignite

The West German reserves of lignite are much less extensive than those of the East. Over 81 per cent are in the Ville region between Bonn and Cologne but there are also small fields near Göttingen and Hanover, in Hesse north of Frankfurt, and in the Bavarian Foreland near the Bohemian border. The brown coal is quarried in vast open pits and its cheapness of production and ease of working offset its low calorific value and price. The main quarries occur in the Oligocene-Miocene deposits of the Ville, where downfaulting in the Erft basin has preserved the beds in the hill country west of the Rhine.[2] Some of the largest open cuts have been made at Knapsack, where the lignite is converted into briquettes in works adjacent to the pit or supplied to nearby power

[1] C. C. Held: ' The New Saarland ', *Geog. Review*, Vol. 41, 1951, pp. 590–605. H. A. Bauer: ' The Geographical Background to the Saar Problem ', *Geog. Review*, Vol. 24, 1934, pp. 555–65.

[2] T. H. Elkins: ' The Brown Coal Industry of Germany ', *Geography*, Vol. 38, 1953, and *idem*: ' The Cologne Brown Coal Field ', *Trans. Inst. Br. Geographers*, Vol. 19, 1953, pp. 131–43.

stations. The network of high-tension transmission lines which spans this somewhat desolate region between Bonn and Cologne is a striking feature of this otherwise rural landscape. Some of the current is fed into the main German grid and thus supplies Cologne and the Ruhr as well as the cities of southern Germany. In 1963, out of a total production of 106 million metric tons from the Ville, 10 per cent of the briquettes produced were exported, especially by barge from Wesseling on the Rhine, thence either downstream to the Netherlands or upstream to Strasbourg and Basle. Austria is also an important market for briquettes. The post-war regrowth of industry in the Cologne region has resulted in an increased need for electrical power and new pits are now being opened.

Potash and Rock Salt

Deposits of potash (*Kali* salts), as well as of rock salt, have long been worked in the Permian beds (*Zechstein*) of North Germany, especially at the northern foot of the Harz and at Lüneburg. They formed the basis of the chemical industry of Stassfurt and Magdeburg in the late 19th century, and the production of sulphuric acid was the source of those chemical fertilizers which were destined to improve especially the poor acid soils of the north German heaths. Small deposits of potash also occur in Baden, in the upper Rhine valley between Freiburg and Basle. The total output of potash in 1963 was 18 million tons.

Petroleum

The existence of petroleum in the Hanover and Brunswick region was realized before the 1939–45 War and oil has been actively exploited both here and in the Ems valley, near the Dutch frontier. Shafts have also been sunk successfully in Schleswig-Holstein and around Rastadt in Thuringia, while production has begun along the North Sea coast at Bremerhaven and also in Bavaria. These supplies have for some years formed a useful addition to the petroleum produced by the Fischer-Tropsch hydrogenation process developed in pre-war Germany, especially in the Ruhr where there was ready access to coal and coke, and production is again steadily increasing, reaching over 7 million metric tons in 1963; while natural gas production amounted to 915 million cubic metres.

Electricity

The production of electrical power in Western Germany is mainly thermal, using either Ruhr coal or lignite briquettes from the Ville. The large power stations are, therefore, either on the coalfields or adjacent to waterways for the cheap movement of fuel and also to provide large supplies of water for the cooling towers where necessary. Only 15 per cent of the total electricity supply is derived from falling water and these hydro-electric power stations are mainly in the Bavarian Alps, along the Swiss-German Rhine, where the power generated at Ryburg-Schwörstadt and at Rhein-felden is used by both Switzerland and Germany. There are two hydro-electric stations in the Black Forest, one at Schluchsee, where the current is taken by the Black Forest railway, and another in the north in the Schwarzenbach valley. A new barrage has recently been completed on the Lech, north of Augsburg. The great barrages of the Sauerland, such as the Möhne and Eger dams, were designed to conserve water for the Ruhr industrial region and not to produce power. Germany is an importer of electricity from Austria, notably from the Achensee station in the Tyrol, which feeds current into the Bavarian grid as do stations in the Vorarlberg.

Iron Ore

Germany's iron and steel industry has access to very limited supplies of raw material within the Federal Republic, and the steel industry has long made large-scale use of scrap metal. The chief reserves of manganiferous iron ore are in the Siegerland, Dill and Lahn valleys, where conditions of extraction are difficult and the Lower Devonian beds yield only 30 per cent of iron. Under the National Socialist régime, the Dogger beds of the Jurassic rocks were worked near Hanover but the seams are thin and strongly folded. Although West Germany depends largely on imported high-grade hæmatite from Sweden and low-grade minette ore from Lorraine, there has recently been a marked increase in the home production of iron ore, the annual production of which increased from 9 million tons in 1949 to 12·8 million metric tons in 1963.

Non-ferrous Metals

The traditional centres of copper mining in the Mansfeld region of the western Harz continue to produce small quantities of the metal, but the bulk of the copper needed in German industry is imported from the New World via Hamburg. There is also some working of lead in the Clausthal district of the Harz but the lead mines of the Eupen and Moresnet areas were lost to Belgium after the 1914–18 War, although there is still some refining of zinc at Aachen based on deposits in the Eifel. After the 1939–45 War, the zinc industry of Upper Silesia passed to Poland. Tin is im-ported up the Rhine for smelting at Essen and Duisburg, while bauxite is also conveyed to the aluminium plants on the German-Swiss section of the Rhine above Basle, where large quantities of hydro-electric power are directly available, notably at Neuhausen.

THE INDUSTRIAL PATTERN OF WEST GERMANY

The post-war industrial organization of the German Federal Republic involved the break-up of the great pre-war concerns into smaller units, the steel assets of the *Vereinigte Stahlwerke* being distributed among some thirteen new companies, while *I.G. Farben* was divided into three large units. Whereas, before the war, three-fifths of the Ruhr coal was produced by the great steel trusts, under the Potsdam Agreement no steel firm was to have coke ovens capable of producing more than three-quarters of its needs of coke. Since the establishment of the European Coal and Steel Community, however, the situation has changed and some amalgamations have taken place, for example that of the Phoenix works, producing semi-finished steel, and the *Rheinische Röhrenwerke*, producing steel tubes. It is once more characteristic of German manufacturing industry that it is mainly in the hands of large concerns, though there are some small plants located off the Ruhr coalfield and the Rhine, as well as in West Berlin, the North Sea ports, regional centres and rural upland areas, where there is a tradition of craft industries or where refugees from the East have established new factories.

The most obvious feature of German manufacturing industry is the continued concentration on the Ruhr coalfield, the ' economic metropolis ' of Germany. Here are the great concerns, combining concentration and integration. The part played by the Ruhr has been accentuated since the war, for the population of the Rhineland-Westphalia is now over 13 million, an increase of 12 per cent on 1939, representing 22 per cent of the total population of West Germany. This figure includes the increase brought about by the influx of refugees from the East. Today, out of nearly 5 million industrial workers, 3 million are concentrated in the Ruhr region and, compared with these figures, the mining population of 450,000 represents a minority group. Here are grouped the great steel, chemical, engineering, textile and food industries. The *Vereinigte Stahlwerke* represent the post-war merging of the steel firms such as Krupp and Hoesch, and such corporations aim at the production of over a million tons of pig iron a year as well as comparable amounts of coking coal. In 1950, Neu-Oberhausen produced 2·6 million tons of coal and 500,000 tons of coke, employing 11,500 workmen in the process. The whole region of the Ruhr forms a vast conurbation, with a population density of over 3,000 per square mile. This major European industrial region is the product of the last century, for mining communities and industrial centres have developed in a region of prosperous agriculture and ancient rural settlement, especially along the *Hellweg* route following the Haarstrang at the foot of the Sauerland. The late 19th-century transformation of this rural landscape proceeded in orderly fashion and some towns such as Essen had their workmen's garden cities, associated with such industrial families as that of Krupp. During the 20th century, factories and coal-mines have spread north and west of the Ruhr and across the Rhine, where Krefeld and Mönchen-Gladbach are important producers of textiles, especially silk and synthetic fibres (*Vereinigte Glanzstoff*), notably *perlon*.

South of the Ruhr coalfield, traditional centres of craft industries were transformed in the late 19th century by the advent of steam power. In the deeply incised Wupper valley which was originally provided with water power, the women find employment in the cotton- and wool-spinning and weaving mills and the men in mechanical engineering. Nearby is the reconstructed ' steel ' town of Solingen, the noted cutlery centre of West Germany. With the development of the Ville lignite field and the availability of large supplies of electrical power, Cologne, together with Deutz across the Rhine, developed as a tentacle of the Ruhr industrial region. It is a centre of consumer goods production, including silk manufacture, car assembly (Ford works), pharmaceutical products and perfume (Maria Farina), and also of mechanical engineering. The significance of the Rhine as a waterway has led to the siting of the *I.G. Farben* synthetic rubber and chemical plant at Leverkusen (*Bayer*) as well as to the oil refinery at Wesseling. To offset the loss of the Siemens-Schuckert works in the Eastern sector of Berlin, the Swiss firm of Brown-Boveri has established an electrical engineering plant at Mannheim on the upper Rhine, while the pre-war heavy chemical plant of *I.G. Farben* across the Rhine at Ludwigshafen has been revived. Another *I.G. Farben* plant, concerned especially with dyestuffs, is at Höchst, on the lower Main below Frankfurt.

In contrast with the large industrial establishments directly related to the Ruhr coalfield, there are the localized industries deriving their original capital from trading activity and with a tradition of skilled handicrafts or advantages of water transport. The former ' free city ' of Hamburg, with its Hansa traditions, has now revived its major pre-war industries of petroleum refining, the working of copper, lead, tin and other imported metals, as well as the processing of tobacco and foodstuffs. Shipbuilding is also prospering at Bremen and Emden, the total tonnage of shipping launched exceeding that of the United Kingdom since 1958. The population of Hamburg, which was reduced to 700,000 in 1945, rose to 1·8 million in 1963. Another city to benefit from water transport is Frankfurt-am-Main, the regional capital of Lower Franconia, with a long tradition as a centre of business and banking. Apart from the light industries of food processing, textiles and clothing established in the city, Frankfurt is the headquarters of *I.G. Farben*, though the plant for the manufacture of dyes, drugs and fertilizers is downstream at Höchst. Adjacent to this industrial site is the giant Opel car assembly plant at Rüsselsheim.

The industrial region of Lower Saxony around Hanover and Brunswick differs from that of the Ruhr, for its pre-war industrial development depended not on immediate access to coal, for this had to be transported *via* the *Mittelland* canal from the Ruhr, but on local resources, traditional skill and ease of communication. Nearby is the Harz, with its ancient lead, copper, zinc and silver mines, part of which remain in West Germany (Clausthal and Goslar). Other local assets include the rock salt and potash of Salzgitter, the petroleum of Hanover and the low-grade Jurassic iron ores of Peine and Salzgitter. After the war, the steel centre of Wattenstedt-Salzgitter was dismantled but, after the establishment of the European Coal and Steel Community, it has again been revived as the *Reichswerke*, now the largest iron and steel complex in the Federal Republic outside the Ruhr. It has a potential output of 2·5 million tons of steel a year. The plant has been rebuilt by refugees from East Germany. The chief centres of industry in this region are the traditional foci of commerce and medieval trade, notably Hanover, with a population of over 567,000 in 1963. This city is noted for its production of steel cables, locomotives and lorries (*Hanomag*), as well as for its rolling stock, chemical industries (including synthetic rubber) and consumer goods, and also woollen textiles. Outside Brunswick is the *Volkswagen* works at Wolfsburg, which sells its cars all over the world. The cathedral town of Hildesheim is a centre for the production of agricultural machinery, furniture, clocks and textiles.

In central and southern Germany, there are several regional centres which have attracted a variety of industries. Munich (München), the hub of Catholic Bavaria and a city of over a million inhabitants, produces a wide range of manufactures, apart from its breweries, and these include rolling stock, synthetic rubber, optical goods, shoes and leather articles, clothing and other consumer goods. Nürnberg, the city of medieval gilds *par excellence*, the regional capital of Upper Franconia, now produces synthetic rubber as well as bicycles and the traditional toys and dolls. Stuttgart, the formerly ornate 18th-century baroque city, half-surrounded by the hills of the upper Neckar valley, largely obliterated by war-time bombardment and fire, has now been rebuilt in such a way that occasional relics of baroque statuary and ornamentation break incongruously upon the new glass and concrete structures of the main streets in the centre of the town. To the south, on a wooded eminence, the *Fernsehturm* (television mast) rises over 500 ft. high and is a land-mark for several miles. The city of Stuttgart remains noted for its Mercedes-Benz works and for its electrical industries. In extreme contrast is the 18th-century planned town of Mannheim, at the confluence of the Neckar and the Rhine, where half the city was completely destroyed and a quarter half-destroyed. This is ' a town of work and not beauty '. Its riverside quays handle Ruhr coal and coke and refined petroleum, as well as salt from Heilbronn on the upper Neckar. The main industrial plants here are those of *I.G. Farben*, Lever Bros. and Brown-Boveri. Another nodal centre which was almost completely destroyed by air raids is Kassel, formerly capital of Hesse. This town, in the Fulda valley, has now been completely rebuilt, with a new main street known as the *Ständeplatz*, with separate lanes for through and stopping traffic, and the *Treppenstrasse*, a series of stairways designed for pedestrians only.

ECONOMIC SUMMARY

West Germany is once again a major producer of industrial goods for the world market. From 1945 to 1949, her economy and external trade were controlled by the occupying powers, French and Anglo-American. Since 1949 she has received extensive credits, especially from the U.S.A., for the rebuilding of industry, towns and means of communication. In 1953, West Germany entered the European Coal and Steel Community under the Schuman Plan. This pooling of her basic industrial resources at once widened the market for Ruhr coal and coke, as well as steel, while reducing by 25 per cent the cost of Lorraine and Luxemburg iron ore. By 1964, Germany's steel output had reached a new high annual record, with a production of over 37 million metric tons, with in addition 4·2 million tons from the Saar. These figures represent an increased production of 33 per cent since 1955 and Germany has made more progress in steel production than any other member of the European Coal and Steel Community, to which she now contributes over half the total production.

FINISHED STEEL PRODUCTION OF WEST GERMANY, 1962–4[1]

(Million ingot long tons)

	Production	Imports	Exports	Net Exports
1963	20·7	3·42	4·95	1·52
1964	24·7	4·05	5·34	1·28
1965	24·5	4·35	6·28	1·92

It is significant as a measure of Germany's recent progress, especially since she joined the Western Defence Pact, that she is no longer a significant exporter of raw and semi-manufactured steel, but of engineering products. In particular, there has been great recent expansion in the production of rolling stock and in ship-building, while the firm of Krupp is now permitted to produce jet aircraft. Competition with Great Britain is intensifying as far as world markets are concerned. Progress in coal production is, on the other hand, much slower but nevertheless the main increase in the European Coal and Steel Community pool has come from West Germany, where production has expanded by over 4 per cent since the scheme came into operation. The output of the Saarland has recently suffered a slight decrease, as has her export of coal. West Germany accounts for over half of the total pool of coal under the Schuman Plan and is the greatest exporter of coal and coke. The following table offers a useful comparison.

PRODUCTION OF COAL IN WEST EUROPE IN 1964[2]

(Million metric tons)

	Production	Imports	Exports
W. Germany	148[2]	7·3	13·9
France	52	14·7	0·9
Belgium	21	7·1	2·5
Netherlands	11	9·2	2·9
Austria	0·9	3·8	nil
Switzerland	nil	1·4	nil

[1] European Economic Community: *Iron and Steel Yearbook*, 1966.
[2] United Nations: *Economic Survey of Europe*, 1964.
[3] Including the Saarland.

The External Trade of West Germany

The main market for West Germany's products and the chief source of her imports is in western Europe, where about 70 per cent of the goods exported are sold in return for nearly half her imports. From the Netherlands, Belgium and France, West Germany imports ' colonial ' produce, petroleum and raw materials, as well as foodstuffs, especially wheat and butter. Much of this trade originates overseas and is handled by Rotterdam and Antwerp, moving thence *via* the Rhine or by rail to the German industrial and urban markets, especially in the Ruhr and Rhineland. Iron ore is imported from Sweden and Lorraine, while France supplies bauxite as well as olive oil and North African phosphates. In return, Germany exports coal, coke, raw and semi-manufactured steel, as well as engineering products, especially machinery, cars, tractors, rolling stock and industrial equipment, together with chemical products, manufactured synthetic fibres such as *perlon*, leather goods, glass and porcelain.

West Germany's trade with the U.S.A. is greater than that with any single European country and West Germany is a market for American metals such as copper; petroleum, foodstuffs and certain types of machinery. In return, West Germany sells a wide range of high-priced manufactures, including optical instruments, photographic apparatus, drugs, porcelain (*Rosenthal*), and specialized types of equipment. In addition, Germany does a growing amount of trade with the underdeveloped lands of the New World and South-east Asia, sending, for example, structural steel and power station equipment to Latin America, textile machinery to South-east Asia and mining equipment to Australia. An assembly plant for the production of the *Volkswagen* has recently been sent to South Africa and port equipment to Basra, on the Persian Gulf. Thus the external trade of West Germany closely reflects her industrial structure, as it did between the two world wars. The table on the next page illustrates the trade between West Germany and her major world markets.

In conclusion, it may be said that, if the general industrial and external trade pattern appears little changed as the result of the last war, certain fundamental elements of the superstructure have been drastically modified. In the first place, Germany's two great pre-war axes of circulation, the north–south axis of the Rhine and the east–west axis of the Elbe-*Mittelland* canal are now reduced to that of the Rhine. West and East Germany are severed economically by the boundary running south from Lübeck to the Elbe

EXTERNAL TRADE OF WEST GERMANY IN 1964[1]

(Million DM)

	Imports	Exports
EUROPE		
France	6,270	7,424
The Netherlands	5,350	6,735
Italy	4,467	4,592
Belgium-Luxembourg	4,304	4,878
United Kingdom	2,782	2,716
Sweden	2,304	3,258
Switzerland	1,839	4,561
Austria	1,523	3,295
Denmark	1,262	2,103
U.S.A.	8,068	4,784

above Lauenburg, thence along the Elbe for 38 miles and then west to Helmstedt. It finally crosses the Harz in the region of the Brocken, leaving most of Thuringia in East Germany, and follows the Werra valley to the Czech frontier at Asch. In consequence, the trade of the North Sea ports, especially that of Hamburg, has been greatly modified, for the Czechoslovak hinterland has been lost, as have the lands east of the Elbe. The internal waterway traffic, except on the Rhine and on the Ruhr-Dortmund-Ems canal system, has been greatly curtailed. On the other hand, there is intense rail and road traffic, for the railway network is only surpassed in western Europe by that of Belgium, and the amount of rail-borne traffic is probably the greatest in the world. Over 40 per cent of the railway lines are double tracked and the number of passengers carried per annum is two and a half times that of the U.S.A., while the ratio of tons/km. is alone surpassed by Canada. With the reconstruction of the great *Autobahn* system and the extension of some of the highways planned before the war, there has been a marked increase in road traffic, especially for the conveyance of long-distance freight by means of articulated lorries.

Another fundamental change in post-war West Germany is the urban scene. Most of the historic towns, with the exception of Heidelberg and small remote places such as Limburg on the Lahn, Rothenburg and Dinkelsbühl in the Tauber valley, have had their ' core ' areas destroyed by aerial bombardment. Some of the

[1] *The Statesman's Year-Book* 1966-67

worst-damaged cities of historic interest are Cologne, Hamburg, Frankfurt, Munich, Würzburg, Mainz and Lübeck. The medieval part of Nürnberg has been remarkably restored, and, in a number

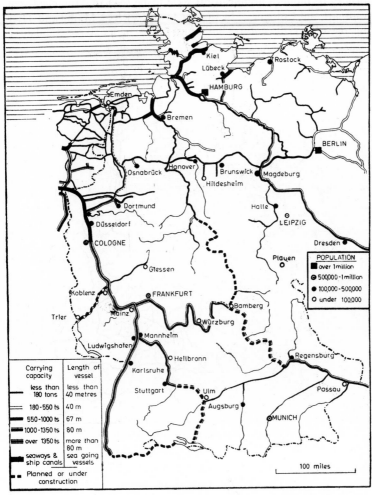

FIG. 96. Germany: navigable waterways and ports served.

of towns, the medieval cathedral, however shattered, has survived to dominate the centre of the city, as in Cologne, Freiburg-im-Breisgau, Frankfurt-am-Main and Münster. In most urban centres, with the exception of such little-damaged places as Heidelberg and

Wiesbaden, the congested core of the old town has been replaced by blocks of offices, shops and apartment houses, in the style of an American business centre. There is in fact an appalling uniformity of modern architectural style to be seen in Munich, Essen, Stuttgart and Cologne. In smaller towns, such as Mainz and Trier, the massive 19th-century buildings, often in local red sandstone,

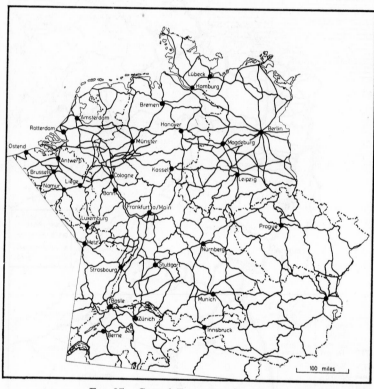

FIG. 97. Central Europe: main railways.

have survived to provide a sharp contrast with post-war housing developments. The federal capital of Bonn, with none of the traditions of such an historic city as Frankfurt-am-Main or Cologne, yet serves to combine the functions of a busy market town and tourist centre with its new rôle symbolized by the ultra-modern *Bundeshaus*, which, with its adjacent legations, presents its main façade to the Rhine.

In the rural areas, the life of the villages has been frequently changed by the influx of bombed-out people and by refugees. Workers on the land have become in many districts a minority, for the inhabitants of the village travel daily or weekly to the nearest town, where their employment is. Some rural areas have seen the building of new settlements, often in wooded surroundings, such as Neu Gablonz which accommodates refugees from the Sudetenland. This new town, with thriving glass and jewellery trades, has arisen outside Kaufbeuren, in the Allgäu. Similarly, pottery and porcelain factories may be found in the Palatinate, moved from Saxony, in the same way as part of the Carl Zeiss works has been transferred from Jena to Göttingen. Another element in the German 'cultural landscape' is the military township which was established by the occupying powers, by the British in the north and by the Americans in the upper Rhineland and Bavaria. Outside Heidelberg and Frank-furt-am-Main, huge tenement blocks have been built, American style, for occupation by troops now maintained under N.A.T.O.

EAST GERMANY

East Germany presents a shattering contrast with the West. It is an impoverished, defeated and once savagely occupied country which has seen the entire reorganization of its economy since the Russian Occupation. Heavy industry has been nationalized and completely reorganized, while agrarian reforms have been ruthlessly carried out. East Germany includes only one metropolitan city with over a million people, that of East Berlin, which records 1·0 million inhabitants (1963). Leipzig, with 588,000, and Dresden, with 499,000, together with Magdeburg (267,000), were all heavily bombed but although they have now been largely rebuilt they are cities in decline.[1] A new centre of heavy industry has been created at Eisenhüttenstadt, south of Frankfurt-am-Oder, as part of the present Seven Year Plan.

Before the 1939–45 War, 20 per cent of the population of Eastern Germany was employed in agriculture. In fact, the 'lost' lands east of the Oder-Neisse line were regarded as semi-colonial territory, the domain of the *Junker* estates. They produced cereals, potatoes, meat and dairy produce, and also sugar beet for the urban markets, ranging from the capital city of Berlin to the industrial towns of the Ruhr, which in return supplied coal and coke. Since the monetary reform of the West in 1948 and the devaluation of the *Deutsche Mark* in East Germany since 1961, trade has been at a

[1] R. E. H. Mellor: 'The German Democratic Republic's Falling Population', *Geography*, Vol. 47, 1962.

standstill between East and West Germany. East Germany now looks inevitably to the countries of the Soviet *bloc* for her markets.

The first agrarian reforms took place in 1946–7 and they involved the confiscation of estates of over 100 hectares, as well as those belonging to war criminals and Nazis. A third of the total area of East Germany is said to have been affected. Those who benefited most from these reforms were the peasants and some refugees from the ' lost lands ' beyond the Oder-Neisse line, though a small amount of land was requisitioned for rebuilding and for ' recreational purposes '. Attempts have been made to mechanize agriculture, and today there are nearly 600 machine and tractor stations. There has been an increase in the number of stock reared, especially pigs, and also poultry and dairy cattle. In 1964, there were over 16,000 collective farms covering 5·47 m. hectares and 658 state farms totalling 406,414 ha.

Compared with West Germany, East Germany has greater brown coal reserves but fewer capital goods and far more consumer goods which depend on imports. East Germany has to face heavy reparation payments and, under Communist planning, there was first a marked emphasis on heavy industry. The slight increase in the production of foodstuffs has been offset by a fall in the output of light industries. It is claimed that the ratio of consumer goods to the total production is now comparable with that of West Germany, so that the pre-war relative importance of these industries has been considerably reduced. In contrast, there has been a marked increase in the production of brown coal, heavy chemicals, pig iron and cement. In consequence, West and East Germany are now no longer so complementary as before the war, for in both areas there is about the same proportion of the labour force employed in basic industries, namely 28 per cent, and about 33 per cent in metallurgical industries. This new emphasis on mining, especially of lignite, on heavy industry and chemicals, is designed to compensate East Germany for war-time losses and post-war dismantling by order of the Russians, and to re-deploy the steel and engineering industries. Compared with West Germany, the East is poor in resources of bituminous coal, for the mines around Karl-Marx-Stadt in Saxony produced only 2·3 million tons in 1964. The East is compensated by abundant reserves of brown coal, rock salt and potash. Cut off from her pre-war supplies of coal and coke from the Ruhr *via* the *Mittelland* canal and from Upper Silesian coal and chemicals by the Oder-Neisse line, East Germany is basing its reconstructed industries increasingly on thermal power produced from brown coal. The output of briquettes is two and a half times that before the war, the production of lignite reaching 256 million metric tons in 1964,[1] mainly in the Cottbus field. The production of aluminium from imported Hungarian bauxite began here in 1964.

The complete reorganization of industry in East Germany and the change of emphasis is illustrated by the five-fold increase in iron ore production between 1936 and 1964, when the output was 1·63 million tons. There was a seven-fold increase in pig iron production, which amounted to 2·89 million metric tons in 1959, but compared with 2·25 million tons as the figure for 1964. The output of crude steel (3·85 million tons) and rolled steel products (2·81 million tons) has increased by a third since 1939. Moreover, before the 1939–45 War, steel products such as heavy engineering, including shipbuilding and the making of rolling stock as well as the production of ball bearings, formed only 6 per cent of the total industrial turnover in East Germany and there was more specialization in textiles, office equipment, printing and paper production, as well as the manufacture of optical instruments, notably by the firm of Carl Zeiss at Jena. Since the onset of Soviet planning, the emphasis has been on the production of generators, mining and metallurgical equipment, heavy machine tools and structural steel. Shipbuilding, which before the war was of minor importance compared with that of the great shipyards of Hamburg and Bremen, has now been given priority, especially at Rostock; while the output of rolling stock has been expanded and that of machine tools doubled. Fewer vehicles are made than in the West, though optical and precision instruments are produced for the Soviet market. Since wool cannot easily be imported through the North Sea ports, there has been an expansion of the synthetic fibre industry, as well as an import of textile fibres, including cotton, from the Soviet Union. The ready-made clothing industry of Saxony has lost its market in West Germany and in West Berlin and there is no appreciable market in the Soviet satellite states to compensate for this loss, on account of their low purchasing power. The production of textiles and textile machinery in Chemnitz (now renamed Karl-Marx-Stadt) and Zwickau; the optical glass industry of Jena and Wetzlar; and the porcelain factory at Meissen near Dresden, have been greatly handicapped by the migration of capital and skilled labour to the West. The dismantling and removal of the Carl Zeiss works from Jena took place in 1946 and the Agfa works at Bitterfeld were also closed. The only monopoly which the Eastern Zone retained was the electrical engineering industry of East Berlin (Siemens-Schuckert

[1] T. H. Elkins: ' East Germany's Changing Brown Coal Industry ', *Geography*, Vol. 41, 1956, pp. 192–5.

and *A.E.G.*). It is estimated that 65 per cent of the industrial capacity of the Eastern Zone was removed to Soviet Russia in 1947, as well as the whole of the armaments industry and 45 per cent of the normal peacetime industrial capacity. The production of crude steel was reduced by Russian dismantling to about 100,000 tons in 1947, 6 per cent that of 1938.

During the 1939–45 War, East Germany suffered relatively little damage, apart from the bombing of the great cities, but by 1947 only the Maximilianshütte at Unterwellenborn in Thuringia and the steel plants at Thale in the Harz and at Hettstedt remained intact. Before the war, the Thuringian plants produced 200,000 tons of pig iron, namely 1·3 per cent of the German total. In addition, there were the metallurgical centres of Riesa and Pirna in Saxony, Grödlitz and Brandenburg in Prussia, while Berlin produced special steels, as well as being the centre of great electrical engineering works. In all, the East produced 1·2 million tons of raw steel and 900,000 tons of rolled steel, mainly with the aid of Ruhr coal and coke, together with lignite, and using iron ore from the Harz and Thuringia, as well as the low-grade Jurassic and Cretaceous ores of the Salzgitter region. After the war, not only did the Russians reduce the capacity of the iron foundries by 50 per cent and that of the steel rolling mills by 80 per cent, but they also removed or destroyed much of the generating plant which used briquettes for the production of thermal electricity.

Today, with the nationalization of the steel industry of East Germany, the State owns 77 per cent of the steel capacity. Under the 1950–5 Plan, the output of electrical power, crude and rolled steel was considerably increased, while the output of thermal power is now at least 100 per cent more than in 1936. On the other hand, the capacity of the generating plant has been increased by only 20 per cent, a measure of its improved efficiency. The aim of the 1955–60 Plan was to produce 3·5 million tons of steel ingots and 2·6 million tons of rolled steel and these figures were exceeded in 1964. The production of 2·5 million tons of steel ingots by 1955 was achieved by reconstructing former plant, such as the Maximilianhütte in Thuringia, where there are now three blast furnaces using local ore and four Bessemer converters, as well as electric-arc furnaces. The steel works at Riesa in Saxony and at Calbe near Magdeburg are also again in operation, both using local low-grade iron ore, including some from the Harz; while limestone is brought from quarries near Magdeburg, and a type of coke, produced at Schwarze Pumpe near Lauchhammer, is derived from lignite. The steel works at Brandenburg produce ½ million tons of crude steel per annum and much of this is sent to the mills at Risa for rolling. Another site is at Döhlen near Dresden, where the *Edelstahlwerk* is the largest special steel plant in East Germany, using both open-hearth and electric-arc furnaces. There are also modern centres of steel production, such as Kirchmöser, where ten open-hearth furnaces were completed by 1950. Under the first Five Year Plan, an integrated steel works was built at Schönfliess near Eisenhütten-stadt (formerly Fürstenberg-am-Oder). This ultra-modern plant, which was to include six blast furnaces, was to have been a vital element in the ' Eastern Combine ', depending upon some 800,000 tons of coke per annum imported from Upper Silesia and one million tons of iron ore from Krivoi Rog.[1] The Oder waterway was to be used to transport the coke and to convey the raw steel *via* the Spree canal system to the Berlin market. The first blast furnaces went into operation in 1951 and by 1954 each was turning out be-tween 400 and 600 tons of pig iron a day. Their capacity is over 500,000 tons of pig iron a year and in addition there is a steel smelting and rolling plant. The city of Eisenhüttenstadt, (until 1961 known as Stalinstadt), a creation of steel and concrete, with its massive blocks of workers' flats, has arisen amidst pine woods and tracts of sandy heath. The town was designed to accommodate 45,000 people but in 1965 had only 24,000 inhabitants.[2]

The ' Western Combine ', which was part of the 1959–65 Seven Year Plan for East Germany, appears to have made less progress. It depends largely on iron ore from the Harz Mountains, serving such plants as Unterwellenborn; the Krupp-Gruson works near Magdeburg having been first bombed and then largely dismantled by the Russians. Today this site, now known as the Thälmann *Schwermaschinenbau*, is an industrial slum, using old machinery, but turning out, for example, heavy crankshafts, steel ingot cutting machinery for China, heavy gearing for the Soviet Union, wire-stranding machinery for the Netherlands and overhead cranes for India. There is an acute labour shortage here, as throughout East Germany.

Under the second Seven Year Plan, there was a vigorous attempt to increase the extractive industries, especially lignite, and today the German Democratic Republic is the chief world producer.[3]

[1] British Iron and Steel Federation: *Steel Developments in Eastern Germany*, 1954.

[2] K. A. Sinnhuber: 'Eisenhüttenstadt and other New Industrial Locations East of Berlin ', *Festschrift Leopold G. Scheidl*, I. Teil, Wien, 1965.

[3] T. H. Elkins: ' The Central German Chemical Industry ', *Geography*, Vol. 42, 1957, pp. 183–6 and also ' East Germany's New Industrial Plan ', *Geography*, Vol. 45, 1960.

Briquettes, made from brown coal, form the basis of the chemical industry, especially the manufacture of synthetic petrol, rubber and plastics, the production of which was at first forbidden. Today, the main thermal stations are closely related to the *I.G.* plants at Schkopau (*Bunawerk*), Bitterfeld, Leuna Zschornewitz, Harbke, Espenhain and Böhlen. A new plant has also been built on the Elbe at Vockerode, as well as at Trattendorf and Bergdorf. Others are under construction, especially in the Erz-Gebirge and in the Thüringerwald. East Germany produced no less than 256 million tons of lignite in 1964, a marked increase on the pre-war output of about 115 million tons, mainly for briquetting and local consumption. Today, an alternative fuel has to be found for Ruhr coke, and the doubling of the pre-war output of briquettes is an attempt to overcome the shortage of domestic fuel and of thermal electricity. Lack of labour has slowed down the construction of power stations and deliveries of electrical equipment are also delayed. Before the war, the main sources of lignite which were exploited were west of the Elbe, near Halle and Leipzig, while there were other workings in Lower Lusatia (Nieder Lausitz), around Helmstedt-Magdeburg and in the Harz foreland. Today the reserves of the middle Oder basin are being opened up, notably around Fürstenberg, to supply a new thermal station south of Frankfurt-am-Oder. There are also large reserves in the Neisse valley around Cottbus which are now being exploited.

The older lignite workings in the Eocene deposits of the Halle-Leipzig region include seams varying from 30 to 60 ft. thick and the great producing field in East Germany lies here. On account of the high water content (60 per cent) and consequent low calorific value, the lignite is converted on the spot into briquettes for use in thermal stations. These briquettes were moved by rail before the war to the great industrial complex of Merseburg-Leuna, with its synthetic petroleum and rubber industries, as well as to the chemical works of Bitterfeld (*Agfa*) and Salzgitter. The lignite of the Helmstedt-Magdeburg zone has long been used in the refining of sugar beet, as well as in the engineering and chemical industries of that region, with its great reserves of potash and rock salt. The lignite of Nieder Lausitz supplies mainly briquettes for the Berlin market. In view of the large reserves here, a new industrial complex is being created, under which the output of lignite is to be increased to 107 million tons, compared with 60 million tons in 1953. Coke is now being produced at high cost from lignite at the Mátás Rákosi plant, with tar, benzene and phenol as by-products. Since 1955 there has been a gas pipe-line to the Fischer-Tropsch plant, producing syn-

(a) Walled town of Nördlingen.

21. TWO MEDIEVAL TOWNS OF SOUTHERN GERMANY FROM THE AIR

(b) Walled town of Rothenburg ob der Tauber.

(a) The new water-front at Frankfurt-am-Main, dominated by the sandstone spire of the Gothic cathedral.

(b) The re-built business 'core' of Frankfurt from the air.

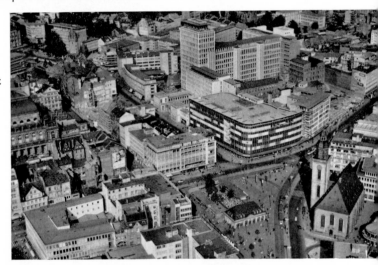

(c) The new town of Neu-Gablonz near Kaufbeuren, founded by Sudetenland Roman Catholic refugees.

thetic petroleum at Schwarzheide, and another to the steel works at Gröditz and Risa on the Elbe.[1] The future demand for briquettes in East Germany may be modified by the electrification of the railways and also by the atomic production of electricity from plants which will use uranium from the mines at Aue in the Erz-Gebirge and at Saalfeld in Thuringia.

The output of non-ferrous metals remains below pre-war level, the production of aluminium being particularly reduced by Russian dismantling, notably at the formerly important centre of Bitterfeld, though a new plant has been completed at Lauta. The production of pyrites in the Harz is the basis of the heavy acid and chemical fertilizer industries of the Magdeburg region, of growing importance. Other long-established industries which have been maintained are the manufacture of porcelain at the Meissen works near Dresden, where the tradition of highly skilled craftsmanship dates from the foundation of the firm in 1710 when it came under royal patronage. Recent developments have been the establishment of a precision instruments factory at Weimar and the production of synthetic rubber. In conclusion, it appears that the former pattern of industry in East Germany, with its bias towards the manufacture of textiles (especially from synthetic fibres), textile machinery, electrical equipment, rolling stock, synthetic petroleum and *buna* rubber, is being further emphasized. In addition, precision instruments, pharmaceutical products and chemical fertilizers are also manufactured. There is now a marked stress on lignite production, thermal power and heavy industry, especially under the new Seven Year Plan (1964–70), designed to increase the production of power supplies, petro-chemicals and electronics. A major project is the oil refinery at Schwedt, where a petro-chemical combine is to come into operation by 1975. The crude oil is now sent by pipeline from Mosur (Kuibyshev) on the Volga. Means of transport are gradually being improved and the problem of access by water to the Eastern sector of Berlin and the western regions of the Democratic Republic is being overcome by a canal by-passing West Berlin. In recent years the shipbuilding industry at Rostock has been greatly expanded. There now appears to be a slight easement in trade between East and West, which hitherto has been paralysed by the blocking of East German marks. It remains to be seen how far the establishment of a European Common Market and also the European Free Trade Area will modify the dependence of East Germany on the Soviet *bloc* as a source of raw materials and as a

[1] T. H. Elkins: 'East Germany's Changing Brown Coal Industry', *Geography*, Vol. 41, 1956, pp. 192–5.

market for her industrial products.   The solution to the problem of the political reunification of West and East Germany awaits the future.

REFERENCES

The best account of post-war Germany, though now dated, is given in P. George and J. Tricart: *L'Europe Centrale*, Vol. 2, *Les Etats*, 1954. There is much useful material in R. E. Dickinson: *Germany. A General and Regional Geography*, 1953.   E. Ottremba: *Die deutsche Agrarlandschaft*, 1956, deals with the rural landscape.   The annual reports of the United Nations, especially *The Economic Survey of Europe*, provide useful up-to-date material, including tables of statistical production and trade. The geography of the Ruhr coalfield is summarized by N. J. G. Pounds: *The Ruhr*, 1952.   Useful papers in English are those of C. D. Harris: ' The Ruhr Coal Mining District ', *Geog. Review*, Vol. 36, 1946, and N. J. G. Pounds: ' The Ruhr Area: A Problem in Definition ', *Geography*, Vol. 36, 1951.   Lignite production has been described by T. H. Elkins: ' The Brown Coal Industry of Germany ', *Geography*, Vol. 38, 1953; *idem: The Cologne Brown Coal Field*, Trans. Inst. Br. Geographers, Vol. 19, 1954; *idem:* ' East Germany's Changing Brown Coal Industry ', *Geography*, Vol. 41, 1956.   There are two useful papers in English on the Saar coalfield, one published at the time of the pre-war plebiscite by H. A. Bauer: ' The Geographical Background of the Saar Problem ', *Geog. Review*, Vol. 24, 1934, the other by C. C. Held: ' The New Saarland ', *Geog. Review*, Vol. 41, 1951.   The *Saar Atlas* was published in 1934.   An *Atlas von Niedersachsen* appeared in 1950.   Useful studies of German towns are included in R. E. Dickinson: *City, Region and Regionalism*, 1947, and the handbook by E. von Seydlitz: *Deutschland*, 1925, is still convenient for reference.   N. J. G. Pounds and W. N. Parker: *Coal and Steel in Western Europe*, 1957, deals with the growth of heavy industry in Germany and the Saar.   Statistical data for the German Federal Republic are published annually in the *Statistisches Jahrbuch* and for the German Democratic Republic in the *Jahrbuch der Deutschen Demokratischen Republik*.

CHAPTER 13

GERMANY: REGIONAL STUDIES: SOUTHERN GERMANY

UPPER BAVARIA AND THE MAIN-NECKAR BASINS

A DEFINITION of southern Germany may be based on both physical and historical considerations. The east–west valley of the Main provides a convenient northern limit, the northern rim of the basin marking the boundary of Bavaria. To the west, the highlands of the Black Forest and the Odenwald-Spessart divide the Rhineland from the Danube and Neckar-Main drainage. The former duchies of Baden and Rhenish-Hesse are described in the section on the Rhineland; whereas Württemberg, together with the historic provinces of Swabia and Franconia, are to be regarded with Bavaria and the Bavarian Palatinate as an integral part of southern Germany. To the east, the boundary of Bavaria marches with that of Czechoslovakia and Austria.

On the physical map, southern Germany appears as almost entirely highland or upland. In fact, it consists of a variety of regions: Alpine ranges in the south, worn down and re-uplifted Hercynian highlands on the eastern and western borders, and, in the centre, scarpland country drained by the Danube, Main and Neckar. This is a complex region, lying on a continental water-parting (Rhine-Danube drainage), in which the divides do not occur on the highest ground, and in which much water has been gained by the Rhine at the expense of the Danube since the diversion north-wards of the Rhine and the Oligocene-Miocene sinking of the Rhine rift valley.

The Danube rises in two headstreams, the Brege and Brigach, on the eastern slope of the Black Forest, and these unite at Donaueschingen, the traditional source of the river. Below this point, the stream turns away north-eastward, keeping to the base of the Swabian Jura as far as Donauwörth. To the south, the Bavarian Foreland slopes up to the base of the Bavarian Alps. Ulm marks the limit of navigation on the Danube for 500-ton barges, but there is little traffic on the upper river above the section between Passau, on the Austrian frontier, and Ratisbon (Regensburg). The volume of the Danube as it flows over the Jurassic limestones of Swabia is very variable; the bed is stony and the stream is shallow, especially in summer, when it partly dries up. At New Ulm, the Danube is joined by its Alpine tributary, the Iller, but there is no significant surface drainage from the Jura. Below the Nördlingen Gate (Donauwörth), the Lech comes in from the Foreland, with its source far back in the Austrian Lechtaler Alps. From the north, the Franconian Jura are crossed by the Altmühl and, from the Fichtel-Gebirge, the Naab flows southwards to join the Danube above Ratisbon, where the Regen comes in from the Bavarian Forest. The foreland of eastern Bavaria is crossed diagonally by a number of streams with their source in the Alps, notably the Isar and Inn (which forms the frontier between Bavaria and Upper Austria). Between Ratisbon and Passau, the Danube winds along the base of the Bavarian Forest in one of its wildest and most picturesque reaches.

The divide between the Rhine-Danube drainage is very devious. It may be traced westwards from the Allgäu Alps across the Alpine Foreland north of lake Constance to the Black Forest (Brege-Wutach divide). It then swings back into the Swabian Jura south of the Neckar valley, following the crest of the scarpland as far as the Ries basin. Through this depression, known also as the Nördlingen ' gate ', the Wörnitz has maintained its southerly flow to the Danube; while the Altmühl also rises to the north of the Franconian Jura in the Franconian Heights. Otherwise drainage has been drawn off north-westwards to the Neckar and the Main. To the north-east of the Franconian Jura, the Fichtel-Gebirge throw off streams to all points of the compass. The sources of the Main, Naab, Thuringian Saale, and Bohemian Ohře interlace here.

Only around lake Constance is the drainage of southern Germany direct to the Rhine. Here, too, water appears to seep through from the Danube to the Aach tributary of the upper Rhine. Elsewhere the Neckar and Main collect the Rhine drainage east of the Black Forest and Odenwald-Spessart highlands. Rising in the north-east of the Black Forest, the Neckar meanders north-eastwards along the base of the Swabian scarpland before turning north through the Neckarland *en route* to its gorge through the southern Odenwald. Its catchment basin is much smaller than that of the Main, but its scenery is rather more picturesque, especially on account of the incised character of the meandering river. The Main has its sources in the Fichtel-Gebirge, and its course is highly irregular, being marked by a number of elbow bends where capture has occurred. As the Neckar traverses scarp and vale country to which the local names ' Berge ' and ' Filder ' are given, so the Main crosses a variety of rocks of unequal resistance in its course westwards towards the Rhine. These rocks belong to the Triassic group, once the Franconian Jura are passed, and they range through Keuper marls and *Muschelkalk* (shelly limestone) to the Bunter sandstone of the Odenwald-Spessart highlands. The last stretch of the Main is across the plain of Rhenish-Hesse.

A description of southern Germany resolves itself into a study of its diverse regions. Upper Bavaria and Swabia include the outermost Alpine ranges, forming the frontier with Austria in the east, and with Switzerland in the west. These *Flysch* and Cretaceous limestone Pre-Alps rise steeply from the Bavarian Foreland to a general altitude of 5,250–6,500 ft. The culminating peak is the Zugspitze (9,720 ft.), in the Wetterstein group. Breaks occur in these west–east ranges where the Alpine tributaries of the Danube and the upper Rhine leave their mountainous tract for the Foreland. These streams, such as the Iller, Lech, Isar and Inn, have filled in the geosyncline of the Bavarian Foreland, which they cross in shallow valleys excavated mainly in the fluvioglacial deposits laid down during the Pleistocene glaciation. Great thicknesses of drift in the form of outwash gravels (*Deckenschotter*), terminal moraines and sheets of boulder clay, bear witness to the deposition work of the *Würm* ice as it retreated towards the Alps, and Tertiary rocks seldom appear except where they project through the skin of drift as local ridges, especially in the *Molasse*. These features account for the hummocky character and soil variety of the Foreland. Glaciation is absent from the low ground elsewhere in southern Germany, but local ice caps have left their mark on the Hercynian highlands, notably the southern Black Forest, the Bohemian Forest and the Fichtel-Gebirge. Only in the upper Main and Danube valleys does glacial drift occur outside the Foreland, but there are local deposits of loess, notably in the Main valley around Würzburg, in the Wetterau and lower Main plain, on the terraces of the Neckar, and also in the upper Danube valley, especially in the Dungau at the base of the Bavarian Forest. Sand dunes have been piled up to the east of Nürnberg, and there are extensive tracts of loess on the Franconian uplands, especially in the open limestone country, and these features, combined with the absence of hindrances to movement in the *Steppenheide* country, have long favoured penetration and rural settlement.

North of the Danube valley, Lower Bavaria and Swabia are characterized by the development of a scarpland landscape. This feature is most conspicuous in the great diagonal sweep of the Swabian and Franconian Jura, where the Jurassic uplands are broken by the peculiar depression of the Ries, and by the post-glacial Rhine gorge at the southern end, where the Rhine falls occur. Parallel to the Jura or Alb, a further series of broken scarps and vales may be traced, developed on Triassic rocks and drained by the Neckar and Main to the Rhine. This varied and dissected country will be described more fully later. Finally, the Hercynian massifs which form the marginal framework of southern Germany must be mentioned. To the west they are represented by the Black Forest, divided from the Odenwald by the sag or saddle of the Kraichgau, and, on the east, by the frontier highlands of the Bavarian and Bohemian Forests, together with the Fichtel-Gebirge. These are barrier regions, averaging over 3,300 ft. in altitude, and, as the names suggest, they are heavily forested. They have served to isolate southern Germany from the north, especially Prussia, a fact which has gone far towards preserving the individuality of Bavaria both from the point of view of its historical and economic development, as well as its physical geography.

Southern Germany, excluding the Rhine and the lower Neckar and Main valleys, is thinly settled compared with the Börde region at the northern foot of the Central Highlands (Fig. 89). Generally high relief, poor soils and a rigorous winter climate repel population, with the exception of parts of so-called 'smiling' Swabia and the Neckarland, and the Main valley around Würzburg. The rest of the Main valley is not so favoured, Upper Franconia assuming a more 'severe' aspect. The upper Danube is no longer a routeway of major importance, and Upper Bavaria has the character of a national parkland, on account of its share of Alpine scenery. Yet for centuries past routes have threaded this region, an essential passage land linking the Germano-Polish lowland, the North Sea and the Baltic coasts with Italy and the Mediterranean. Along the early 'salt' roads over the Alps moved medieval traders; small market towns developing in southern Germany, where fairs were held. Augsburg, on the Lech, compared in importance in medieval times with Nürnberg, with Ratisbon on the Danube, and with Frankfurt-am-Main. Stuttgart and Munich (München) represent more modern and artificial growths, whereas Dinkelsbühl and Rothenburg are small but notable survivals of medieval charm, remote from modern highways of trade. Industrialism, except in Munich, Nürnberg and Stuttgart, has hardly touched southern Germany east of the Rhine and south of the Main, and the resources of the region lie chiefly in its varied land economy and scenic attractiveness, especially in Upper Bavaria.

THE BAVARIAN ALPS

The Bavarian Alps lie along Germany's southern boundary with the Austrian Tyrol for a distance of about 180 miles. As part of the Alps, they attain the highest altitudes in Germany, the culminating point being the Zugspitze (9,720 ft.). The Bavarian Alps, however, represent only the northern outer ranges of the whole Alpine system, and they can hardly be said to form a complete region in themselves, but rather must they be related to the outermost ripples of the Alpine folds which die out northwards against the Bavarian Foreland. *Flysch* and Cretaceous limestones are the commonest rocks involved in the building of the Pre-Alps, and they give rise to fold ranges, rising ridge behind ridge, from the eastern end of lake Constance to Salzburg. Their general elevation is about 6,500 ft., with many peaks rising to over 8,500 ft.

The Bavarian Alps may be divided into three sections. From Lindau, on lake Constance, the Allgäu Alps curve away to the east as far as the Lech valley. This western section of the Pre-Alps lies in Swabia. East of the Lech, the Bavarian Alps begin and they include such magnificent and well-known ranges as the Wetterstein, Karwendel and Berchtesgaden Alps, the latter forming a separate region. East of this district, the Austrian frontier turns northwards from Salzburg, following the Salzach valley to the point where it joins the Inn.

The Pre-Alps, lying in the southern Allgäu, exhibit typical Alpine land forms. They present a series of arcs, trending generally west-east and they are continued across the Austrian frontier in the Vorarlberg and the Lechtaler Alps. The Allgäu Alps comprise the main Calcareous Pre-Alps, the outer Alpine ranges composed of Cretaceous limestones and *Flysch*, and the foothill ridges developed on *Molasse*, a sandstone of Oligocene and Miocene age.

The Allgäu Alps include some attractive mountain scenery; bold, rocky peaks dominating precipitous slopes, divided by deep, narrow valleys, the sides of which are scored by ravines and mantled with rock débris. The ranges rise to narrow crest lines, notched by *cirques* partly filled with rock waste. The main transverse valleys such as the Lech and the Iller are overdeepened by ice, and the side streams, which drop over steep ledges, hang in relation to the main valley. In this part of the Alps, limestones of both Triassic and Jurassic age were involved in the Miocene folding. These relatively resistant rocks form the ribs of the outer Alpine mountain system, while more easily eroded rocks, such as the Lias clays and the Keuper marls, have been preserved in the synclines between the

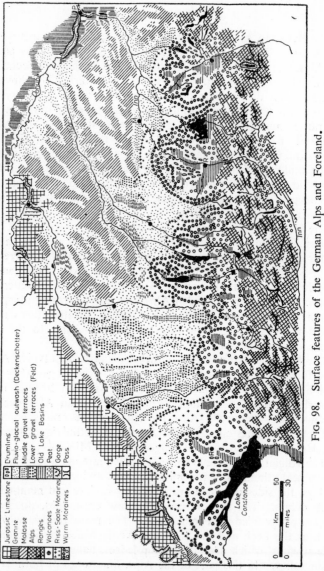

Legend:

Jurassic Limestone
Granite
Molasse
Alps
Ranges
Volcanoes
Riss-Saale Moraines
Würm Moraines

Drumlins
Fluvio-glacial outwash (Deckenschotter)
Middle gravel terraces
Lower gravel terraces (Feld)
Old Lake Basins
Peat
Gorge
Pass

Lake Constance

Km 0 ———— 50
miles 0 ——— 30

FIG. 98. Surface features of the German Alps and Foreland.

folds.   In places the sediments have been thrust forward in super-incumbent or *nappe* fashion.   This feature applies especially to the limestone range which hems in the head of the Iller valley, where the main peaks are the Hochvogel (8,494 ft.) and the Mädele Gabel

(8.815 ft.), along the crest of which runs the boundary between Swabia and Upper Austria. Here the hard dolomitic limestone has weathered into pyramidal-shaped peaks, on the slopes of which much bare, greyish-white limestone is exposed. The highest parts of the range rise above the permanent snow-line (about 8,200 ft.), but there is not a sufficient accumulation of snow for glaciers to remain at this altitude, except where local conditions of shelter and shade have enabled a small one to be preserved on the western side of the Mädele Gabel.

Füssen is the regional centre of the Allgäu Alps. It lies on the left bank of the Lech, at the point where the river leaves its gorge, cut through the outermost Alpine ranges, for the Foreland. Immediately to the south of this small tourist centre, the sheer edge of the limestone Pre-Alps rises to 5,000 ft., attaining 6,715 ft. in the Säuling, nearby peaks forming secondary heights. These continue the frontier eastwards until it zigzags in the direction of the Wetterstein range, east of the Lech valley. The second structural feature of the Allgäu Alps is well represented in this district, where ranges of somewhat lower elevation are developed on Cretaceous rocks, which may be traced from the Swiss frontier through the Bregenzerwald to the west of Oberstdorf, where they form such lofty peaks as the Hohe Ifen (7,316 ft.) and the high, plateau-like country known as Gottesäcker. To the east of the Iller valley, from Sonthofen to Nesselwang on the Vils, the outcrop of the Cretaceous rocks is very narrow, although it forms an outlying ridge to the west of Pfronten on the Vils. To the east, the Cretaceous rocks peter out, to be replaced by the Eocene *Flysch*. This easily weathered, crumbly rock is frequently preserved by faulting and it accounts for the line of flat-topped ridges at the foot of the main Alpine ranges, exemplified by the Hohe Trauchberg (3,471 ft.), east of Füssen.

Low ridges are also developed on the *Nagelfluh* and *Molasse* formations. These conglomerates and sandstones form broken, east–west ridges in the Foreland country, rising to about 3,000 ft., through which the Lech cuts a miniature gorge north of Füssen. Both the Lech and the Vils, a left-bank tributary, exhibit the same alternation of broad, trough-like valleys hemmed in by ridges and steep slopes, in contrast with the gorge sections cut transversely through the limestone ridges, a feature reminiscent of the French Pre-Alps. All these streams have a characteristically Alpine flow and régime, for in spring they are swollen with snow-melt and they flood wide areas, but in summer these torrents shrink to a shallow, braided channel swinging between great banks of shingle and gravel.

The Alps in the vicinity of Füssen are noted for a number of small but beautiful lakes, some of which lie embedded in deep and largely hidden valleys, such as the Alpsee and Schwansee, close to the fantastic castles of Neuschwanstein and Hohenschwangau. Other lakes are held up by morainic ridges along the edge of the Foreland and the rising line of the Alps to the south. These include the Hopfen, Weissen and Bannwald lakes, all of which are in slow process of silting. There is also much peat or *Moos* in the ill-drained hollows.

The Bavarian Alps to the east of the Lech valley continue the features of the Allgäu Alps and they include the tourist centres of Oberammergau, Mittenwald and Garmisch-Partenkirchen. The Pre-Alps attain their greatest altitudes here; only the Inn valley dividing them from the High Alps to the south. The two main ranges are the Wetterstein, culminating in the Zugspitze, and the Karwendel Alps, both of which rise to over 8,000 ft. They are drained northwards by the Ammer, Isar and Inn tributaries of the Danube, and access to the Tyrol is not quite so easy here as in the Allgäu Alps along the trench of the Lech. The main approaches are either from Reutte in the Lech valley or from Garmisch, skirting the Zugspitze, to Leermoos and the Fern pass. This historic routeway links Augsburg and Upper Bavaria with the Tyrol and Innsbruck. There is an alternative route from Scharnitz on the frontier, involving tunnels through the Seefeld pass to the Inn valley, and so along the great terrace to Innsbruck and thence to the Brenner pass and Italy. This is the ' Porta Claudia ' route. The main line from Munich, on the other hand, utilizes the Inn valley from Rosenheim upstream to Kufstein, and this route links southern Germany with northern Italy *via* the Brenner and with Switzerland *via* the upper Inn valley and the Arlberg tunnel.

The Bavarian Alps are notable for their scenic splendour, the sharp form of which is the result partly of geological youth and partly of ice sculpture. Today, only small glaciers occur in the Pre-Alps, notably in *cirques* on the Zugspitze, where, on account of its considerable elevation (9,720 ft.), snow lies longer than elsewhere, and avalanches are common. The peak is a typical arête, knife-like rock ridges radiating from the summit in characteristic fashion, so that from the point of view of form and difficulty of ascent, the peak ranks with those of the High Alps. The Zugspitze is, in fact, the culmination of the Wetterstein range, for everywhere the same rocky precipices are to be found descending to trough-like, overdeepened valleys. Some of the northward opening valleys contain glacial lakes, such as the Kochelsee in the Loisach valley and the Tergensee below the Achen pass. Waterfalls are fairly numerous, and they occur where side streams plunge down into the main valleys. There is a hydro-electric power station below the Walchen-see.

To the north of the main ranges, subsidiary ridges occur in *Flysch*, and this feature extends from the Ammer mountains to Rosenheim in the Inn valley. It then disappears temporarily south of the Chiemsee, but it gives rise to flat-topped foothill country in the neighbourhood of Traunstein further east. A notable feature of this outer zone of the Alps is the formation of basins at the foot of the mountains, usually drift-filled and occupied by well-known Bavarian resorts, such as Oberammergau. This village, which lies in the Ammer valley at the foot of precipitous mountains, has a particularly dramatic setting, in keeping with its association with the Passion Play. Similar sites are Lengries and Bayrischzell.

The last section of the Bavarian Alps to be described is the country around Berchtesgaden, on the border between Bavaria and the Tyrol. The boundary is formed by the Salzach river here, leaving Salzburg to the east. A main road follows the Saalach tributary east of the Stein pass into the Tyrol but the valley in which lies Berchtesgaden allows of no escape southwards, on account of the mountain rim which hems it in at the head. This amphitheatre is crowned by such magnificent mountains as the Watzmann (8,993 ft.) and the Hoher Göll (8,264 ft.). These are formed mainly in dolomitic limestone, and they were intensely glaciated. At the foot lies the long, finger lake of Königssee, held up by moraines. Precipitous rocky slopes which descend almost to the edge of the lake exhibit the steeply dipping limestone of which they are composed. The lower slopes are partly covered by scree, weathered from the bare face of the rock by frost action. In places, torrents cascade into the main valley, and down these forbidding slopes avalanches are apt to descend from the Eiskapelle snowfield on the Watzmann.

There are not many arêtes or *cirques* in this district, but bare limestone slopes and rocky basins are very characteristic. The flats, which in the Allgäu carry the *Almen* or summer mountain pastures, are also absent from this district. Much of the country remains under forest. The feature which first attracted settlement to this region was the existence of salt in the Triassic rocks, especially at Reichenhall in the Saalach valley and at Traunstein, and again in the Inn valley at Rosenheim. The mining of rock salt, associated especially with the town of Salzburg, led to the development of traffic in salt from Celto-Roman times onwards and to the construction of the so-called ' salt ' roads over the Alps.

THE BAVARIAN FORELAND

The Bavarian Foreland is a clearly defined triangular region, with its base extending for 200 miles along the foot of the Bavarian Alps. It narrows westwards and crosses the Swiss frontier at lake Constance and extends eastwards into Austria beyond the Inn valley. Its greatest width north–south, measured from Regensburg on the Danube to Rosenheim on the Inn, is 80 miles, while in the west it shrinks to less than 40 miles, between the Swabian Alb and lake Constance. In the north the Danube forms a clear limit, except where the limestones of the Alb cross to the southern side of the river, as between Tuttlingen and Sigmaringen, Kelheim and Regensburg. Below Regensburg the Danube is incised into the crystalline rocks of the Bohemian block, and, between Vilshofen and Passau, on the Austrian frontier, these resistant rocks give rise to rapids in the course of the river, which here follows an epigenetic course.

The Bavarian Foreland is a great geosynclinal depression between the folded and uplifted Alps and the resistant Hercynian massifs of the Black Forest and Bohemia. The rocks of the Foreland are all Oligocene-Miocene or Recent deposits, the oldest formations lying on the margins and the youngest in the centre; the Tertiary sands, clays and marls being laid down on the floor of the Pliocene Sea which extended from the Pannonic basin westwards into the present upper Danube valley. *Molasse*, derived from the Alps, was locally compacted into a sandstone, and, on account of its relative resistance, it now forms upstanding, whale-backed ridges in the southern part of the Foreland, as described elsewhere. *Nagelfluh*, so-called because it contains nail-like pebbles, also gives rise to local ridges. Otherwise the varied surface of the Foreland results from the deposition of glacial drift, brought by the Würm ice from the Alps. Melt-water from these glaciers reached as far as the line of the Danube in the north and the Rhine and lake Constance in the west. In consequence, the surface features and soil pattern of the Foreland may best be described in relation to the deposition of the drift.

During the last or Würm glacial period, valley glaciers extended from the Alps for varying distances over the Foreland (Fig. 98), leaving outwash material piled up at the end and along the sides of the retreating glacier, forming the great morainic ridges which today characterize the Foreland. In the west, these occur in a series of festoons around lake Constance, where the glacial drift has to a large extent determined the configuration of the lake. Here the over-deepening of the Rhine valley was carried out by the ice in a region of structural weakness, fractures running parallel to the arms of the lake.   Drumlin ridges also abound to the north of the lake and are responsible for much marsh and ill-drained country.   In the All-gäu Foreland, the moraines trend generally parallel with the line of the Alps, the glaciers having been less extensive here than to the west and east, on account of the smaller snowfields in this part of the Alps.   East of the Lech, the great valley glaciers of Bavaria spread over the Isar section of the Foreland.   Moraines lie parallel to the Lech, where they form ridges 300 ft. to 450 ft. high which encircle the Würm and Ammer lakes to the north.   Here no less than four glaciers coalesced on descending from the highest part of the Bavarian Alps (the Wetterstein and Karwendel Ranges).   Similarly, to the east, glaciers converged from the Mangfall and Berchtesgaden Alps in the neighbourhood of the Chiemsee.   This belt of moraines continues eastwards as far as the Salzach valley on the Austrian frontier.   These morainic ridges form some of the best drained country of the Foreland.   Their slopes are frequently cut into terraces which provide suitable sites for settlement.   Between the moraines the land is usually flat and ill-drained, with much boulder clay and drumlins.   Peat bogs, marshes and lakes abound.   Along the southern edge of the Alpine Foreland, most of the lakes are held up by moraines and in the vicinity of these peat bogs occur, marking the former extent of the lake, for example the Murnau Moos, a large swamp.   Scattered widely over the Foreland are erratic boulders carried from the Alps by the action of ice or melt-water.

In front of the moraines, gravelly and sandy outwash material (*Deckenschotter*) was spread over the Foreland by the streams fed by the melting glaciers.   The drift was laid down in fairly thick sheets, giving rise to plateau features such as those between the Iller and the Lech.   This plateau slopes from 2,500 ft. in the south to 1,400 ft. in the north.   Elsewhere these gravels occur at lower levels, forming local plains, such as that of which Munich is the centre. Gravel terraces also fringe the main river valleys above the wide band of alluvium which represents the flood stage of the river when swollen by glacial melt-water.   These alluvial strips sometimes contain only a minor stream, but there are widespread tracts of marsh and peat bog on either side.   One such notorious marsh is the *Dachau Moos* to the north-west of Munich.

In addition to the deposits laid down by the action of ice and running water, there are also important areas of loess.   This light, porous, sandy material is partly inter-glacial and partly a periglacial wind-borne deposit.   It occurs to the north of the main belt of moraines and is especially important adjacent to the Danube.   It

also forms a capping on some of the older moraines.   Loess weathers
into the best soil of the Foreland, especially where it combines with
clay to form a rich, easily worked loam.   One such region occurs
to the north-east of the Danube, at the foot of the Bavarian Forest,
where the loess gives rise to a strip of open country between Strau-
bing and Vilshofen, known as the Dungau.   The greater proportion
of land under strip cultivation near the Danube, in contrast with

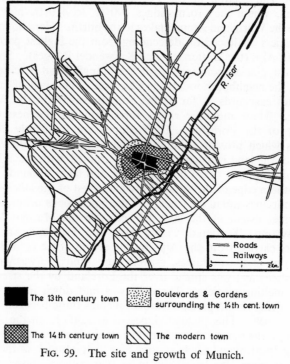

FIG. 99.   The site and growth of Munich.

the predominately pastoral Foreland in the vicinity of the Alps,
may be explained by this difference in soils; the heavy, ill-drained
glacial soils being unsuitable for the plough.

In the triangle between lake Constance, the Rhine and the Danube
lies the Hegau, a line of isolated volcanic hills.   Like other eruptive
features in southern Germany, they appeared during the Miocene
upheaval.   Their steep slopes and cone-like form make a sharp
contrast with the flat, cultivated land at their foot.   The soils
weathered from these basalts are very productive, since they are

mingled with the drift of the Foreland. The highest point is the Hohenstoffeln (2,775 ft.).

A notable feature of the Foreland is that the course of the Danube, which is its real axis, lies along the northern margin. It drops steadily from an altitude of 1,850 ft. at Scheer, where it leaves the limestone country of the Alb, to 900 ft. at Passau, on the frontier, over a distance of over 200 miles. It is navigable for 500-ton barges below Ulm. From the Alps come its longest tributaries, the Iller, Lech, Isar and Inn. These are all swift-flowing streams, of irregular volume and flow, the period of greatest depth and velocity being in early summer (June) when the rate of snow-melt in the High Alps is the swiftest. They are chiefly used for log floating, for example the Lech. In Swabia, the Iller and Lech drain directly south–north across the Foreland to join the Danube at Ulm and below Donauwörth respectively. The Isar and the Inn cross the Foreland diagonally, collecting a number of tributaries as they flow north-east towards the main river. The Inn, which forms the frontier divide, joins the Danube at Passau. Various factors contribute to the flooding of the upper Danube and not least in importance is the irregular volume of the Alpine tributaries. These streams come down in spate after the spring thaw and so augment the early summer floods of the Foreland. The wide tracts of marsh and the strips of alluvial water-meadow which border the Danube and also its left-bank tributaries bear this out. Between Ulm and Donauwörth there is a strip of marsh known as the Donau Ried, now partly drained and reclaimed, and at Ingolstadt, lower down the valley, lies the Donau Moos, another region of poor surface drainage. In the south-west of the Foreland a region which formerly drained to the Danube now contributes to the Rhine, while in the neighbourhood of lake Constance there is much evidence of reversed flow towards the lake on the northern side. It has also been proved that a certain amount of water filters through from the Danube to the Rhine by means of subterranean fissures in the limestone, notably between Tuttlingen and Aach.

THE SWABIAN AND FRANCONIAN ALB AND THE BASIN OF THE RIES[1]

The Jurassic scarplands of southern Germany form a crescentic belt of plateau country, dividing the Neckar and Main drainage from that of the Danube. This region of the Alb extends from the Rhine falls at Schaffhausen in the south-west, where it is continued across the Rhine in the Plateau Jura of Switzerland, to the upper

[1] C. Scherzer and others: *Franken*, 1955.

Main valley in the north-east. It may be divided into the Swabian Alb, stretching from south-west to north-east for a distance of 125 miles from the Swiss frontier to the Nördlingen ' gate '; and the

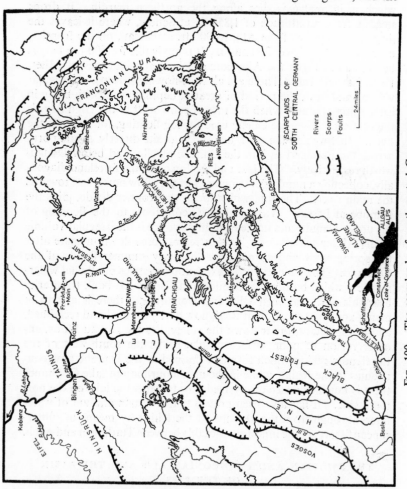

Fig. 100. The scarplands of south-central Germany.

Franconian Alb, an eastern and northern continuation of the scarp-land, covering a distance of 100 miles. Marking the break between the two is the historic Nördlingen ' gate ', corresponding to the tectonic basin of the Ries with its low volcanic hills, through which once passed the Roman *limes Germaniæ*, built from the Main to the Danube.

This predominantly limestone country presents a steep but fretted scarp edge to the north-west and west, overlooking the basins of the Neckar and the Regnitz, a headstream of the Main (Fig. 100). In contrast, the south-eastern slope towards the Danube valley is much more gentle and appears as a dissected plateau, with a general altitude of 950–1,300 ft. and a width of 18–25 miles. The highest points naturally occur near the crest of the scarp. The Swabian Alb attains its greatest altitude in the south (Lemberg, 3,330 ft.); while there is a broadening of the plateau as it swings northward, and the maximum altitudes in the Franconian Alb are much lower (Hahnen Kamm, 1,808 ft.). This is generally open, windswept country, lacking surface water. The soils, weathered from marl and limestone (the *Malm*), are stony, and the climate is cold and raw; hence its unattractiveness to settlement and the aptness of the name, *Rauhe Alb*.

The fact that this diagonal scarpland belt forms part of a continental water-parting rather than the higher Primary massifs to east and west calls for brief explanation. Whereas the greater part of the drainage is down the scarp slope of the Alb to the Neckar and the upper Main, comparatively few streams cross the limestone plateau or rise on the dip slope to drain to the Danube. This river has fought a losing battle with the Rhine since the foundering of the Rhine trough and the development of the rift valley. Today the Danube flows at a higher level than the Neckar and Main tributaries of the Rhine, and much water has been lost to the Black Sea in favour of the North Sea. This process of river capture may be traced from the eastern slope of the Black Forest, where the Eschach headstream of the Neckar has been deflected northwards, leaving the Brege and Brigach to flow eastwards as the sources of the Danube. No important left-bank tributary joins the Danube from the Swabian Jura. The first gap occurs where the Wörnitz breaks through the scarpland in the Ries basin (Nördlingen Gate), forming the main line of approach from the Main to the Danube valley. The Altmühl also rises to the north of the limestone scarp and winds its way eastwards towards the Danube. Along the eastern edge of the Franconian Jura, the Laber, Vils, and Naab flow towards the Danube; converging in the narrow depression which lies between the scarpland of Franconia and the Bavarian Forest.

The soils of these limestone cuestas are of the brown earth type. They are highly calcareous and, where the humus content is very high, they are almost black. Loess covers wide tracts of country, often extending up to 3,000 ft., and, in these districts, tractable loamy soils result, suitable for arable farming on the lower slopes.

The thin soils of the scarp face are mainly under forest, in contrast with the open plateau above, where peat has accumulated locally. This is a region of ' steppe-heath ' (*Steppenheide*),[1] inviting pre-historic settlement on account of its relative freedom from forest, but today it is sparsely populated, averaging only about 150 people to the square mile.

The Swabian Jura

From the Swiss Rhine at Schaffhausen to the Ries basin, a distance of 125 miles, the Swabian Jura or Alb extend in a broad sweep from south-west to north-east.[2]   The uplands present a sinuous but steep and rugged scarp slope to the north-west, and a long, gentle dip slope to the Danube which flows along the base of the limestone. The scarp edge rises in general to over 1,650 ft., forming a series of bastions dominating the Neckar basin to the west (Fig. 100).   The surface of the scarpland is tabular but it is broken by a number of narrow, deep-cut valleys.   There are no surface streams on the plateau top, but springs break out at the junction of the Dogger and Lias formations at the base of the scarp, and, less regularly, on the dip slope.   The shales and sandstone of the Dogger or ' Brown Jura ' are associated with iron-o re-bearing beds and vary in thick-ness from 200 ft. to 400 ft.   The middle and upper slopes of the scarp are formed of massive white dolomitic limestone, with inter-bedded clays and marls, and they form the ' White Jura ' or *Malm*. These beds give rise to local cliff features, as in the epigenetic section of the Danube gorge between Tuttlingen and Sigmaringen, hence the term *Riffkalke*.   Because of its porous character, the *Malm* acts as a sponge, so that there is an absence of surface drainage, water making its way along subterranean channels.   In consequence, karst scenery appears, streams disappear from the surface and plunge down into swallow-holes.   These features occur notably in the bed of the Danube at Immendingen, where, especially during a dry summer, the Danube shrinks in volume, and water percolates through the river gravels into the limestone, so seeping through to the Rhine. Farms derive their water supply largely from roof tanks, otherwise settlements are located in the scarp foot zone along the spring line, at the junction of the Dogger sandstones and shales and the Lias clay.   Other settlements are scattered over the south-eastern slope, with a preference for the point in the valley where a perennial stream begins.

An extraneous feature of this limestone country is the occurrence of volcanic rocks, as in the Hegau.   A number of small volcanic

[1] R. Gradmann: *Süddeutschland*, Vol. 1, 1931, p. 65.

[2] T. H. Elkins and E. M. Yates: ' The South German karplands in the vicinity of Tübinger ', *Geography*, Vol. 48, 1963.

outbursts also occur within the Swabian Jura, 'volcanoes in embryo ', which give rise to local eminences, such as the Römerstein (2,867 ft.). These conical hills are formed of either tuff or basalt, but they die out north-east of the Ries. The Alb is, in consequence, somewhat varied in its relief, and erosion has further emphasized this feature. Deep gorges dissecting the scarp have left steep, conical hills dominating the crest line and sometimes wrapped in mist and cloud. Some exceed 3,000 ft., thus providing dominating sites for castles, notably the Hohenzollern Hörnle (2,808 ft.), south of Tübingen. The plateau is cut into separate blocks by deep but often dry valleys, which facilitate penetration. Bare rock seldom outcrops, and much of the exposed north-western slope remains forested. The windswept plateau forms desolate country devoid of running water, in contrast with the more tractable land found on the dip slope. Here, the Pliocene covering of clays, sands and marls is partly preserved, and the soils are also enriched by lime washed down from the higher slopes. The gentle gradients and loamy soils, amenable to the plough, have favoured arable land in contrast with the upland pasture of the High Alb.

The Ries

The basin of the Ries is a polygonal depression, 12 to 15 miles wide, breaking the continuity of the Alb scarpland, and draining southwards to the Danube. It is associated especially with the Nördlingen ' gate ', the walled town of that name lying to the south-west of the basin, where routes from Mannheim, Frankfurt and Würzburg to Augsburg and Munich converge. The Ries owes its existence to volcanic activity, a number of explosive vents occurring within the basin. Granite and Tertiary limestones occur around the rim, while the centre consists of drift (loess and alluvium) overlying Keuper and Jurassic rocks. Hot springs break out on the margin of the basin which is bordered by fault scarps. These steep slopes remain fairly thickly wooded and contrast sharply with the undulating floor of the basin, which is intensely cultivated. The soils, weathered from such a variety of rocks and drift, are very productive, and the density of rural population is much higher than on the surrounding uplands. Moreover, this Ries basin has played the rôle of a corridor for centuries, hence the growth of such centres as Öttingen and Nördlingen. This gap between the Swabian and Franconian Jura is drained by the Wörnitz, a stream which rises like the Altmühl in the Franconian Heights to the north-west of the Alb, crossing the scarpland in a meandering fashion from Dinkelsbühl to Donauwörth, where it joins the Danube.

The Franconian Jura

North-east of the Ries, the Alb assumes a crescentic form, swing-ing from a south-west to north-east direction to south–north in Upper Franconia. The scarp feature continues as far as the Altmühl gap, then it dies away near the source of the Regnitz, to appear again east of Nürnberg, where great bastions jut out towards the basin of the Regnitz in Middle Franconia, extending as far as Bamberg. Examples of eminences include the Hahnen Kamm (2,122 ft.) in the south, and the isolated crest of the Hessel Berg (2,260 ft.). The Franconian Jura rise to much lower altitudes than their counterpart in Swabia, and they maintain a general alti-tude of only 1,500 ft., rising only occasionally to over 2,000 ft. This is not a typical scarpland on account of the gentle dip of the beds, but it is a broad plateau, broken by faults but devoid of volcanic features, and cut by deep, narrow valleys. Over wide tracts, Pliocene sands and clays are preserved, and, to a considerable extent, the lower slopes are mantled with loess, notably above the Altmühl valley. The upper limit of the loess seems to be about 1,300 ft. At the base of the scarp, the same iron-ore-bearing Dogger beds occur as in the Swabian Jura, the massive dolomitic limestones forming the cliff features of the main escarpment. There is a line of dissected foothills along the base. Where the scarp feature is pronounced, the crest is often covered with forests. The surface of the *Malm* plateau is waterless and the soils are thin and stony, except where the residual patches of Pliocene sand and clay remain. Settlement is concentrated where springs break out at the junction of wooded slopes and the cleared and cultivated valley floor. There are large limestone quarries at Solnhofen, in the Altmühl valley. Here, and also in the Pegnitz valley, subterranean solution has led to the development of underground streams, caves, and grottoes with stalactites.

The Franconian Jura drain almost entirely to the Main *via* the Regnitz, which has been deflected from its original course to the Danube, flowing northwards to join the Main at Bamberg. Only in the south have the Wörnitz and the Altmühl maintained their flow to the Danube; the latter turning eastwards and following a deep-cut and picturesque valley parallel to the Danube, to the point where it is joined by the Main-Danube canal. It eventually joins the mainstream at Kelheim, where the Danube cuts into the limestone which forms steep banks on both sides of the river down to Ratisbon (Regensburg).

THE NECKAR BASIN

The country drained by the Neckar extends from the eastern slope of the Black Forest to the scarp of the Swabian Alb, and from the plateau of the Baar in the south to the Odenwald in the north. The course of the river is remarkable, for it is superimposed upon a variety of Secondary rocks, irrespective of hardness, in a highly meandering fashion. The final course of the Neckar is through the Bunter sandstones of the Odenwald, into which it has cut a deep and narrow gorge, the approach to which is commanded by the castle town of Heidelberg, situated at the point where the river emerges on to the upper Rhine plain. The general character of the Neckar basin is that of scarp and vale country, the beds dipping gently south-eastwards, so that the more resistant, slightly tilted rocks form ridges trending from south-west to north-east, parallel to the Swabian Alb, with a broken but distinct line of scarps facing north-west.

The divide between the Neckar and Danube drainage on the plateau of the Baar, east of the Black Forest, is very narrow, and, with the progressive deepening of the Rhine trough, much water has been diverted from the Danube to the Neckar. The Eschach, flowing south along the eastern slope of the Black Forest before turning north to join the Neckar above Rottweil, provides a striking example of stream capture. This town of Roman origin has an impressive site and lay-out, above the incised meander of the Neckar. From the Swabian Alb a number of streams break through the scarp in deep water gaps *en route* to the Neckar, notably the Kocher and Jägst, both of which rise in the Härtfeld at the north-eastern end of the Swabian Jura. Other tributaries are derived from the northern Black Forest, such as the Nagold and Enz, and these converge on Pforsheim, and below this town the Enz flows eastwards to join the Neckar.

The Baar, Oberes Gau, and the Swabian Keuper Hills

The Neckar rises near the south-western end of the Swabian Jura in the Triassic country of the Baar. This narrow, open corridor region lies between the forested eastern slope of the Black Forest and the rising ground of the Swabian Jura. A narrow clay vale lies at the base of this scarp, where springs break out at the junction of the Dogger and the Lias clay. The highest point in the scarp is reached in the Kleine Heuberg (2,290 ft.). In contrast with the well-watered clay country, the Triassic limestone of the Baar and Upper Gau offers a striking scenic contrast. The *Muschelkalk* landscape is open, the surface dry and the soils stony, so that the land remains largely under pasture. Where, however, there is a superficial covering of loess, rich, loamy soils occur and strip cultivation prevails.

Further variety is introduced into the Neckar region where the Neckar leaves the *Muschelkalk* for the Keuper marls and sandstones. This belt of country widens to the north-east, and the more resistant Keuper sandstone gives rise to local scarp features, known locally as the *Berge*. These hills are thickly forested and contrast with the closely farmed Keuper marl country across which the Neckar drains *en route* from Tübingen to Cannstatt. Damp soils and a high water-table correspond with a region which is primarily devoted to stock rearing. Peat occurs locally but along the banks of the Neckar there are strips of excellent water-meadow, with vineyards and fruit trees above on the well-drained slopes and terraces. Stuttgart, lying in a side valley of the Neckar to the south-east of Canstatt, is the largest and one of the most dynamic cities in southern Germany. Its setting is in an amphitheatre of hills, where springs break out at the base, providing an excellent water supply. Stuttgart is the meeting place of routes from the Rhine valley (Karlsruhe), Frankfurt-am-Main, Nürnberg, Munich and Constance. It marks the break between the Upper and Lower Gau and is today a rapidly growing city of 634,713 people. The post-war development of buildings of steel and concrete have largely replaced the finely laid-out town planned in the 18th century. The pre-war engineering industries have been revived, especially those associated with the firm of Mercedes-Benz, while many new plants have been established by refugees from the East, especially concerned with electrical plant and equipment.

The Plain of Middle Swabia and Hohenloher

The Neckar continues its incised meandering course northwards from Cannstatt to Heilbronn across the Keuper marl country of the Lower Gau. To the west lies the thickly populated region of the Strohgäu, where loess overlying limestone has long favoured agricultural settlement. To the east, the Keuper sandstone scarp of the Löwenstein Berge advances towards the Neckar, its steep slope dominating the winding river. To the west, the Stromberg hills divide the Enz valley from the Kraichgau. Heilbronn, originally a Roman spa, marks the limit of navigation for 500-ton barges on the Neckar, though improvements are projected upstream. The modern chemical industries of the town, based on local salt derived from the Trias as well as on limestone and gypsum, have the advantage of access to a regulated, shortened and canalized waterway. Below Heilbronn, the Keuper hills recede and the river collects its long right-bank tributaries from the Hohenloher plain, namely the Kocher and the Jägst. To the west, the Kraichgau provides an east passageway to the Rhine plain between the Odenwald to the north and the Black Forest to the south.

The Lower Neckar Valley and the Odenwald Gorge

Between the Kraichgau and the Bauland the Neckar has cut a deep and narrow valley in the *Muschelkalk*, varying in depth from 160 to 500 ft., and it continues north-westwards to enter the Bunter sandstone country of the southern Odenwald below Neckarelz. This last section of the Neckar is the most spectacular, for the river has eroded a remarkable epigenetic gorge in the resistant rocks, and, at the same time, has maintained its meandering course. Remnants of terraces provide a route for the road and railway which follow the windings of the river, and also the sites for settlement such as Neckarsteinach. The steepness of the slopes, in contrast with the flatness of the Odenwald plateau above, favours the preservation of forest (the beech predominating), or, alternatively, viticulture and fruit orchards. At the western end of the gorge stands the university town of Heidelberg, with its red sandstone castle dominating the river as it enters its tract across the upper Rhine plain, *en route* for Mannheim. This last stretch of the Neckar, regulated by straightening and deepening, carries a good deal of barge traffic *en route* for Heilbronn and the upper Neckar basin. The landscape is dull and monotonous, the river flowing over a flat alluvial plain, and the gravel terraces are very much eroded. The meadows of the flood-plain extend down to the Rhine at Mannheim, cultivated land being restricted to the higher and better drained terraces. There is no settlement of importance between Heidelberg, the strategic site, and the modern river port of Mannheim (apart from the American N.A.T.O. base of Patrick Henry Town), the countryside assuming a rural aspect. At the great junction of Mannheim, routes strike off across the Rhine bridge to the industrial site of Ludwigshafen and thence to Mainz, Lorraine, and the Saar industrial region.

THE MAIN BASIN

The highlands and plateau which form the framework of the Main valley show marked diversity.[1] To the east lies the

[1] C. Scherzer: *Franken*, 1955, gives a full account of Franconia.

Bohemian massif, with the Fichtel-Gebirge forming the divide between the Main and Danube drainage. From this mountain plexus, the Thuringian highlands strike away to the north-west, but the water parting between the Main and the Weser (*via* its tributary the Werra) lies in the plateau country to the south of this primary massif. Further west, the volcanic masses of the Rhön and Vogelsberg separate the Main basin from the highlands of central Germany, and finally the faulted southern margin of the Taunus block defines the sharp northern limit of the lower Main plain. On the southern side of the basin, the Franconian Jura thrust northwards, deflecting the upper Main into a great bend between Bayreuth and Bamberg. Further west, scarps developed in Triassic formations trend parallel to the Rhine rift valley and are cut across by the Main. The last of these features is represented by the Odenwald-Spessart block, through which the Main turns northwards along the foot of the Spessart scarp before entering the plain of Hesse.

The Main basin may be described according to its regional units. The upper Main valley lies between the Fichtel-Gebirge and the Franconian Jura. Here it receives the Weisser and Roter Main from the Fichtel-Gebirge, streams which rise near the source of the Fichtel and Heide Naab, which flow to the Danube. The two streams unite at Kulmbach and flow through a narrow clay vale eroded in the hill country of Upper Franconia. This section of the valley may be said to end below Bamberg, the limit of barge navigation on the Main-Regnitz. From this point, Ludwig's canal once provided a connection between the Main and the Danube *via* Nürnberg and Regensberg, but today its traffic is negligible.

The middle Main valley lies within the Triassic hill country of the Mainland known as the Bauland, a rich agricultural region. The course of the river is remarkable, for it continues to describe great loops in the form of a broad ' W ', after it has left the Franconian Jura. At first its course lies across Keuper marls at the foot of sandstone escarpments, but, after turning south at Schweinfurt, it cuts down into *Muschelkalk*. The great bend of the river between Schweinfurt, Kitzingen and Würzburg occurs in this resistant formation which characterizes Middle Franconia. At Gemunden, at the central apex of the ' W ', the Main is joined by the Franconian Saale from the north. It then turns south, continuing the direction of its tributary, as it enters the Bunter sandstone country of Lower Franconia. Here it is joined by the Tauber from the south, as the Main turns westwards through its Bunter sandstone defile between the Odenwald and Spessart. The gorge ends at Aschaffenburg, where the Main abuts against the crystalline country of the north-western Spessart. Below this point, the river enters the plain of Rhenish-Hesse, keeping first to the foot of the hills as far as Hanau, where it is joined by the Kinzig, and then swinging westwards past Frankfurt-am-Main to flow into the Rhine opposite Mainz.

The Upper Main Valley and Franconian Heights

The Main has its source in the remote country of the Bavarian Palatinate, bordering Bohemia. On the western slopes of the thickly forested Fichtel-Gebirge, the divide between the Main and Danube drainage is narrow and penetration of the region is not so difficult as the complexity of the physical features would suggest. The upper Main valley, which lies at the base of these highlands and the Franconian Forest, corresponds to a tectonic depression, displaying in its bordering fracture lines a characteristic north-west to south-east Hercynian trend. Apart from narrow bands of Lias clay, the corridor has been etched out mainly in Triassic rocks, notably Keuper marls, but there is much overlying drift. The chief centre of this district is Bayreuth on the White Main, at the northern foot of the Franconian Jura, a town world famous on account of its music festival.

The Middle Franconian Hills (Mainland)

West of the Franconian Jura, the Main traverses a belt of broken and dissected country, developed on Triassic rocks. North and south of the valley below Bamberg, resistant Keuper sandstones give rise to a line of wooded heights, terminating in a north-west-facing escarpment. These Keuper hills are known locally as the Steigerwald south of the Main, where they attain nearly 1,650 ft. (Hohen Landsberg, 1,633 ft.). They are continued northwards in the Hassberg and Coburg hills, which attain similar altitudes. A large number of streams rise on the long, gentle eastern slope of this sandstone scarpland and these flow towards the Regnitz, an important left-bank tributary of the Main, which it joins below Bamberg. This northward-flowing river follows the base of the Franconian Jura, whence it receives the Pegnitz, the willow-bordered stream on the banks of which stands Nürnberg. Fürth is a confluence town and railway junction (Frankfurt–Prague and Vienna). There is much variety of soil in this district, the damp and impervious Lias clays of the Regnitz valley contrasting with the dry and sterile Keuper sandstones east of Nürnberg, with their extensive pine woods. There are also dunes here. The loams and loess soils which occur on the gentle slopes of the Franconian Heights are partly under cultivation, but there remain extensive badly drained tracts, especially north-west of Nürnberg, and the scarps are largely forested, beech and pine predominating. Much water has been drawn off to the Main *via* the Regnitz from the Danube, and only at the southern end of the basin has the Altmühl succeeded in maintaining its southerly flow. Both rivers display a notable development of gravel terraces, in common with the Main, especially between 15 and 40 ft. above the level of the alluvial flood-plain, and other fragments occur at higher levels, though they are less well preserved.

The Lower Franconian Plateau

A short distance below Schweinfurt, the Main has cut down into the *Muschelkalk*. This feature continues below Würzburg, and, because of its resistant character, the Main has incised a flat-floored valley in the limestone, in places 600 ft. deep. The steep slopes are broken by river terraces, marking stages in the Pliocene and Pleistocene erosion of the valley. The sunny, south-facing slopes favour the cultivation of the vine, but the loamy loess soils of the terraces are under strip cultivation. Meadows extend along the stream banks. On the *Muschelkalk* plateau above the Main valley, the waterless nature of the country and the stoniness of the soils result in sparse settlement and a predominance of pastoralism. A local and significant name for this country north of the Main is the Grabfeld, which lies at about 1,200 ft., a height comparable with the sandstone plateau of the Odenwald. Bluffs frequently mark the edge of the *Muschelkalk*, eroded by the Main and its tributaries during the post-Pliocene excavation of the present valley. The remarkable ' elbow ' bend below Kitzingen may be related to the former course of the river southwards, prior to the deflection to the Rhine *via* Würzburg. This town is an important junction, for from it routes lead to Bamberg and the upper Main valley, as well as to Nürnberg and *via* the Uffenheim ' gate ' to Ansbach and the Danube valley, while from the west routes converge from the Rhine valley and also from the lower Main and Neckar. Würzburg, the seat of a medieval bishopric and of the dukes of Franconia, is the centre of a prosperous agricultural region where loess occurs, at the limit of viticulture in central Germany. The castle of Marienburg stands high on a bluff dominating the left bank of the Main and vineyards extend over terraces up the steep slope below the castle walls. A renowned centre of baroque architecture, Würzburg has been spared its magnificent bishop's palace (the *Residenz*) and also, high above the Main on the south bank, ' die Käppele ', a jewel of rococo style. Downstream, the Main receives the Franconian Saale from the north, the direction of which it retains until it again turns westwards, after being joined by the Tauber from the south. In this latter valley is the walled town of Rothenburg, a 'fossilized' medieval settlement of great charm, comparable with Dinkelbühl on the southern side of the Franconian Heights. Unlike Nürnberg, both these centres of medieval gild industries have escaped modern industrialism and, on account of their relative inaccessibility, albeit on the *Romantische Strasse*, they have retained their late medieval character and both are artistic gems.

The Spessart-Odenwald Gorge

The great loop described by the Main as it divides the two Hercynian massifs of Lower Franconia and Rhenish-Hesse occurs in a deep defile cut in the Triassic sandstone. This epigenetic gorge provides a routeway of only secondary importance, on account of the devious course of the river, though the valley is thickly settled. The terraces above the narrow flood-plain provide the sites for village settlement and are either under strip cultivation or fruit orchards. The steep, well-drained and sunny slopes are frequently terraced for the vine. Aschaffenburg marks the end of the highland section of the Main, where the chief route eastwards from the central Rhine valley strikes off across the Spessart.

The Lower Main Plain

This lowland embayment represents an extension of Rhenish-Hesse, east of the Rhine rift valley. To the north, the eroded fault scarp of the Taunus rises steeply from the terraced plain of the Rheingau. In this thickly populated region, the *Weinstrasse* offers analogies with the *Bergstrasse* of the Odenwald margin. Loam soils, derived largely from loess deposits, provide the basis of intensive arable farming and there is also some black earth here. Fruit orchards are numerous and the vineyards on the lower slopes of the Taunus are well known. At their foot lies the industrialized village of Rüsselsheim, the site of the Opel car factory, and nearby is Höchst, with its long established chemical plant and dye works. The city of Frankfurt-am-Main serves to integrate the life of the region. Here the sandstone Gothic cathedral dominates the new flats along the waterfront by the Main and nearby the restored Renaissance houses of the Römer, with their stepped gables, persist amidst the new concrete blocks, shops and business houses. Frankfurt remains a city of commerce, banking and industry, and it is also a river port and bridge town on the Main. It is linked by

Autobahn with Kassel, through the corridor of the Wetterau, and also with Mannheim and southern Germany.

THE HIGHLANDS OF EASTERN BAVARIA AND THE BAVARIAN PALATINATE

The north-eastern highland rim of Bavaria forms the historical frontier with western Bohemia and the whole region really belongs to the *Mittelgebirge* of central Europe. The section of the Hercynian massif which comprises Bohemia is represented in western Germany by the Bavarian and Bohemian Forests, the Forest of the Upper Palatinate (*Oberpfalz*), the Fir (*Fichtel*) Mountains and the Franconian Forest (*der Wald*). The greatest altitudes occur in the south in the Böhmerwald, where the great forested range extends from north-west to south-east for over 60 miles from the Cham-Fürth gap to the Austrian frontier. Parallel to it lies the Bayrischerwald, rather lower in altitude but forming part of a double rampart between Bavaria and Bohemia. North of the Regen valley, the Bohemian Forest continues towards the Fichtel-Gebirge for another 70 miles; the Palatinate Forest forming another subsidiary range. To the north-west, the Franconian Forest strikes away from the complex massif of the Fichtel-Gebirge but the divide between the two is not very clear.

The Bohemian, Bavarian and Palatinate Forests

These highlands are alike in structure, land forms and scenery. They are fractured and tilted blocks, trending north-west–south-east, strongly dissected and consisting mainly of crystalline rocks. The Bavarian Forest presents a steep scarp edge towards the Danube, which flows along its base through the Dungau, while the ancient frontier of Bohemia follows the water parting along the Böhmerwald. The Bavarian Forest attains a general altitude of 3,000 ft., and it dominates the Danube valley from Passau on the Austrian frontier, where the gneissic rocks cross the Danube, almost to Regensburg. The Bohemian Forest rises in general to over 4,000 ft., with the Arber Mountain (4,780 ft.) as the culminating point on the frontier. On the rounded summit of this mountain, the forest gives way to open moorland, as on the highest and most exposed slopes of the Black Forest; elsewhere there is an almost continuous forest cover. A number of small glacial lakes occur, hidden within the forest at levels varying from 3,000 to 3,500 ft., for the highest parts of these highlands experienced local Pleistocene glaciation. As is so characteristic of the Hercynian highlands of central Europe, the sky line is broken by a confusion of rounded summits, developed on granite and gneissic rocks and cut by a number of minor valleys and gorges. A narrow strip of more easily eroded mica schists outcrops between the Bohemian and Bavarian Forests, marking an ancient line of fracture, and these rocks underlie the upper Cham basin. This stream, a tributary of the Regen (which it joins at Cham), forms the only main break in the highland barrier throughout its extent of 130 miles; hence the significance of the Fürth gap, comparable to that of the Ohře (Eger) at the northern end of the range.

The granitic bosses of the Bavarian Forest are continued north of the Regen valley in the Upper Palatinate Forest. This broken, crystalline country presents the appearance of an undulating plateau, largely forested, except where the timber has been cleared for pasture and cultivation in the valleys and depressions. This is a region of much more mild relief than the Bohemian Forest and seldom exceeds 3,000 ft. A number of basins occur at about 1,500 ft., often ill-drained, with numerous ponds. These regions form foci of rural settlement, and there is some local utilization of kaolin, as the basis of a pottery industry. The chief centres of population lie, however, along the junction of the crystalline highlands and the Jurassic scarplands, notably Bayreuth in the northern Palatinate, already described in connection with the Main valley, and Amberg, in the south. A main north–south route leads from the Fichtel-Gebirge along the Naab and lower Regen valleys to Regensburg (Ratisbon) and the Danube, and so into Austria.

The Fichtel-Gebirge and Franconian Forest

This complex Hercynian country forms part of a physiographic divide between southern and central Germany. The Fichtel-Gebirge massif throws off drainage southwards *via* the Naab to the Danube, westwards *via* the Red and White Main to the Rhine, and northwards *via* the Saale to the Elbe basin. Its greatest heights are in the west and south-west (Schneeberg, 3,455 ft. ; Ochsenkopf, 3,360 ft.). The core of the massif is formed by gneiss and granite, with Cambrian slates to north and south. The block was folded in Carbo-Permian times along both north-west–south-east and north-east–south-west lines, and subsequently worn down prior to re-uplift and block faulting during Miocene times. The Fichtel-Gebirge appear to have been glaciated above 1,500 ft., and rock basin lakes occur in the granitic country. Bare rock is exposed on the steep, rugged slopes, but much of the region is covered with fir forests, as its name suggests, and there has been rather a limited amount of clearance for pasture and cultivation, on account of the remoteness of the region and its negative attraction to settlement. This broken highland country occupies an important position in relation to approaches from the Main basin to western Bohemia, and it is threaded by several routes converging on Cheb (Eger) across the Bohemian frontier. The main line from Nürnberg to Prague winds its way through the Fichtel-Gebirge from south-west to north-east making for Cheb, where it meets the Danube-Naab route. From the north, two lines penetrate into this difficult forested highland, diverging south of Hof to the Naab valley and to Aš (Asch), a frontier station in Bohemia.

North-west of the Fichtel-Gebirge, the Franconian Forest continues the highland border of the Main basin towards the Thuringian Forest (Münchberg massif), where it rises to an altitude of 2,258 ft. This Hercynian ridge, with its characteristic north-west to south-east trend, has been fractured along its south-western edge, and presents a steep slope to the upper Main valley. From Würzburg, the line from the Main valley enters the Franconian Forest at Kulmbach, *en route* for Hof, and so northwards to Leipzig.

CHAPTER 14

WESTERN GERMANY: THE RHINELAND

WESTERN GERMANY is in essence the German part of the Rhine basin. Only the swift Alpine section of the upper Rhine and the broad, navigable waterway of the Dutch Rijn and its distributaries, the Waal and the Lek, lie outside the German Federal Republic. The Rhine is the most important waterway of Europe, linking land-locked Switzerland through the port of Basle with the North Sea and the Dutch ports, notably Rotterdam. In its lower reaches it also serves the greatest centre of coal-mining and heavy industry on the Continent, *viz.* the Ruhr-Westphalian region, the post-war recovery of which has been remarkable. The Rhine valley provides the easiest routeway from Alpine Europe to the North German lowland, hence its significance in relation to national and international rail and road routes, including the modern *Autobahnen.* Express rail services, such as that of the *Trans-Europa* express *Rheingold,* provide excellent connections between Rotterdam, Cologne, Mainz and Basle, with extensions southwards to Zürich, Milan and Rome. The Rhine valley is also crossed by highly important routes, such as that between Mainz, Frankfurt, Würzburg, Nürnberg and Vienna, while the northern branch of the pre-war Orient Express line from Paris *via* Strasbourg crosses the Rhine at Kehl *en route* to Karlsruhe, Munich and Vienna, with main-line connections with Prague, Buda Pesth, Belgrade and Istanbul. A third international service operates between Brussels, Aachen and Cologne, continuing *via* Düsseldorf to the Ruhr and also to Berlin and Hamburg.

The Rhine is, therefore, the great unifying feature of the German Federal Republic, although its source lies over 200 miles inside Switzerland and its deltaic mouth in the Netherlands. Together with its great tributaries, the Main, Neckar, Mosel and Meuse (Dutch Maas), the Rhine drains a wide variety of regions, such as the Neckar and Main basins, some of which are dealt with in another chapter. Only the lower Mosel below the Saar confluence falls within western Germany, while the Dutch Maas flows entirely outside the German frontier. In this chapter, the part of the Rhine basin to be described is that which extends from the Swiss frontier to the Netherlands, including the marginal Hercynian highlands and

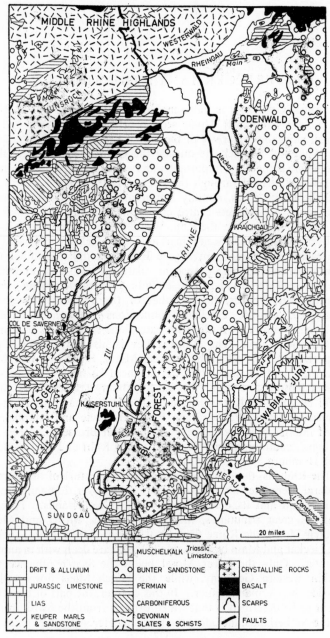

FIG. 101.   The structure of south-west Germany.

THE BLACK FOREST
(SCHWARZWALD)

(a) Summit of the Feldberg (4,905 ft.) in summer.

(b) Forested slopes of the Feldberg with settlement in forest clearing.

(c) Eastern 'dip slope' of the Black Forest from the Feldberg, with the Feldsee in foreground.

(a) Freiburg-im-Breisgau, in embayment at the foot of the Black Forest.

24. THE RHINE RIFT VALLEY

(b) The upper Rhine plain from the Münstertal in the Black Forest.

(c) The Rhine flood plain with *Auenwald* (poplar, alder and swamp vegetation) near Breisach.

their connecting saddles, depressions and valleys. Considered regionally, western Germany may be considered as follows: the upper Rhine plain with its bordering mountains, the middle Rhine highlands with their gorges and flanking coalfields of the Saar[1] and the Ruhr, and the lower Rhine plain below the Cologne ' bay ' and the Ville lignite field.

The upper Rhine plain or rift valley extends for some 200 miles between Basle and Mainz. The trench has an average width of 20 miles and is sharply delimited by the marginal Hercynian highlands, whose faulted edges rise steeply on both sides, though in a broken ascent. These Palæozoic massifs occur symmetrically, the Vosges having their counterpart in the Black Forest (*Schwarzwald*), while the Hardt are offset by the Odenwald-Spessart block. Transverse depressions separate these highlands, notably the Saverne ' gap ', which provides a devious route to Lorraine across the Low Vosges; while the Pforzheim ' gate ', a little to the north of the Black Forest, provides a major routeway through the Kraichgau to Stuttgart and the upper Danube valley. The Neckar offers an alternative route from the Rhine valley at Mannheim following the gorge from Heidelberg through the southern Odenwald towards Würzburg and also to Stuttgart in the upper Neckar valley. Another line of diagonal routes follows the southern base of the Rhine Slate Plateau, linking the Lorraine ironfield through the ' gate ' of Kaiserslautern and the Saar-Nahe hill country with the Rhine at Mainz. Here the line crosses the Rhine to Darmstadt and so to Frankfurt-am-Main. Aschaffenburg is situated on the Main where it cuts through the Spessart, at the junction of routes from Mannheim, Frankfurt and Nürnberg, and, from this point, railways and roads strike away eastwards to the middle Main valley at Würzburg and to the upper Main and to Nürnberg in the Regnitz valley.

The middle Rhine highlands form an irregular block across the Rhine valley between Bingen and Bonn and here the river has cut a post-Pliocene epigenetic gorge extending from south-east to north-west for a distance of over 80 miles. The resistant slates which form the greater part of these highlands are also trenched diagonally by the Mosel and Lahn tributaries of the Rhine, and again by the right-bank tributaries of the Sieg and the Wupper. The plateau is divided therefore into separate blocks of highland, forming asymmetrical massifs, like the Vosges and the Black Forest from which, however, they differ structurally. The Hunsrück in the south-west has its counterpart in the Taunus in the south-east ; the

---

[1] Under the agreement signed between France and Germany in June, 1956, the Saar district became German territory on 1 January, 1957.

C.E.—M

Eifel, divided from the Hunsrück by the gorge of the Mosel, has affinities with the Westerwald, for volcanic rocks outcrop on both sides of the Rhine gorge, notably in the Vor-Eifel and in the Siebengebirge. The Eifel has its continuation in the Belgian Ardenne massif, and the Westerwald, together with the Rothaar-Gebirge, are linked with the Siegerland and Sauerland and also with the uplands of the *Mittelgebirge*. At the foot of these massifs, folded in Carbo-Permian times, the coal measures have been preserved in synclinal basins. A minor field is worked near Aachen at the base of the Ardenne, and is a structural continuation of the Sambre-Meuse coalfield of Belgium, while the largest single coalfield in western Europe, namely the Ruhr, lies along the Ruhr, Emscher and Lippe valleys. The main routes through this vital but difficult region are on each side of the Rhine gorge. The Mosel and Lahn valleys are of minor importance as routeways, especially when compared with the more direct alternative thoroughfares skirting the base of the highlands. These include the main line from Brussels or Paris through Aachen to Cologne and so across the Rhine bridge to Düsseldorf, the Ruhr, Hanover and Berlin. An alternative route between the Rhine valley and northern Germany runs from Mainz through Frankfurt-am-Main, thence through the Fulda or Wetterau depressions to Kassel and so to Hanover. Minor routes cross the middle Rhine highlands diagonally, for example from Trier to Cologne, following the Roman road from *Augusta Treverorum* over the Eifel to *Colonia Agrippina*; while others thread their way up the Sieg and Wupper valleys to the Ruhr. There is also a line which links the upper Sieg and Lahn valleys through Giessen to Frankfurt.

The last division of western Germany is the lower Rhine plain between the middle Rhine highlands and the delta region of the Netherlands. In this flat, rather featureless region, the Rhine receives the Ruhr, Emscher and Lippe right-bank tributaries which flow through the Ruhr-Westphalian coalfield. South of this industrial region, the plain forms a re-entrant in the middle Rhine highlands known as the Cologne 'bay'. This feature extends from the end of the gorge at Bonn to Düsseldorf and below this point the plain of Westphalia extends to the east of the Rhine. To the west of the Rhine and parallel with it rises the faulted Oligocene-Miocene ridge of the Ville, the main scene of lignite working in the German Federal Republic, though brown coal is now also obtained in the Roer valley at Düren, halfway between Aachen and Cologne. Towards the Dutch frontier, the countryside provides little of scenic interest, except for the appearance of glacial drift

derived from the Riss-Saale ice sheet and the development of Pliocene
and Pleistocene river terraces. Below Wesel, the Rhine swings
westwards and finally crosses the Dutch frontier between Emmerich
and Nijmegen.

THE UPPER RHINE PLAIN OR RIFT VALLEY

The Rhine valley from Basle to Mainz is one of the most striking
features on the map of west-central Europe, especially on account
of its flat and monotonous relief compared with the highlands which
border it on both sides. The trench extends from the Sundgau,
at the foot of the Plateau Jura, to the gorge section at Bingen,
covering a distance of 186 miles, and it maintains a continuous
width of between 20 and 30 miles. The distance from south to
north through the valley is equal to that from Basle to Milan or
to Lyon. The outer limit of the rift valley is clearly defined by fault
line scarps which strike south-south-west to north-north-east, parallel
to the trend of the bordering highlands, and these faults are continued
beyond the limit of the Rhine plain in the depression of the Wetterau,
north-east of Frankfurt. Locally, where a series of fractures occurs,
the straight edge of the valley is broken, for example in the Freiburg
and Saverne embayments, in the Lemberg rift and in the Kraichgau
depression. The foothills which mark the change from the drift-
covered plain to the faulted edge of the highlands also occur rather
irregularly along the edge of the valley both in Baden and Alsace
as well as in the Rhenish Palatinate and Rhenish Hesse.

This section of the Rhine basin may be described as a rift valley
on account of its origin; or as the upper Rhine plain on account
of its position and broad physical character; or, perhaps, as the upper
Rhine lowland, on account of diversified relief within the region.
A geological map of the valley showing the drift deposits overlying
the Tertiaries and older rocks makes a division into sub-regions clear.
These are the foothill belt, the ' bays ', and the marginal depressions.
There is the isolated massif of the Kaiserstuhl, north-west of Freiburg, and at the upper end of the valley lies the region of the Sundgau,
on the Franco-Swiss frontier. Parallel to the Rhine and the marginal
highlands is the main Pleistocene terrace of the rift valley, known
as the *Hauptterrasse*, rather wider on the Alsatian than the German
side of the Rhine, though here it is dissected by the Ill. The zone
of terraces ends abruptly against the flood-plain of the Rhine, which
marks the main axis of the valley, though the river is not always
centrally placed. The present channel of the Rhine is entirely
artificial, as the result of the straightening and regulation of the

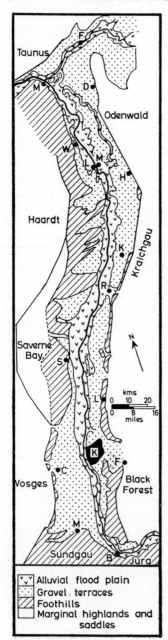

Alluvial flood plain
Gravel terraces
Foothills
Marginal highlands and saddles

river carried out for the improvement of navigation in the 19th century, when the numerous meanders were cut through (Fig. 103). Today these artificially abandoned meanders survive as backwaters.

The steep and broken descent from the highlands through the foothills results from the fracturing and foundering of the rift valley in Oligocene-Miocene times. From the base of the foothills on the west to the margin of those on the east, faults which underlie the centre of the valley are buried beneath the covering of fluvioglacial and alluvial deposits. Consequently, in spite of its sub-surface features, the upper Rhine plain appears strikingly flat. On the margin, the foothills and terrace fragments provide variety, especially the Markgräfler hills of the Breisgau, the foothills of the Black Forest around the Freiburg embayment, and the basalt mass of the Kaiserstuhl. North of the Kraichgau depression, the *Bergstrasse* forms a notable strip of thickly settled agricultural and fruit-farming country at the base of the Odenwald, but foothills are absent east of the Rhine, though they are a conspicuous feature where the Hardt mountains descend by a series of steep fault scarps to the Rhine. Many of these structural terraces are fragments of Jurassic limestone, forming flat-topped features cut through by V-shaped valleys, especially those open-

FIG. 102. Surface features of the Rhine rift valley.

ing from the Black Forest on to the Rhine plain. The Markgräfler hills south of Freiburg rise generally to 1,250 ft., but the
Schönberg, an isolated fault block, attains 2,112 ft. Between
Freiburg and Breisach, the fault-bounded block of the Tuniberg
rises abruptly from the plain and, like most of these loess-covered
limestone hills, is terraced for the vine.

The Kaiserstuhl provides a distinctive feature to the north
of the former fortress site of Breisach, where basalt reaches to

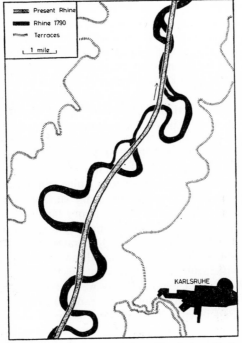

FIG. 103. The flood-plain of the Rhine below Karlsruhe.

the Rhine.[1] This volcanic mass compares with the denuded Tertiary
basalts of the Vogelsberg and the Hegau.   The core of the Kaiserstuhl reaches 1,827 ft. but the volcanic rocks seldom appear at
the surface as the result of the widespread covering of loess, which
serves to smooth surface irregularities, though the loess itself forms
cliff-like features and high banks where minor roads are deeply

[1] N. Creutzburg, H. Eggers, W. Noack and M. Pfannenstiel: *Freiburg und der
Breisgau*, 1954.

sunk into it. In places, these loess deposits have been excavated to provide cellars for the storage of local crops, especially wine and potatoes. This is one of the richest agricultural regions in 'the garden of Germany'. Long, hot and sunny summer days, together with deep, rich soils weathered from the basalt and loess, give high crop yields.

At the upper end of the Rhine plain, the Sundgau forms a threshold region, on the divide between streams draining to the Rhône (*via* the Doubs and the Belfort 'gate') and to the Rhine below Basle. The divide is crossed by the Rhine-Rhône canal. This platform region slopes from the Plateau Jura of Switzerland to the edge of the Rhine plain and descends from 1,650 ft. to 800 ft. It is a region of faulted and fractured Tertiary rocks, mainly *Molasse*, but the solid rocks are partly masked by loess and fluvioglacial gravels, often to a depth of 100 to 130 ft. A number of streams trench the easily eroded material as they flow north-east to the Rhine. The Sundgau forms a thinly populated frontier region, quite thickly wooded, with lines of poplars bordering the streams. It ends where the *Hauptterrasse* of the upper Rhine valley begins. This terrace, which is partly loess-covered, extends on both sides of the Rhine plain and lies at about 50 ft. above sea-level. It has been partly cut by the Rhine but it is also dissected by the various Rhine tributaries, such as the Kinzig and the lower Neckar. The dry surface provided by the terrace gravels and the pure water supply favoured settlement by the Franks and Alemanni, the place names in *-ing*, *-ingen* and *-heim* pointing to the thick spread of agglomerated villages dating from the occupation of the region in the 4th and 5th centuries. These Germanic settlements took place during the early part of the *Völkerwanderung* in a region already well served by Roman roads, where some Roman settlement had already taken place, as at Baden-Baden and Badenweiler, both famous as health resorts, endowed with mineral springs. Beneath the surface covering of drift, potash (*Kali*) salts are obtained from the Triassic beds on both sides of the Rhine and the white conical tips are a striking feature between Freiburg and Basle. The plain has long supported a high density of rural population, the soils giving good yields. The land is parcelled out into innumerable long narrow strips, running usually at right angles to the Rhine, and these result from the subdivision of the land through the system of inheritance, known as *Realerbteilung*.[1] The region is, therefore, characterized by holdings which are often too small to be economic and make difficult modern methods of

[1] G. Pfeifer: 'The Quality of Peasant Living in Europe'. Contribution to *Man's Rôle in Changing the Face of the Earth*, 1956.

working.[1] The variety of crops grown is remarkable, including wheat, maize, lucerne, tobacco and hops; while fruit trees are interspersed through the arable land (*Fruchtwechselwirtschaft*).

Below the loess-mantled *Hauptterrasse* and the main line of villages lies the flood-plain of the Rhine, below the 50-ft. level. Over this flat, alluvial surface the Rhine formerly followed a changing and meandering course, in contrast with its present straight channel, which is confined between fairly steep and artificially reinforced banks. The backwaters, swamps and marshland or *Ried* indicate the abandoned courses of the former Rhine. Here swamp-loving vegetation prevails, especially the poplar and alder, which are interspersed amidst water meadows, forming *Auewald*. This is a natural barrier region, largely uninhabited, except where firm ground comes close to the river, as at Kehl, the bridge town opposite Strasbourg, and at Mannheim-Ludwigshafen. In parts of the plain, former hunting forests are still preserved as in the *Hanauer Wald* between Kehl and Rastatt, where strips of Scots pine and mixed timber occur parallel to the Rhine.

THE BLACK FOREST ('SCHWARZWALD')

The Hercynian massif of the Black Forest consists of a highly broken and dissected triangular-shaped plateau. It lies mainly in the *Land* of Baden but continues north-eastwards into Württemberg. It extends from the upper Rhine valley between Basle and Waldshut to Pforzheim for a distance of over 100 miles, with an east–west extent of 40 miles in the south, but tapering north-eastwards. It is sharply delimited on the west by the line of foothills bordering the Rhine plain, and here the survival of the various regional names with the suffix 'gau', such as Breis*gau*, Klett*gau*, Kraich*gau*, etc., bear witness to settlement of the regions marginal to the Forest by the Alemanni prior to penetration of the wooded valleys in the later Middle Ages, during the forest-clearing phase or *Rodungszeit*. To the south, the Black Forest slopes steeply down to the Rhine and the Swiss frontier but to the north the descent to the Pforzheim or Maulbronn 'gate' is much more gradual. The eastern limit of the Forest is not nearly so clear cut as that on the west, for the long, gentle 'dip' slope merges gradually into the plateau country of the Triassic sandstone. The most striking contrast is shown in the vegetation, for the thickly forested Bunter

---

[1] A M. Lambert: 'Farm Consolidation in Western Europe', *Geography*, Vol. 48, 1963.

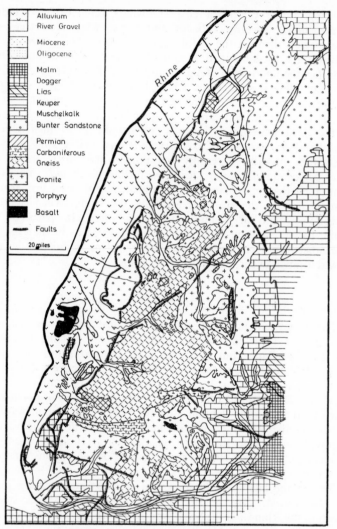

Alluvium
River Gravel

Miocene
Oligocene

Malm
Dogger
Lias
Keuper
Muschelkalk
Bunter Sandstone

Permian
Carboniferous
Gneiss

Granite

Porphyry

Basalt

Faults

20 miles

FIG. 104.   Geology of the Black Forest.

sandstone country gives way abruptly to the open pastoral and arable land of the *Muschelkalk*, known as the Baar.

The Black Forest massif attains its greatest altitudes towards the south (Feldberg, 4,905 ft., the Belchen, 4,672 ft., and the Schauinsland, 4,118 ft.), and these rounded eminences correspond to the outcrop of highly resistant granites. These igneous rocks form similar if less extensive hill masses to the south and they also underlie the culminating height of the northern Black Forest, the Hornisgrinde (3,820 ft.). Further irregular masses are found around the central core of Pre-Cambrian rocks, for example in the Blauen, which rises to 3,825 ft., forming a conspicuous mass behind Badenweiler, between Freiburg and Basle. To the south-east of the culminating Feldberg massif, the valleys are deeply incised into the granites and some are glacially overdeepened, such as the Himmelreich east of Freiburg leading to the ravine of the Höllental.

The general trend of the Black Forest is Variscan, that is, northeast to south-west, parallel with the Vosges, with which it formed a continuous, if denuded, mountain system until Oligocene-Miocene times. This region of Carbo-Permian folding appears to have experienced a series of peneplanations and the older erosion surfaces are exhumed only in the south, for the Permian beds and Bunter sandstones conceal this feature in the north-east.[1] In the south-centre of the Black Forest, a number of erosion surfaces are clearly preserved between 2,000 and 2,500 ft., notably around the villages of St. Peter and St. Märgen, where the bevelling of the surface facilitated the early clearance of the forest during the period of medieval monastic settlement, and today the amount of land used for stock rearing and the cultivation of crops in long narrow strips is very striking, in contrast with the thickly wooded slopes which fall away from these platforms on all sides.

The Bunter sandstones cover an area approximately equal to that of the crystalline rocks but they offer a striking contrast in land forms, extent of forest cover, and density of settlement. The Bunter covering is best preserved in the north-east, where it outcrops over a belt of country 20 miles wide. This uplifted erosion surface is deeply cut by the Murg and Enz rivers, the latter a tributary of the Neckar, to such an extent that the basement crystalline rocks are exposed along the valley gorges. On the eastern side of the Black Forest, the distinctive red rocks of the Bunter form a continuous outcrop from Pforzheim to the rift of Bonndorf. However, where the divide between the Rhine and Neckar drainage is narrowest, the outcrop contracts to a width of only 5 miles. In the south-east, patches of Bunter sandstone have been preserved, particularly in the long and narrow faulted block of the Hühnersiedel (2,448 ft.), between the Elz and the Kinzig valleys. In the highest parts of the Black Forest (as in the High Vosges), the sandstone covering has been completely stripped from the crystalline core.

[1] E. de Martonne: *Europe Centrale*, Géog. Univ., Vol. 4, p. 143 and map.

The *Muschelkalk* forms a continuous though narrow band, 7 to 10 miles wide, along the eastern edge of the Forest. On the western margin, as the result of the down-faulting of the Rhine rift valley, the *Muschelkalk* has been preserved as a series of narrow and discontinuous platforms, above those of the Jurassic already described, marking a step in the steep descent from the highland to the plain. It is best preserved in the fault block of the Dinkelberg plateau, to the south-west of the Black Forest. Important lines of fracture also cross the central Black Forest diagonally in a north-east to south-west direction, along which the Elz has cut its valley, thereby offering a relatively easy way into the heart of the massif. Other routes lead from the Rhine plain into the Forest along the flat-floored but steep-sided valleys which lie south of the Elz, such as the Dreisam, and the Wiese behind Basle. To the north, the Kinzig valley is followed by the Black Forest railway *en route* to the Danube valley *via* the spiral tunnels above Triberg, where the line crosses the divide between the Rhine and Danube drainage. This railway is joined by the electrified line from Freiburg and the Höllental (Ravennaschlucht viaduct) to Donaueschingen, the hydro-electric power station at Schluchsee providing the current. Short feeder lines extend into the Forest to the north, but the main railway from Karlsruhe follows the Murg valley from Rastatt to Freudenstadt and so to Stuttgart. Thus the dissected character of the Black Forest and its deep, rejuvenated valleys have invited penetration at a number of points.

During the Pleistocene glaciation, the highest parts of the Black Forest, like the Vosges, were centres of small independent ice caps. From such foci as the Feldberg and the Hornisgrinde, where snow and ice covered the summits, small glaciers streamed down the valleys which radiate from these massifs, extending eastwards to the edge of the Baar and westwards to the Rhine plain. On the eastern side of the Feldberg, the stages in the retreat of this local ice are marked by the moraines which lie at the lower end of Titisee, a ' finger ' lake at the site of which glaciers coalesced. In contrast, the circular Feldsee, at the eastern foot of the Feldberg, is a clear example of a *Kar* or rock basin lake, 1,000 ft. below the summit. On the eastern side of the massif, the steep, rejuvenated valley of the Höllental, with its scattering of erratics, leads to the flat-floored Himmelreich, where the Dreisam flows along a broad valley, thickly settled and intensely cultivated. Several of the valleys on the eastern slope favoured the accumulation of ice, on account of their aspect and gentle slope, and, in some of these, moraines occur. In the northern Black Forest, lakes similar to the Feldsee occupy basins eroded in sandstone, apparently below the limit of the ice.[1]

THE ODENWALD

North of the Kraichgau depression, the Hercynian highlands re-appear in the Odenwald, which, together with the Spessart, bears many resemblances to the Black Forest, though the general altitude is much lower. Each displays the Variscan north-north-east to south-south-west trend and they each exemplify two contrasted types of landscape developed on crystalline and sandstone formations. The slope to the Rhine is abrupt and broken by major north–south faults, in contrast with that to the east which is long and gentle. All are barrier regions, thinly populated when compared with the productive valleys and plains to which they descend, and, with important exceptions, routes through these regions are few and difficult. Much of the land is under mixed forest, the soils being too poor and thin and the slopes generally too steep to permit of clearance for pasture or cultivation.

The triangular region of the Odenwald extends from the south of Heidelberg northwards for thirty miles. The straight western edge overlooking the Rhine plain corresponds to a major fault line fracture and there is an abrupt ascent to the rugged country which rises to the east. At the foot of the western scarp edge lies the *Bergstrasse*, a rich and thickly settled strip where the loess is weathered into highly productive soils. This region is famous for its early Germanic settlement and for the number of villages, with their half-timbered houses aligned along the road, the names of which end in *-heim*.[2] It is also noted for its agricultural richness and variety of production; its meadowlands and cultivated fields being thickly interspersed with fruit trees, notably the cherry, pear and apple, and these generally line the roadside.

The approach to the Odenwald from the south is very gentle, while in the north the high and broken country of the crystalline Odenwald sinks beneath a covering of younger rocks in the vicinity of Darmstadt. Granite, gneiss and other crystalline rocks give rise to rounded summits above the general level of the plateau. Two such viewpoints which rise above the tree-line are the Neunkircher Höhe (1,985 ft.) and the Malchenburg or Melibocus (1,690 ft.). In the south, the upwelling of basalt accounts for the eminence called the Katzenbuckel (2,053 ft.). In the western Odenwald,

[1] E. de Martonne: *Europe Centrale*, Vol. 1, map on p. 159.
[2] R. Gradmann: *Süddeutschland*, Vol. 2, 1931, p. 62.

the valleys are wide and shallow at the head but they are deeply cut into the resistant rocks in their lower sections and provide striking examples of inverted relief. These valleys are threaded by a number of minor routeways into the Odenwald from the Rhine plain, though the Neckar gorge, at the lower end of which stands the castle and university town of Heidelberg, offers the main means of penetration. The crystalline rocks of the Odenwald show abundant surface run-off and the rushing torrents provide local water power, though there is not the same development of craft industries as in the Black Forest. It is estimated that 36 per cent of the Odenwald is forested but much of the land has been cleared for hill grazing and strip cultivation. Within the Forst there are a few picturesque small towns and villages, notably Michelstadt and Erbach, the former a small market town with half-timbered houses, steeply pitched gables and narrow, cobbled streets in late medieval style.

The Bunter sandstone country of the eastern Odenwald is sparsely settled on account of the lack of surface water and the isolated farms in forest clearings are far apart. The proportion of land under forest increases in general to over 60 per cent but in places it is much higher, 90 per cent of the land being covered with fir forest. This is monotonous plateau country with a fairly uniform altitude of 1,200 ft., draining southwards to the Neckar and north and east to the Main valley. The Odenwald dies out eastwards where the *Muschelkalk* country begins. This open region is drained by the Tauber tributary of the Main, in the district known as the Taubergrund.

The drainage of the Neckar and Main through the region of the Odenwald-Spessart block offers a striking example of epigenetic drainage and the gorge scenery is very impressive. Where the Main has cut a deep cleft between the Odenwald and the Spessart, its red cliffs form a sharp contrast with the dark green of the fir forests which mantle the slopes above the valley. The river is incised below terraces on both sides, and these provide the flat surface utilized by the road and railway which thread the valley. The big sweeps of the Main make the river valley route too indirect for the railway from Frankfurt to Würzburg, and it leaves the Main at Aschaffenburg to cross the Spessart, rejoining the Main valley at Lohr. The valley of this river contrasts markedly with the steep slopes above it, for there is a dense spread of settlement along the valley and viticulture is important on the terraced slopes, with orchards and strip cultivation also in evidence. This region was settled at an early date by the Franks, as villages such as Wert*heim* suggest. This is a confluence site, where the Tauber joins the Main. The Neckar has been canalized by means of a number of locks and weirs above Heidelberg as far as Heilbronn,[1] carrying quite a considerable amount of barge traffic, notably salt. The Main, however, is of negligible importance as a waterway above Aschaffenburg, though there have long been schemes to link the river with the upper Danube, and also the Neckar with that river (Fig. 96).

THE SPESSART

North of the Main, the highlands of the Odenwald are continued in the Spessart mountains. Here the Variscan trend is repeated but the general elevation compares with that of the Odenwald rather than with the Hardt across the Rhine or with the Vosges-Black Forest. The highest point is that of the Geyersberg (1,985 ft.) but the general line of crests seldom exceeds 1,640 ft. and the upland as a whole lies at about 1,500 ft. The Spessart consists of two types of country, that developed on the Archæan basement rocks and that on the Bunter sandstone. In the west, the crystalline rocks, especially mica schists and gneiss, form rugged, broken country between the Main and Kinzig valleys. The culminating point is reached in the ridge known as the Hahnenkamm (1,430 ft.). This feature is a fault line escarpment and, to the east, the greater part of the Spessart is developed on Bunter sandstone, forming a gently sloping plateau which is virtually waterless, the streams being few and flowing in deep-cut gorges. The slope to the Main between Aschaffenburg and Hanau is broken by a second escarpment rising to 1,800 ft. and this ridge provides a number of good viewpoints over the surrounding forested country, such as that from the Lern Höhe (1,725 ft.), in the north, and the Geishöhe (1,706 ft.), in the south. The population density is very low here and seldom exceeds 150 to the square mile. The Bunter formation crosses the Main valley and subsequently ends against the *Muschelkalk*, which forms the rim of the lower Franconian basin. To the north of the Kinzig valley, the sandstone country is continued in the Fulda depression which divides the volcanic masses of the Vogelsberg and Hohe Rhön. The whole of this district is scenically rather monotonous. Miles of forested plateau country, without the lakes which enhance the beauty of the Black Forest, are the essence of the Spessart. This is an upland region remarkable for its isolation and sparse population, in spite of its relatively low altitude.

[1] *Heimatatlas der Sudwestmark Baden*, first edition, 1934.

THE RHENISH PALATINATE (THE HARDT MOUNTAINS AND HILLS OF RHENISH HESSE)

North of the Lauter valley, where the Franco-German frontier swings west from the Rhine, the highlands of the Palatinate begin.[1] As the Vosges and Black Forest balance each other across the Rhine, so the Hardt mountains and the Odenwald, divided by the lower Rhine rift valley, complete the symmetrical arrangement of highland and lowland in south-west Germany. These mountains of the eastern Palatinate divide the Rhine valley from the Kaiserslautern depression and there is a general slope westwards to the Saar valley and eastwards to the Rhine. The Hardt mountains differ, however, from the other highlands which margin the Rhine rift valley in the completeness of the sandstone covering. Only where valleys have cut very deeply into these fairly resistant rocks, or where local faults occur, are the fundamental gneisses revealed, but they form the core of the block none the less. The Variscan north-east–south-west trend, parallel to the Odenwald-Spessart blocks, with which it was once continuous, is apparent. This is a region of rather monotonous features, though the general altitude is rather higher than that of the Odenwald, averaging 2,000 ft. In some districts the sandstone has weathered into sharp ridges which rise above the general level of the plateau and these jagged crests, rocky pinnacles and stacks appear to resemble ' Saxon Switzerland ', south of Dresden. The highest points in the Hardt mountains are the Kalmit (2,241 ft.), overlooking the Rhine plain at Speyer, and also the Drachenfels (1,873 ft.). These heights occur in the region of greatest Miocene uplift, though the divide between the Rhine and Mosel drainage lies to the west of the main crest, as the result of progressive river capture. The contrast between the short torrential streams draining to the Rhine and the long, winding rivers which flow towards the Mosel and the Saar is very marked, the Rhine tributaries providing sites for water power at a number of points, especially along the Lauter and Speyer. These streams have cut deep notches in the steep fault line escarpment of the Hardt, thus dominating the Rhine plain and the thickly settled *Hauptterrasse*, which is followed by the *Weinstrasse* along the foot of the hills. The terraced descent from the Hardt to the Rhine rift valley thus contrasts strikingly with the back slope which has the form of an uplifted peneplain. Much of the Hardt is thickly forested, the conifers of the upper slopes giving way to mixed woodland and beech in the foothills.

[1] J. Wagner: *Hessen*, 1961.

To the west of the Hardt, the forest is replaced by open land developed on *Muschelkalk*, in the district of Westrich. To the north lies the Palatinate depression, with the key town of Kaiserslautern, on the ancient route from Châlons-s.-Marne–Metz–Saarbrücken–Kaiserslautern–Mannheim. The depression is also known as the Saar-Nahe rift valley and is drained westwards by the Blies to the Saar and eastwards by the Lauter to the Nahe, which joins the Rhine at the entrance to the gorge at Bingen. The corridor is floored by Triassic, Permian and Carboniferous rocks and is a region of low but diversified relief, with some fairly productive soils and an abundant water supply. The average height is about 1,200 ft. but the Carboniferous limestones form residual buttes such as the Pots Berg (1,844 ft.). To the east, porphyry rocks give rise to a line of heights known as the Saar-Nahe hills, culminating in the Donnersberg (2,254 ft.), a fine viewpoint overlooking the foothill country of Rhenish Hesse. The region is mainly rural, lacking large towns and industries, in sharp contrast with the Saar coalfield region to the west. Green meadows appear intermingled with rich red plough land, with forests of fir and beech on the hill slopes. To the north of this depression, the Nahe has cut a narrow, incised valley, especially where it encounters hard, eruptive rocks, for example near the Birkenfeld. The Nahe valley consists of a series of gorges excavated at the base of the Hunsrück, the last occurring just before the river enters the Rhine at Bingen. To the north, the Palatinate extends to the Rhine-Hesse hill country, within the area delimited by the towns of Worms, Kreuznach, Bingen and Mainz. This foothill country is developed on easily eroded Pliocene sands and clays; the Rhine and Nahe terraces being partly covered by loess, forming strips above the river alluvium. This is a highly productive region, under intensive crop cultivation; the long, narrow strips being interspersed with vineyards and orchards.

THE SAARLAND

In view of the agreement reached in June, 1956 between France and Germany, the vexed question of the ownership of the Saar coalfield was once more resolved. There is no real geological or physical unity in the Saarland, for it consists of that part of the middle Saar basin which contains the coalfield returned to Germany by plebiscite in 1935 and the population of which voted once more in 1955 for union with the post-war Republic. The economic life of the region has been dominated since 1870 by the exploitation of the coalfield on the Franco-German frontier, though the Saar basin also includes the incised valley of the meandering Saar between Saarlouis and Trier and the south-western slopes of the Hunsrück.

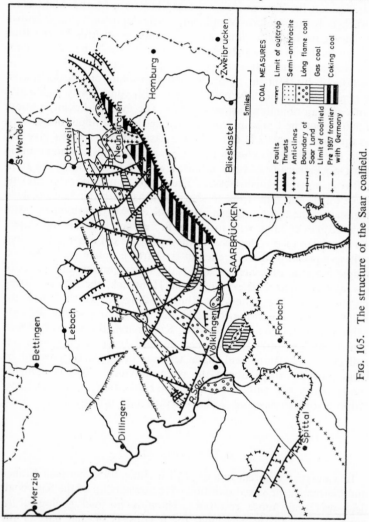

Fig. 105. The structure of the Saar coalfield.

The coalfield itself lies on the northern flanks of the Saar-Nahe rift valley and has the same north-east–south-west trend. The region has been lightly folded into a series of basins and swells, the apex of the main anticline being under Saarbrücken, the town which functions as the capital of the *Land*, and it is the hub of the industrial region. Coal is exploited over an elliptical area lying between Neunkirchen, Ottweiler, Saarlouis and the Warndt, extending south-west across the Saar valley.[1] The coal measures dip gradually westwards beneath younger rocks, especially Triassic sandstones and limestones which extend into Lorraine. To the south-east, a great thrust fault results in the coal being buried to unworkable depths in the neighbourhood of St. Ingbert. In the older parts of the coal-field, shafts are sunk to depths of about 500 ft. but in recent years deeper shafts have been sunk in the Warndt to 3,000 ft. The horizontal bedding of the coal seams greatly facilitates mining and there is not the same extensive displacement of seams by faulting as occurs in the Belgian field at the northern base of the Ardenne. The seams of the Saar coalfield, numbering about 300, are inter-bedded with sandstones and shales and they vary in thickness from 3 to 10 ft. The coalfield has been developed in a fairly thickly populated region, the miners travelling daily to the mines from outlying villages; as do the workers in the blast furnaces, steel mills, glass and pottery works. The coal may be used for coking, though it is not particularly suited for this purpose, an unfortunate circum-stance in view of the proximity of the ' minette ' ores of Lorraine. The Saar coal is mainly of the long flame and household type, so that, although much of the coal has a local demand in gas works and factories, a large proportion of the market lies in the cities of the Rhineland and southern Germany, as well as in Switzerland and northern Italy. In addition, the industrial areas of Lorraine and Luxembourg are integrated with the Saar as members of the European Coal and Steel Community. Coal production in 1964 was 14·6 million tons.

To the east of the Saar coalfield, the country becomes more rugged; the Bunter sandstones giving rise to low hills trending south-west–north-east, and manufacturing industry peters out. This is the open country drained by the Blies and called the Bliesgau. Woods crown the heights, while intermediate slopes are under pasture; the river terraces being cultivated and the streams fringed with water meadows. The valley of the Blies is particularly marshy where it leaves the uplands at Neunkirchen for the western continuation of the Palatinate. The main railway and *Autobahn* from Landstuhl to Homburg, on the Kaiserslautern–Saarbrücken route, keep well to the south of this marsh. To the north of the coalfield, the land slopes up to the Hunsrück through the Saar hills and here the highest point is the Höcher Berg, 1,700 ft. In this district, the Permian

[1] The *Saar Atlas*, 1934.

sandstones and quartzites are replaced by Devonian and Cambrian formations, typical of the Schwarzwalder Hochwald to the south-west of the Hunsrück.   In this rugged country, the headstreams of the Nahe interlace with the left-bank tributaries of the Saar.   The resistant slates are weathered into ridges trending south-west–north-east, and these rise above the general level of the Bunter sandstone plateau, the average elevation of which is about 1,800 ft.   The highest point in the Hochwald is the Erbeskopf (2,677 ft.) and, at the western end of the forest, rises the Teufelskopf (3,133 ft.).   In these high, windswept districts, open moorland with highland peat bogs extend above the forest which covers many of the slopes of the plateau.   Some of the forest has been cleared along the valleys for pasture and settlement, but the highest levels are devoid of population.

Along the western edge of the Hunsrück, the Saar has cut a deeply incised valley of great scenic attractiveness.   The gorge is particularly narrow where the river leaves the Triassic sandstones for the more resistant Primary rocks, notably between Merzig and Serrig.   A spectacular viewpoint occurs at Kloev, where the Saar describes a complete loop within the sandstone bluff which overlooks the river here.   The opposite slope is gradual and smooth and the forest which elsewhere comes almost to the river's edge is here cleared for pasture.   In the distance, the long, even sky line of the 2,000-ft. erosion surface is conspicuous, in contrast with the rejuvenated character of the gorge.   The smooth outline of the Hunsrück is further enhanced by the almost continuous forest cover on the western slope of the Saar valley.   To the west, the scarp and vale country of Lorraine and Luxembourg begins, and with it the industrial landscape of the ironfield.

THE MIDDLE RHINE HIGHLANDS

The Middle Rhine Highlands or Rhine Slate Plateau (*Schiefergebirge*) form a compact block, cut diagonally from north-west to south-east by the Rhine in its epigenetic gorge section.   The massif, which resembles in shape a butterfly with wings outstretched, extends for 93 miles from north to south and for 150 miles from east to west.   Its strikingly level plateau surfaces form monotonous, thinly populated, highland country, in marked contrast with the deep rejuvenated gorges of the Rhine, Mosel and Lahn, along the narrow floors of which settlement is elongated.   These valleys break up the massif into separate blocks; the Hunsrück rising to the south-west, divided by the Mosel gorge from the Eifel to the north-west; while

the Taunus and Westerwald are similarly divided by the incised
valley of the Lahn. Along the southern edge of the massif, a
dissected fault line scarp provides a sharp limit to the region against

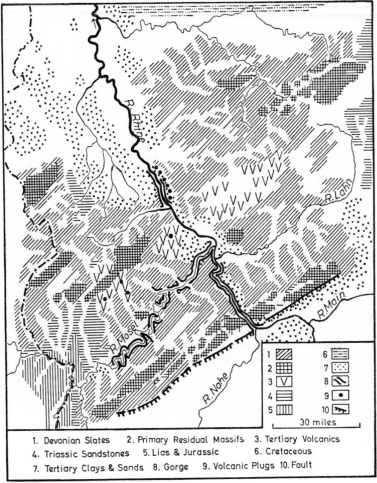

FIG. 106. The structure of the Middle Rhine Highlands.

1. Devonian Slates   2. Primary Residual Massifs 3. Tertiary Volcanics
4. Triassic Sandstones 5. Lias & Jurassic   6. Cretaceous
7. Tertiary Clays & Sands 8. Gorge   9. Volcanic Plugs 10. Fault

the Saar-Nahe rift and the lower Main plain. The Rhine gorge
between Bingen and Koblenz severs the slab of the Hunsrück from
that of the Taunus, two very similar regions. In contrast, the
broken, partly volcanic country of the Eifel and Westerwald has

its continuation in the Belgian Ardenne to the north-west of the Eifel and in the Rothaar-Gebirge, north-east of the Westerwald. East of the Rhine below Andernach, the Siegerland and Sauerland form distinctive regions, drained to the Rhine by the Sieg, Wupper and Ruhr tributaries.

The middle Rhine highlands are not so spectacular scenically as the Black Forest-Vosges blocks but they form part of the same type of Carbo-Permian fold-mountain system. The Palæozoic rocks were folded and metamorphosed, worn down and partly covered by Mesozoic rocks and again uplifted in Miocene times, with accompanying vulcanism and dissection by deep gorges. This contrast between the level surface of the plateau with its even sky lines and the deeply trenched streams is one of the most significant features of this distinctive region of western Germany. The Mesozoic rocks (mainly Triassic) have been preserved on the flanks of the highlands, notably in the Trier ' bay ', where colourful red sandstone cliffs form a line of bluffs overlooking the Mosel opposite the city of Trier. Triassic rocks also occur in the wooded country south of Düren and again at Malmédy, near the Belgian frontier. With the exception of the volcanic regions (the Pellenz district of the Eifel, the Siebengebirge and the Westerwald) and the special region of the Hohes Fenn where Cambrian rocks are exposed, the highlands are formed very largely of Devonian slates, quartzites and sandstones, folded in Carbo-Permian times along an east-north-east–west-south-west axis. The slates are a particularly striking feature on account of their association with Rhenish and Mosel viticulture, for the ubiquitous slate walls support the terraces which run like scars across the steep slopes of the Rhine gorge, e.g. at Rudesheim. These uplands form part of a significant barrier region between the rift valley of south-west Germany and the lower Rhine plain, i.e. athwart the most vital routeway of western Germany. Much importance is therefore attached to the gorges which provide diagonal routes across the region.

The Hunsrück Mountains

These ' Dog's Back ' highlands form the south-westerly block of the middle Rhine highlands. They consist of rather rugged country, forming a quadrilateral area between the Saar, Mosel and Rhine valleys, with a steep scarp edge overlooking the Saar-Nahe rift to the south-east. Since the block underwent maximum uplift in the south, where fracturing also took place during the Alpine orogeny, the greatest heights are to be found here; the Erbeskopf attaining 2,677 ft. to the north of Birkenfeld. There is a gradual slope to the Mosel valley across the Mosel hills, themselves cut into a series of terraces during stages in the downcutting of the river. The folded form of the highlands is preserved in the series of ridges and depressions which characterize the region but the resistant quartzites give rise to such local features as the Hochwald, Idarwald and Sonnwald. In some areas, the underlying Cambrian rocks are exposed, as in the Schwarzwalder Hochwald, and also in the neighbourhood of Bingen, where the Nahe has cut a deep gorge into the slates before joining the Rhine. The Hunsrück form, as a whole, a desolate highland region partly under pasture, rough hill grazing and forest, but with large tracts of open waste land and a very small proportion of the total area under cultivation (there are relics of the open-field system here). There has been some reclamation of moorland and rough pasture of recent years by means of peat cutting, draining and marling, by afforestation, and also by the improvment of upland pasture, though the population density remains low and there is a persistent exodus to the towns on the margin.

The Taunus

The contrasts between the loess-covered plain of the lower Main valley, the vineyards of the Rheingau, and the sombre pine forests of the Taunus, are very pronounced. These highlands attain their greatest altitude in the Grosser Feldberg (2,887 ft.) and the Königstein (2,618 ft.), the highest points in the southern Rhine highlands. As in the Hunsrück, the west-south-west to east-north-east trend prevails; the Taunus ending in a steep fault scarp along the south-eastern margin of the block in the district of the Rheingau, while the slope towards the Lahn valley is gentle, though broken. Westwards, the Taunus descend almost precipitously to the Rhine gorge, notably where the fortress of Ehrenbreitstein opposite Koblenz commands the confluence of the Mosel and Rhine. Valleys, notably the Lahn dominated by the medieval cathedral town of Limburg, and the Wisper, are markedly rejuvenated. The latter is associated with a local wind known as the *Wisperwind*, a cold, down-valley wind which brings abnormally low temperatures to the district in winter. The Taunus was recognized as a frontier region in Roman times, when the *limes Germaniæ* crossed the upland from the Rhine at the site of Andernach to the Main. Along the southern edge of the Taunus mineral springs occur, utilized by the Romans at Wiesbaden and Homburg, and these are both noted modern health resorts, Wiesbaden surviving with little war-time damage. The foothill region of the Rheingau has in fact been settled continuously since prehistoric times; the intensively farmed region between Frankfurt and Wiesbaden being rich in early Frankish place-name endings in *-heim*, etc. In contrast the dark line of the Taunus rises in the distance; the lower slopes being covered with fine stands of beech, with firs above. The forest was partly cleared during the *Rodungszeit*, and *Waldhufendörfer* survive in the street village of Waldorf; while Oberrod provides an example of a *Gewanndorf*, surrounded by fields of wheat, oats, rye and potatoes. Survivals of the open-field system occur here and most cultivation above 2,000 ft. is of the subsistence type. Towards Limburg the intensity of arable farming is marked; crops of wheat, oats and potatoes predominating; while the vine and maize appear in the Lahn valley.

The Eifel

The north-western sector of the middle Rhine highlands exhibits greater scenic variety than the regions so far described. It covers a much larger area than the Hunsrück and is bounded structurally by the Brabant massif north of the Ardenne; by the Cologne ' bay ' to the north-east, balanced by the Trier ' bay ' to the south-west; and by the Rhine gorge between Koblenz and Bonn; while the incised valley of the Mosel forms the southern limit of the Eifel. An extraneous element may be traced through the region from the vicinity of Trier through the *Bitburgerland* and Hillesheim towards Düren, and along this line ran the Roman road and the modern railway from Trier through Euskirchen to Cologne. In the *Bitburgerland*, the Triassic rocks have been preserved in a downfold of the Eifel and the exposure of the red Bunter sandstone, with its frequent mantle of spruce forest, forms a sharp contrast with the dull grey of the slates or the sombre hues of the basalt. This sandstone was used by the Romans in the Porta Nigra, the amphitheatre and other Roman buildings still preserved in Trier. South-west of this city, the *Muschelkalk* outcrop continues into the adjacent Duchy of Luxembourg. Here the open pastoral landscape is combined with strip cultivation, especially of cereals, fodder crops (including maize), as well as fruit orchards; the trees being frequently scattered through the cultivated fields (*Fruchtwechselwirtschaft*) and along the roads.

The Eifel massif consists of three structurally contrasted elements: the Hohe Eifel, forming the core of the region and rising to 2,493 ft. in the Hohe Acht; the volcanic regions of Pellenz and the Vor Eifel; and the Hohes Fenn south of Aachen. The Hohe Eifel displays the dominant east-north-east to west-south-west trend of the whole block. This is part of the Pre-Cambrian core of the middle Rhine highlands and is strongly dissected by streams draining to the Mosel, Rhine and Meuse. The Hohe Eifel has been cut into distinct ridges such as the Schnee Eifel, which rises to 2,280 ft.; the Aar-Gebirge; and the Vor Eifel, which attains only 1,150 ft. This last foothill region consists of broken, dissected country characterized by the development of river terraces, the counterpart of the Moselberge, and likewise cut by the Mosel tributaries. The volcanic Eifel presents further regional contrasts, many of the valleys having been blocked by lava flows; while remnants of volcanic cones may be seen in the Pellenz country west of Andernach (Mosenberg, 1,670 ft.). Another feature of the volcanic Eifel is the occurrence of crater lakes, such as the Pulvermaar, 246 ft. deep, and also the Laacher-See. Much of the basalt country is forested but the tuff regions, with their frequent loess covering and waterless surfaces, form open country. This is a sparsely settled district, the population having been drawn off to the industrial regions at the base of the highlands (Aachen and Ruhr coalfields, and also the Cologne industrial region). Salt springs occur and Burtscheid, south of Aachen, served as a small Roman spa. There is much quarrying of basalt for building stone and road metal; while Düren functions as an industrial town, supplied by power from the thermal stations on the Ville lignite field.

Within the Eifel region, the Hohes Fenn is a district of special note, for here Cambrian slates have been preserved in a major downfold between the Ardenne-Eifel block and the Brabant massif. The slates and quartzites occur over a spindle-shaped area, aligned north-east to south-west, with a Caledonian fold trend antedating the folding of the Hercynian highlands. Much of this region is bare and windswept, and largely devoid of settlement. In the peaty depressions between the ridges, turf cutting is carried on, but most of the upland is covered by desolate moorland.

The Westerwald

Bounded by the Rhine and Lahn gorges and by the Sieg and Dill valleys, the Westerwald forms the north-eastern sector of the middle Rhine highlands and closely resembles the Eifel in its scenery. The massif consists of highly folded and contorted slates and quartzites of Devonian age, showing the typical Variscan trend, while it also includes some Tertiary volcanics. The slate outcrops give rise to high plateau country, with flat-topped summits and deeply cut valleys, some of the highest points being the Fuchskante (2,156 ft.) and the Stepkopf (2,145 ft.). The soils weathered from the slates are heavy clays, much of the land being maintained under forest which it is useless to clear. The exposure of Pliocene clays, covered in part with Recent deposits, has been preserved over a wide area, especially around Limburg in the Lahn valley, and here the soils are more amenable to improvement for pasture and cultivation. Between Bonn and Königswinter, and again on the margin of the Neuwied basin, basalt and trachyte appear, notably in the Sieben-gebirge which dominate the right bank of the Rhine from Linz to Königswinter. A core of trachyte forms the Drachenfels, the pyramidal peak which rises to a culminating height of 1,066 ft. In these eruptive areas, the well-drained soils are richer than those derived from the slates and, except where the slopes are too steep for use other than forestry, they are under hill pasture or cultivation. Fir and beech woods commonly occur, forming wind breaks in these exposed uplands. There is some quarrying of building stone as in the Siebengebirge, and iron ore has long been worked in the Dill and upper Lahn valleys. Settlement, however, remains notably peripheral, and it is concentrated especially into the Neuwied basin[1] and into the Sieg, Dill and Lahn valleys, as well as extending along the Rhine gorge; where some of the villages, such as Andernach, date from Roman times, for here the *limes Germaniæ* took off for the Danube.

The Siegerland and Sauerland

Except for the rugged country of the Rothaar-Gebirge to the north-east, itself a continuation of the Westerwald, and the parallel ridge of the Ebbe-Gebirge, where the headstreams of the Ruhr and Wupper interlace, these northern extensions of the Rhine highlands are regions of generally lower relief than those so far described. The Rothaar-Gebirge rise to a general height of 2,000 ft., though the Kahlen Asten reaches 2,763 ft. To the west, the plateau descends to the Bergische Höhe which fringe the eastern margin of the Cologne ' bay '. To the north, the countryside becomes increasingly indus-trialized as the Wupper and eventually the Ruhr valleys are ap-proached. In fact, the development of the manganiferous iron ore deposits of the Sieg valley and the industrial growth of the towns in the Wupper valley strike a contrasting note in this otherwise rural area. This is a region of broken relief, where streams provide a number of sites for the use of water power. Access to local iron ore and charcoal give rise to the early metal working industries of the Sieg valley, of which Siegen remains the centre. In the Wupper

[1] T. H. Elkins and E. M. Yates: ' The Neuwied Basin ', *Geography*, Vol. 45, 1960.

valley, the availability of lime-free water and of water power led to the
growth of textile industries, based on local wool, years before the
large-scale exploitation of the coalfield to the north.   The twin towns
of Elberfeld and Barmen (Wuppertal) specialize in spinning and
weaving, dyeing and printing wool, cotton and silk textiles, as does
Hagen, though the outlook of that town is to the Ruhr rather than
the Wupper valley.   In contrast, the lower valley of the Wupper,
long noted for its domestic iron industry, has seen the growth of
such steel centres as Solingen and Remscheid, dependent for many
years on high-grade alloy steel used in the production of stainless
steel, cutlery and machine tools, etc.   The Sauerland serves increasingly as a source of water supply and also as an attractive recrea-
tioned parkland for the population of the industrial Ruhr–Rhineland.

THE GORGES OF THE RHINE HIGHLANDS

The Rhine from Bingen to Bonn

The diagonal gash cut by the Rhine through the resistant rocks
of the Slate Plateau is a comparatively youthful feature, post-dating
the Miocene uplift of the block and the consequent rejuvenation of
drainage.   Except in the volcanic districts, the flat summit levels of
the plateau contrast sharply with the almost precipitous sides of the
gorge cut by the Rhine and its affluents.   This is the Rhine valley
of legend and song, of ruined medieval castles set amidst slatey
slopes terraced for the vine, with villages strung out below, parallel
to the Rhine river.   The narrow terraces on either side of the gorge
provide very limited space for street villages, railways and roads,
and the strips of alluvium below the embanked road are sometimes
used for pasture.   The villages live by viticulture, and their names
such as Bacharach, Rüdesheim, Oberwesel and St. Goar are renowned.   Where side streams join the Rhine, as at Koblenz
(Deutsches Eck), and below Ems on the Lahn, there is a considerable
spread of Pliocene sands and clays, forming terraces above the river
alluvium.   These deposits underlie the productive basins of Maifeld
and Neuwied.   Below Andernach, volcanic downwash partly
accounts for the fertility of the strip known as the ' Golden Mile '.

Koblenz dominates the centre of the gorge as a nodal point where
the Mosel joins the Rhine, almost opposite the confluence with the
Lahn.   Its strategic site has been recognized since the time of the
Roman settlement of Confluentes.   The most spectacular scenery
of the Rhine gorge, apart from that of the Siebengebirge, lies above
Koblenz and includes the precipice of the Lorelei, the quartzite rocks

of which are continued as reefs into the bed of the Rhine. A similar feature occurs at the *Wilde Gefahr*, at Bacharach. Below Koblenz, the terraces begin to recede, first from the left bank below Andernach and then from both, once the Siebengebirge are left behind. Wooded islands and sandbanks appear in the river and vineyards give way to fruit trees on the terraced slopes.

The Mosel Valley from Trier to Koblenz

The Mosel-Lahn trough, cutting the axis of the Rhine gorge at right angles, is a major structural feature of the middle Rhine highlands and is also a complex one. The Mosel, like the Lahn, has eroded its valley since Miocene times, cutting a series of Pliocene and Pleistocene terraces. Fragments of these remain, notably in the Moselberge and in the Vor Eifel, and against the lowest (the *Niederterrasse*) the river impinges as it cuts its gorge more and more deeply. The present course of the Mosel lies to the south of an outcrop of Permian marls which underlie the Wittlich depression. This feature extends from the Trier ' bay ' to the famous meander of the Mosel at Marienburg and is related to the older line of drainage. The main railway from Koblenz to Trier and Luxembourg follows this depression in preference to the devious route along the gorge of the river, but it also tunnels, as at Cochem, to cut through a meander spur. There is today a growing amount of traffic on the recently canalized Mosel, the river meanders having been cut through and the river regulated by a series of locks and weirs. The work was completed in 1963, so that now barges of 1,500 tons may operate between the Ruhr and Thionville in Lorraine.[1] Consequently, Lorraine iron ore is now moved by waterway to the Ruhr blast furnaces and only a small amount goes *via* the Marne–Rhine canal to Strasbourg; thence to Mannheim-Ludwigshafen. The most attractive scenic features of the Mosel gorge are the great incised meanders, leaving bevelled spurs flat enough for arable cultivation or orchards, while vineyards are sited on the steep, undercut and sunny slopes. The *Mittelterrasse* and *Niederterrasse* are frequently under strip cultivation; maize and fodder crops such as colza being common crops, while apple, cherry and pear trees are scattered through the fields. The system of rotation cropping practised in this district, as elsewhere in the Rhineland, is known as *Fruchwechselwirtschaft*. Similarly, the abandoned meander channels marking the Pliocene stage in the erosion of the Mosel valley and lying high above the present valley, are also often under strip cultiva-

---

[1] A.A. Michel: ' The canalization of the Moselle and West European Integration ', *Geog. Review*, Vol. 52, 1962.

tion, with the vine on the steep slopes above. Above 900 ft., however, the forest zone begins and crowns the plateau summits above
the gorge. Below Cochem, the vineyards disappear from the slopes
with a northerly aspect and the woodland descends to lower levels;
for the Mosel valley is near the northern limit of the vine, introduced
by the Romans; some of the vineyards, for example around Trier,
being of great antiquity. This town, *Augusta Treverorum* of the
Romans, lies in the Trier ' bay ', below the confluence of the Saar
and the Mosel. It arose as a bridge point and Roman frontier post,
as the great sandstone Porta Nigra bears witness. In medieval
times the city flourished as a cathedral and market town and as the
headquarters of the Mosel wine industry. Its modern growth has
been handicapped by its nearness to the Luxembourg frontier and
it has developed few industries. Lower down the Mosel valley,
Berncastel and Cochem are also important centres of the Mosel
wine industry and the villages are dominated by the ruins of medieval
castles. The production of fine-quality grapes suffered a severe set-
back when the vines were attacked by phylloxera in the late 19th
century, but resistant varieties were produced by grafting with
American stocks.

The Lahn Valley

Like the Mosel, the course of the Lahn is mainly across resistant
slates and quartzites of Devonian age. It rises on the southern slopes
of the Rothaar-Gebirge, flowing south past the castle towns of
Marburg and Giessen to Wetzlar, where it is joined by the Dill
from the north-west. Limburg, halfway between this point and
the Rhine confluence, is the regional centre of the Lahn valley.
Here the valley widening is related to the tectonic feature known as
the Limburg ' bay '. Below Limburg the gorge of the Lahn begins,
similar in scenery to that of the Mosel. The Lahn meanders constantly over the narrow valley floor, the swings being closely followed by the railway line from Giessen to Niederlahnstein, tunnel-
ling at frequent intervals. Local iron, lead and silver ores gave
rise to an early metal industry in Wetzlar. Today the town specializes in the production of precise and optical instruments, photographic materials and apparatus, etc.

THE LOWER RHINE PLAIN, INCLUDING THE COLOGNE 'BAY'

Bonn, the city which now serves as the capital of the German
Federal Republic, has today a population of over 600,000. Below
it the Rhine enters a region which was covered by the Pliocene sea

and its retreat has left a flat, featureless plain. Apart from the Tertiary sands and clays of the Cologne ' bay ' and the important lignite deposits of the Ville between Bonn and Cologne, the lower Rhine plain is composed mainly of Pleistocene and Recent deposits; the gravels of the Rhine terraces margining a wide flood-plain; while glacial gravels and outwash material appear towards the Dutch frontier, together with peat fen. In the neighbourhood of Xanten and Kalcar, low morainic hills rise to 250 ft. In the neighbourhood of Bonn, the higher gravel terraces lie at 600 ft., descending rapidly towards the Dutch border. They are frequently wooded and serve as local water-partings, notably between the Rhine and the Meuse (Maas). The meanders of the lower Rhine are developed on the heavy alluvial clays of the flood-plain, especially below Emmerich. Prior to the regulation of the river during the 19th century, involving the building of dykes for the protection of the adjacent farm land, the river was liable to flood over a wide area. The lower Rhine has been straightened to improve navigation, for this section of the river carries a very heavy amount of traffic both up and down stream, especially between the Dutch ports and the Ruhr, while sea-faring vessels can proceed to Cologne.

The Cologne ' Bay '

This re-entrant of lowland is primarily the result of Miocene earth movements, the margins of the ' bay ' being defined by lines of fracture. These features also define the margins of the Ville and the Bergische Höhe. The descent to the Rhine plain is by a series of gravel terraces, the dry surface of which provided sites for early settlement above the marshes of the flood-plain. In places, the soils are enriched by the occurrence of loess. In contrast, the Pliocene sands carry tracts of woodland or heath, for example the Golzheimer Heide north of Düsseldorf. The focus of the whole region is, of course, Cologne (Köln), with its great bridges over the Rhine, here 650 yd. wide. Cologne originated as a Roman fortress town, Colonia Agrippina, on the left bank of the Rhine. In medieval times it flourished, like Trier and Mainz, as the seat of one of the great electorates of the German Empire. The medieval thoroughfares of the *Altstadt*, near the cathedral with its great twin Gothic spires, and the Hanseatic *Stapelhaus* survived until the devastation of the recent war. Today, a new city has risen from the ruins and now records a population of 835,859, compared with 768,426 in 1939. Between the wars, Cologne became a flourishing centre of varied industries especially concerned with engineering, and these industrial suburbs lay outside the semi-circle formed by the *Ring* bounding the *Altstadt*, extending into the *Neustadt* and the residential districts of Bayenthal and Lindenthal. Across the Rhine lie the 'Kleinseite' and the industrial suburbs of Deutz and Mülheim. The growth of new industries here has been made possible by the development of the Ville lignite field as a source of cheap fuel for thermal stations serving the Cologne region. The output of lignite from this field has been greatly expanded since the war, especially because of loss of access to the resources of brown coal in East Germany, production in West Germany in 1963 amounting to 106 million tons.

Düsseldorf, a modern river port for the industrial lower Wupper valley and Rhineland, developed as a medieval bridge town across the Rhine and also as a market centre. The town expanded considerably in the late 18th century when it became a noted centre of art and music. Today it is the capital of the *Land Nordrhein-Westfalen* and serves as the administrative headquarters of many of the Ruhr industrial firms. It imports Ruhr coke and Swedish iron ore for its iron and steel plants and also produces chemicals. It also serves as an airport for *Lufthansa* and *B.E.A.* flights. The towns on the left bank of the Rhine include Mönchen-Gladbach, Rheydt and Krefeld. These became centres of textile manufacture in the 17th century, especially silk, as the result of settlement by Dutch Mennonite refugees, the raw silk coming from Italy. Today, they have added the manufacture of synthetic fibres, especially *perlon*. To the south lies Leverkusen where Bayer founded the great chemical plant, and where today 25,000 workers are employed. Wesseling, also on the Rhine, is the centre of a large petro-chemical complex, served by an oil pipeline from Rotterdam.

The Rhine Plain below Duisburg-Ruhrort to the Dutch frontier

Below the industrial zone of the Ruhr-Emscher valleys, the Rhine winds over a wide flood-plain between high banks. The plain is 5 miles wide at Xanten and 15 miles wide at the Dutch frontier. Broad strips of water meadow extend on both sides of the Rhine and its tributaries, including the IJssel. The scenery gradually changes to that of the polder landscape typical of Holland, Emmerich being the last small industrial town before the Dutch frontier is reached.

THE RUHR-WESTPHALIAN COALFIELD AND INDUSTRIAL REGION

The Coal Measures which underlie the major industrial region of Nord-Rhein-Westfalen contain the greatest estimated reserves of workable coal in Europe, and they form the major basic industrial resource of the German Federal Republic, as well as of the European Common Market.   Before the 1939–45 War, 90 per cent of the total bituminous coal reserves of Germany were to be found in the Ruhr district.   The loss of the German section of the Upper Silesian field to Poland and the depletion of the reserves of the minor remaining fields within post-war Germany, especially those of Saxony and Aachen, have increased the figure to 92 per cent, a further 6 per cent being near Aachen.   Moreover, the Ruhr coal-

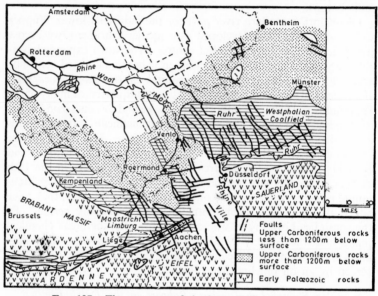

FIG. 107.   The structure of the lower Rhine–Maas basin.

field yields a wide range of types of coal, from semi-anthracite at the base to high-volatile coal at the top of the exposed Coal Measures. The main market for the semi-anthracite is as domestic fuel, the semi-bituminous coal being used for the manufacture of briquettes for central heating, thermal power for industry and also for rail transport.   A major asset of the Ruhr coalfield is the medium-volatile coal which produces high-grade metallurgical coke for the iron and steel industry, the by-products of coal tar being used in the chemical industry.   Other seams yield steam coal; while the non-coking, high-volatile coal is sold to thermal stations for the genera-tion of electricity, as well as being used for gas production for industrial and domestic purposes.   Such coal is also suitable for use in the manufacture of petroleum and synthetic rubber (*Buna*) by the hydrogenation process.

The Coal Measures outcrop for 40 miles along the east–west axis

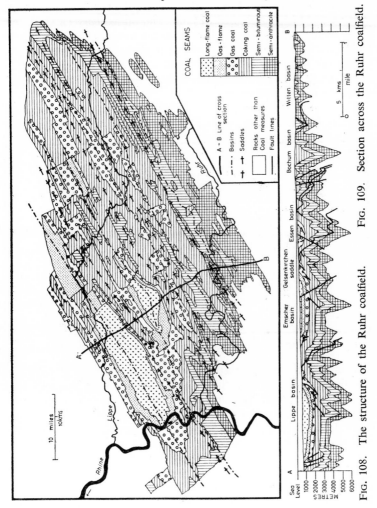

FIG. 108. The structure of the Ruhr coalfield.

FIG. 109. Section across the Ruhr coalfield.

of the Ruhr valley and they extend over the exposed field for 10 miles north of the Ruhr river, beyond which they dip under Mesozoic sediments, mainly Cretaceous rocks which overlie the Coal Measures unconformably. Coal is mined over the concealed field to depths of about 1,000 ft. in the Lippe valley, increasing to 3,000 ft. in the north towards Münster, where the Older Drift partly covers the solid rocks. The coal seams occur in a series of saddles and basins as the result of Carbo-Permian folding, and these include the Essen, Bochum, Emscher and Lippe basins, where the richest seams occur. The coalfield is criss-crossed by faults and buried *horsts* and *graben*, so as to give a ' crazy quilt ' pattern to the surface geology.[1] Great thrust planes also characterize the field, such as the Gelsenkirchen, Sutan and Satanella, so that the depth at which coal is mined varies from 165 ft. at Essen in the lower Ruhr valley to 2,600 ft. at Hamm, some 40 miles to the east.

Large-scale production of coal has characterized the exposed coalfield for the last century and has been closely tied to the German

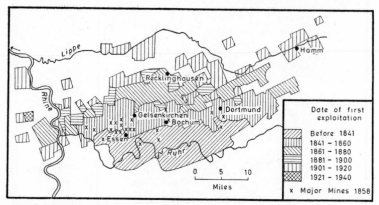

FIG. 110.   Stages in the development of the Ruhr coalfield, 1840–1940.

iron and steel industry, especially after the first use of coke for smelting iron ore at Mülheim in 1849.   In that year, the output of coal from the Ruhr was only about 1·6 million tons.   After the acquisition of the major part of the Lorraine phosphoric iron ores in 1871, the output of Ruhr coking coal increased rapidly, reaching 60 million tons by the turn of the century.   The output of Ruhr coal was curtailed in the 1920's, partly as the result of a ' go slow ' policy during the French occupation of the Ruhr and Rhineland and the demand for coal as Reparations payments, which lasted until 1923. It was also on account of the conversion of much merchant shipping to the use of oil for bunkering, the increasing use of lignite for thermal electricity, and the import of high-grade Swedish hæmatite ore in preference to that from French Lorraine, needing

[1] C. D. Harris: ' The Ruhr Coal-Mining District ', *Geog. Review*, Vol. 36, 1946, pp. 194–221.

(a) The Rhine gorge at Bingen.

25. THREE EPIGENETIC GORGES IN THE HERCYNIAN MASSIFS OF WESTERN GERMANY

(b) The Mosel valley at Berncastel.

(c) The Neckar gorge in the Odenwald.

(a) The business 'core' of the re-built town of Essen from the air.

26. THE INDUSTRIAL LANDSCAPES OF THE RUHR COALFIELD

(b) Coal mines, coke batteries, coal and coke wagons in the Ruhr.

less coke to produce a ton of pig iron. During the drive for economic self-sufficiency in the immediate pre-war years, increasing quantities of scrap were consumed in the steel mills, some of which was imported. By 1937, the Ruhr reached its peak pre-war production of 127 million tons of coal (69 per cent of the German total) and these figures were maintained during the high pressure of the early years of the war. After the 1939–45 War, production was reduced at first to a bare minimum of 33 million tons in 1945, increasing to 103 million tons in 1950, when this figure represented 20 per cent of the total European production outside Soviet Russia. In 1950 dismantling was brought to a halt and coal production began to expand very remarkably, especially with the entry of the German Federal Republic into the European Coal and Steel Community, inaugurated as the Schuman Plan in 1950–1 and coming into force in 1952. Today, West Germany is the greatest single contributor of coal and coke to the Common Market and Free Trade group; the total German output (with the addition of 14 million metric tons from the Saar) being 158 million metric tons in 1967. In that year, West Germany exported 13 million tons of coal and coke, mainly to other industrial countries within the Common Market, especially France and Benelux but also to Switzerland and the Scandinavian countries.

The exploitation of Ruhr coal was first carried out by means of a large number of relatively shallow pits, numbering a maximum of 300 in the 1870's but decreasing subsequently on account of the greater cost of sinking deeper shafts. In 1900, new mines were sunk west of the Rhine but here underground water proved a problem. In 1937, the average production of each mine was of the order of a million tons, 85 per cent of the coal coming from seams between $2\frac{1}{2}$ and 6 ft. thick. About three-quarters of the coal was worked between depths of 1,300 and 2,600 ft., but 13 shafts penetrated to over 3,000 ft. The average output per miner was high, namely 526 short tons, 60 per cent more than in Great Britain. Mechanization had made good progress before the 1939–45 War, the long wall method of mining with back filling being the general practice. Today, the total output of coal and coke is declining, with increasing competition from oil, both home produced and imported *via* Rotterdam. Some of the older pits are also uneconomic, especially in the Bochum field, where many miners have left the pits.[1]

The reserves of coal in the Ruhr today are estimated to be 213,000 million tons; two-thirds of these reserves consisting of coking coal,

[1] Peter Hall: *The World Cities*, 1966, p. 142.

C.E.—N

especially produced in the Essen basin. Little progress has been made with the development of the concealed field west of the Rhine, but a number of modern pits have been sunk north of the Lippe valley through the Cretaceous and drift cover as far as the outskirts of Münster.

It is characteristic of the Ruhr coalfield that its resources of coking coal have been exploited at the expense of other types of coal, for Ruhr coal has been tied to German iron and steel production for the past century. As the late Lord Keynes expressed it: ' The German Empire has been built more truly on coal and iron than on blood and iron.' It has been claimed that ' Germany is a land poor in rich deposits of iron ore but rich in poor deposits '.[1] The domestic reserves are mainly in the Sieg, Lahn and Dill valleys east of the Rhine gorge, where the output amounted to merely half a million tons of ore in the 1930's. In addition to these high-grade deposits, there are the low-grade Jurassic ores, exploited near Salzgitter in Hanover since the 1930's. Germany turned first to the non-phosphoric ores of Bilbao, in northern Spain, to supplement her meagre home supplies, and later to French North Africa and Elba, but for many years the market has been dominated by Lorraine and Sweden. The low-grade phosphoric ores of Lorraine were used increasingly after the application of the Thomas and Gilchrist process in 1878, while the import of Swedish magnetite was facilitated by the completion of the Arctic railway line from Kirunavaara to Narvik in 1902, which enabled supplies of Swedish ore to be shipped directly across the North Sea to Hamburg, Emden and Rotterdam. Internally, the construction of the Dortmund-Ems canal in 1899, with a branch to Herne and the Rhine (1914), greatly cheapened the bulk movement of coal, coke and iron ore. In 1916 another canal was opened, linking Wesel near the mouth of the Lippe to the point where that river is crossed by the Dortmund-Ems canal, thus providing an alternative route from Dortmund to the Rhine. The first stage in the construction of the *Mittelland* canal was completed when the canal reached Hanover in 1910. In the 1930's, this canal was extended to the Elbe at Magdeburg, thus enabling Ruhr coal and coke to supply the then recently developed centres of iron, steel and chemical production in the Hanover–Brunswick–Salzgitter–Merseburg-Leuna region. In spite of the significance of inland waterways, including especially the lower Rhine, in the bulk transport of fuel and raw materials to and from the Ruhr, the railways carry the greater part of the internal traffic of the region. A very close network has been evolved at the foot

[1] N. J. Pounds: *The Ruhr*, 1952, p. 169.

of the Sauerland and extends mainly east–west along the Ruhr, Emscher and Lippe valleys, linking these heavily industrialized areas with the vital artery of the Rhine valley. The great marshalling yards at Hamm mark the point where the railways from central Germany enter the industrial region of the Ruhr. Other railway nodes are Oberhausen, Essen and Dortmund. From Duisburg-Ruhrort, lines branch out to cross the Rhine *en route* to Aachen, to follow the Rhine to Cologne-Deutz and south to Frankfurt-am-Main and the upper Rhineland. In the Ruhr region the road system is antiquated, tortuous and frequently congested by tram lines, thus being neither convenient nor important for anything but local traffic. In the west, the Cologne–Arnhem–Rotterdam or *Holland linie Autobahn* serves the Rhineland. There are two arterial roads through the coalfield: one is the *Ruhrschnellweg*, running from east to west along the Ruhr valley south of Dortmund, north of Bochum and south of Essen, thence to Duisburg. It is paralleled by the *Emscherschnellweg* to the north, extending from Duisburg along the Emscher valley. These roads will eventually be linked with the planned *Autobahnen* from Cologne and the Sauerland to Münster; while another *Autobahn* connects Cologne *via* Gelsenkirchen with Hanover.[1]

The 'core' region of the inner Ruhr district today comprises some fifteen urban centres, forming part of one vast conurbation, the suburbs of which coalesce, and with a total population of some two million people. This high figure includes the great industrial cities of Essen with over 728,000 inhabitants in 1963, Düsseldorf with over 701,000, Dortmund with 652,000, and Duisburg with over 497,000. Since the end of the war, the housing problem of the Ruhr area, already acute on account of wholesale war-time destruction, has been greatly aggravated by the large influx of displaced persons from beyond the Oder-Neisse line, as well as from the Eastern sector of Berlin and the German Democratic Republic. Many of these refugees are highly skilled industrial workers, trained in the steel works of Upper Silesia, the textile mills of Saxony, the production of electrical engineering equipment in Berlin, and the manufacture of optical glass, photographic equipment and in the various light industries of Thuringia and the Sudetenland. In consequence, the traditional heavy industries of the Ruhr have become more diversified, with the establishment of textile mills at Düsseldorf, in the Lippe valley and at Mönchen-Gladbach, while ready-made clothing is now produced at Gelsenkirchen and the traditional linen industry of Aachen has been expanded.

[1] Peter Hall: *The World Cities*, map on pp. 140–1.

The centres of the great industrial cities of Nord-Rhein-Westfalen have seen a marked decrease in population as the result of the destruction of dwellings by bombing and the post-war occupation of many of these sites by modern office blocks and shopping centres.   There has been a major exodus to the suburbs and outlying agricultural and market gardening districts, so that much time is lost by daily travel into the centre of the city by thousands of *Arbeitspendler*. However, the six pre-war heavily-urbanized zones persist, the centres of some of these towns such as Duisburg, Essen and Bochum being originally medieval, though others, such as Gelsenkirchen, were mere agricultural villages in 1870.   Much of the outer Ruhr region is still given over to intensive agriculture, dairy farming and market gardening, notably the loess belt around Recklinghausen; while the Münsterland is noted for its pig rearing for the nearby urban markets in the Ruhr.   To the south of the coalfield lies the detached industrial belt concerned with steel and textile production, extending up the Wupper valley south of Düsseldorf towards Hagen in the upper Ruhr valley.   Here, where some 900,000 people are concentrated, are the steel and cutlery centres of Solingen and Remscheid, where hammer ponds originally supplied the power for the iron industry of the early 19th century and where charcoal was traditionally used for iron smelting.   In 1800, Solingen ceased to produce swords in favour of cutlery.   In the conurbation of Wuppertal (Elberfeld-Barmen) women find employment in the textile mills and the men in mechanical engineering.   Here the firm of Bayer established a dyestuffs industry in 1850, based on coal tar.

The narrow Ruhr valley, aligned east–west along the base of the wooded and pastoral Sauerland, reached its height of prosperity as the centre of coal-mining by the latter half of the 19th century. Today, although still concerned with coal-mining, it lies to the south of the great modern steel centres with which the Ruhr coalfield is associated.   At the mouth of the Ruhr, where it enters the Rhine, are the reconstructed twin river ports of Duisburg-Ruhrort, where the harbour wharves handle more traffic (mainly coal and coke) than those of any other river port in Europe.   To the east, the towns which originated along the *Hellweg* route, extending from Düsseldorf across the Rhine to Mülheim, included Essen, Bochum and Dortmund.   These ancient walled towns, with their medieval core of narrow, winding streets, persisted until the tremendous urban expansion of the late 19th century.   In common with others in this heavily industrialized region, they suffered grim destruction during the war-time *Blitz* on the Ruhr, 30 per cent of the houses in

these towns being destroyed. Since 1945, phenomenal reconstruction has taken place, especially in the business centres of such cities
as Essen and Dortmund, so that they have been completely metamorphosed by the erection of modern steel and concrete structures,
on somewhat American lines. In Essen, many of the old, narrow
streets, in which miners' families live, have survived, terrace housing
fronting directly on to roads paved with basalt blocks from the Eifel.
The ' garden city ' founded by the Krupp family at Margarethen-
hohe, the name of which became synonymous with Essen, has also
been rebuilt. Essen is the traditional ' capital of the Ruhr ' coal
mining and steel industries.

To the north of the lower Ruhr valley, there is a double line of
towns along the Emscher valley, extending from the steel centre of
Oberhausen through Gelsenkirchen and Wanne-Eickel to Herne,
where the Rhine-Herne canal strikes off. All these towns are concerned with coal-mining, coke production, iron and steel manufacture.
North of the Emscher valley are the industrial towns of Hamborn
and Mülheim (formerly identified with the Thyssen family) and the
coal-mining towns of Sterkrade, Bottrop and Recklinghausen.
These towns are essentially the products of the German ' industrial
revolution ' and they lack clearly defined centres and a planned lay-
out. The line of the Lippe valley towns is, by comparison, much
less well developed. Here are the modern collieries, where shafts
have been sunk in the concealed coalfield and where, in place of the
colliery ' villages ' of the older part of the Ruhr, there are the
medieval settlements of Dorsten, Werne and Hamm; the last of
these is notable for its great railway marshalling yards, which, like
Wesel at the lower end of the valley, were both virtually obliterated
by bombing. Along the north-south axis of the Rhine valley are
the ancient towns of Düsseldorf and Duisburg, sited on gravel
terraces on the right bank of the Rhine above the flood-plain
meanders; with Neuss, Krefeld-Uerdingen and Rheinhausen situated
similarly west of the Rhine. These industrial towns, together with
Mönchen-Gladbach, are largely concerned with textile manufacture (see p. 357). Krefeld is also noted for its fine steel. New
industries, such as car assembly, aluminium processing and plastics,
depend largely on thermal electricity produced from the lignite of
the Ville. Outliers of this industrial region are Cologne, with its
pharmaceutical products; its manufacture of the traditional 'eau de
Cologne ' (*Acqua Admirabilis*) by the Farina family dating from the
18th century; its silk industry and car assembly plant (Fords); and
Düren, in the Aachen coalfield region, which has recently developed
a glass manufacturing industry based largely on refugee labour.

Other older industries, such as chemical manufacture, depend upon the by-products of the coking plants, including the production of dyestuffs (aniline dyes) derived from coal tar. These are located at Krefeld-Uerdingen and also at Leverkusen, where *I.G. Farben* began with the production of synthetic ultramarine by Dr. Leverkus in the mid-19th century.

The industrial region of Nord-Rhein-Westfalen makes enormous demands on local water supply for industrial, urban and domestic use. Water is especially needed for cooling and quenching in the blast furnaces, for coal washing, and for steam production in thermal stations. All the rivers draining the coalfield are thus used, including the Ruhr, Emscher, Lippe and also the Rhine itself. Apart from the Rhine, which is the main source of supply, the Ruhr is, perhaps, the most heavily drawn upon, for it has a dependable run-off from the impervious rocks of the Sauerland upland and it discharges relatively slowly into the Rhine. The water also has the advantage of being clean and relatively soft and so is suitable for industrial use. Between 1894 and 1931, several dams were built across the Ruhr and its headstreams, and two of these were seriously damaged by bombing in 1943, taking six years to repair. The Möhne dam was completed in 1908 and it impounds a reservoir with a capacity of 135 million cubic metres, with a regulated flow of 180 cubic metres per annum. Water is pumped regularly from the Ruhr across the low watershed into the Emscher valley, where Gelsenkirchen and Herne have no local sources of supply. The water of the Lippe is hard and saline and so is unsuitable for industrial purposes, although much future industrial development is likely to take place here on the concealed coalfield. In consequence, a reservoir is being built in the Hernetal and another in the Biggetal, to have a capacity of 140 million cubic metres. Electricity supplies in the Ruhr depend entirely on thermal stations, several of which consume lignite briquettes derived from the Ville, and the whole region is integrated with the grid system of north-west Germany. Gas is produced in the Ruhr valley for local needs especially in association with the coking plants and it is also piped to Cologne. The modern competitor is oil, brought either by pipeline or Rhine barge to the modern refineries at Wesseling, below Cologne.

The total population of the Ruhr region was 3·2 million in 1939 but it was reduced to under 2·8 million in 1946. Since then, there was a tremendous influx of refugees from East Germany and also from beyond the ' Iron Curtain ', totalling half a million, until the building of the Berlin Wall in 1961. There has, therefore, been a large reserve of skilled and semi-skilled labour to draw upon for the giant tasks of industrial revival and reconstruction, while, at the same time, there has been an acute housing shortage. About a fifth of the total population is engaged in coal-mining and the same proportion in iron and steel manufacture. In the 'inner Ruhr' area, mining and heavy industry are of overwhelming importance, the only other significant industry being that of glass manufacture, for textiles have hitherto been unrepresented, and there has also been a marked under-development of consumer goods industries. Around this built-up inner core of the Ruhr industrial area, covering some 10 per cent of the coalfield, there is a region of agriculture, pig rearing and dairy farming, associated with the loess soils of the *Haarstrang* near Recklinghausen. These loam terrains produce good crops of wheat, oats, barley, potatoes, vegetables and fodder crops, while the meadow lands along the Ruhr, Emscher and Lippe valleys are used for cattle grazing. There is much waterlogging in these valleys as the result of mining subsidence. Strips of woodland persist even within the 'inner Ruhr', notably in the *Stadtwald* of Duisburg and again north of Recklinghausen, as well as on the steep north-facing slopes of the Sauerland. These belts of natural forest serve as a great local amenity in an otherwise heavily urbanized and industrialized area.

CHAPTER 15

CENTRAL GERMANY: HESSE, THURINGIA AND SAXONY

DIVIDING WESTERN and southern Germany from the north German lowland there lies a belt of country of varying width and height and considerable structural variety and complexity. Central Germany consists of a mosaic of regions of three major types: the Hercynian highlands, the Börde and the coalfields. The zone of Carbo-Permian folding includes a number of important basins and depressions and the sub-Hercynian zone, which lies along the base of the *Mittelgebirge*, with its characteristic loess covering and its various ' bays '. It forms one of the most thickly settled regions in Central Europe, apart from the industrial areas developed on and adjacent to the bituminous coal and lignite fields, for this is a region of great inherent soil fertility and it is also accessible to the large potash deposits of the Stassfurt-Magdeburg region. The major coalfields of West Germany and of post-war Poland lie along the northern edge of the Central Highlands, from the small Aachen field near the German-Belgian border, and the Saar coalfield on the Franco-German border; the Ruhr-Westphalian field, once again the greatest industrial asset of the German Federal Republic; to the Upper Silesian field, now almost entirely Polish except for the Czechoslovak section. The largest reserves and the most important fields of lignite also lie in this zone, especially in the Ville region of the Cologne ' bay ', already described, the Leipzig field, and those fields now being rapidly developed in the upper Spree and middle Oder valleys in the German Democratic Republic.

Central Germany has a certain unity underlying its diversity, since it lies almost entirely within Hercynian Europe and it forms a significant highland and upland barrier between southern and northern Germany, crossed only with difficulty by means of devious routes, other than that through the Rhine and Elbe gorges and the Fulda gap route across the hill country of Hesse. The *Mittelgebirge* form only a minor water-parting; for, of the great rivers draining to the North Sea, only the Weser rises on the northern slope of the Hercynian highlands in the hill country of Hesse; while the Elbe has its course on the southern slope of the Riesen-Gebirge in Czechoslovakia. Similarly, the Oder rises on the south-eastern slope of the Sudetes before turning north-east to enter Poland and the Silesia lowland *en route* to the Baltic at Szczescin (Stettin).

The Palæozoic highlands of central Germany mark the southern limit of the continental or Riss-Saale ice sheet, for the rising ground of the *Mittelgebirge* checked further advance southwards. However, within these highlands, local ice caps developed on the highest summits, as in the Riesen-Gebirge (Schneekoppe, 5,268 ft.). Along the northern margin of the highlands, loess was deposited between the Riss-Saale and Würm phases and this æolian material is also found in the Thuringian basin, as well as in the various bays or re-entrants between the highlands and the northern lowland, notably in the Leipzig region. These Börde lands contain some of the most productive soils in Germany and southern Poland and they support a high density of rural population.

The Central Highlands may be considered as a series of separate units. In the west, the Wetterau and Fulda depressions divide the middle Rhine highlands from the volcanic region of the Hohe Rhön and Vogelsberg. These eruptive massifs partly block the north-eastern extension of the Rhine rift valley, the faults of which are continued through the Wetterau depression; the feature finally terminating in the region of the Fulda gap, where lies the rebuilt town of Kassel. In addition to these basaltic highlands, the secondary folds (Saxonian) are represented by the Teutoburger- wald and the Weser hills, but the chief feature of the *Mittelgebirge* is the series of Palæozoic massifs, folded in Permo-Carboniferous times, subsequently peneplaned and then re-uplifted, faulted and fractured in Miocene times. They are the Thuringian Forest, which thrusts north-westwards from the Franconian Forest, and the Fichtel-Gebirge (Fir Mountains). To the east lie the highland blocks which form the northern framework of the Bohemian massif, the Erz-Gebirge (Ore Mountains) and ' Saxon Switzerland '. The Harz Mountains form an outlying mass of the denuded Hercynian mountain system and they rise as a ' horst ' between the Thuringian basin and the plains of Lower Saxony.

The northern edge of the *Mittelgebirge* is broken by the occurrence of the lowland ' bays ', notably that of Cologne in the west, Münster (or the plain of Westphalia), and Leipzig in the east. Within these regions lie the main coalfields of Central Europe, as already described, and also the minor fields of Saxony and Aachen; while the Ibbenbüren field has been preserved by faulting on the northern flanks of the Teutoburgerwald near Osnabrück.

THE CENTRAL HIGHLANDS OR MITTELGEBIRGE

The Hohe Rhön and the Vogelsberg; the Wetterau and Fulda Depressions

The lava flows of the Hohe Rhön and Vogelsberg massifs form some of the best-preserved regions of eruptive rocks in Germany. Indeed, the Vogelsberg, with its radial valleys scored in basalt flows, exemplifies a landscape similar to that of the Cantal in the Auvergne region of central France.[1] The Vogelsberg does not exceed 2,600 ft., and, although the steeper slopes remain thickly forested, much of the timber has been cleared to provide hill grazing land, and there are also exposures of bare rock where basalt has been quarried. The valleys, often incised 500 ft. into the massif, have ill-drained floors which are frequently filled with peat. They broaden out as they open on to the lowlands to the south-west and north-west, but, in the east, the streams continue to cut narrow trenches in the porous Triassic sandstones. The Vogelsberg is a region of meagre and decreasing rural population. A particularly desolate local region is the *Oberwald*, a stretch of forested country overlooking the Fulda basin. The thick covering of spruce and silver fir on the steep slopes forms a sharp contrast with the bright green of the meadows on the floor of the Fulda depression, the site of a Cistercian monastery, the nucleus of the small town of Fulda.

The Hohe Rhön rises to greater elevations than the Vogelsberg, the Wasserkuppe attaining 3,117 ft. This massif may be described as the ruin of a volcano. Its original radial drainage has been destroyed, with the result that most of the relief is developed on Triassic sandstones and *Muschelkalk*, with basalts crowning the heights, while Eocene clays are preserved in the depression at the foot. This region is even more forbidding than the *Oberwald*; the snow lying longer in winter and the total annual precipitation is greater. The heights have retained their primeval forest cover, beech intermingling with fir on the lower slopes, but with much land in the valleys cleared for pasture and a limited amount of strip cultivation. The region has lost population to the Fulda and Wetterau lowlands and also to the industrial regions of the Ruhr and Siegerland, as well as to those of the Thuringian Forest.

To the south-west of this volcanic region, the Fulda and Wetterau depressions form a continuation of the plain of Rhenish-Hesse, extending into the heart of the forested Bunter sandstone country of Upper Hesse to the north. Of these two corridors, that of the Wetterau lies between the Taunus and the Vogelsberg and here the

[1] E. de Martonne: *Europe Centrale*, Géog. Univ., Vol. 4, p. 268.

Nidda valley provides a passageway from Frankfurt-am-Main to Kassel, the route continuing through Giessen and Marburg on the upper Lahn. The corridor is very narrow where the basalts of the Vogelsberg have flowed over the Eocene and Oligocene clays and sands near Giessen, but it widens considerably to the north-east in the direction of the Kassel ' gate '. The Fulda gap lies to the east, between the Vogelsberg and the Hohe Rhön, and it carries an alternative route from Frankfurt to Kassel *via* the Kinzig valley and the Fulda, a headstream of the Werra. Both these lowlands are floored with easily tilled soils, derived from volcanic downwash and loess, and they have long attracted rural settlement, though the abbey of Fulda was responsible for much of the medieval forest clearance in favour of pasture. There has been much loss of population in recent years to the mining centres of the nearby Lahn and Dill valleys, and this is also true of the Kassel basin; where the town of Kassel, noted before the war as an important centre of locomotive manufacture, has a population of over 211,800.

The Weser Hill Country

The broken upland country which lies between the *Mittelgebirge* and north German lowland is divided from the Münster ' bay ' to the west by the Teutoburger Forest and from the Leipzig-Saale ' bay ' to the east by the massif of the Harz. Below the confluence of the Fulda and Werra at Münden, the Weser begins its meandering course northwards, cutting a series of narrow trenches and deep water gaps through the Weser hills, which trend from south-east to north-west. This region was affected by the Saxonian folding of Jurassic times but the local drainage appears to show no direct relation to it. Erosion has destroyed many of the land forms, though there is marked accordance of summit levels, suggesting Cretaceous peneplanation followed by uplift and dissection. The Riss-Saale ice sheet advanced to the north-eastern foot of the Teutoburgerwald and overrode the Weser hills, so that the deep water gap cut by the Weser at Minden and known locally as the Porta Westfalica, owes its flat floor and steep sides to overdeepening by ice.

In this rather complex region of Mesozoic rocks, the lithology ranges from Bunter sandstone in the south through Liassic clays and Jurassic limestones to Cretaceous rocks. The latter outcrops on the western margin of the region in the Egge-Gebirge, south of the Teutoburgerwald, and on each side of the Leine valley, south of Hanover; while Primary rocks occur to the south-east as the Harz is approached. The dissected hill country of the upper

Weser basin lies between the plain of Westphalia and the flat, drift-covered plains of Hanover and Oldenburg. The Weser and Leine valleys are regions of fairly dense rural settlement, for the drift-derived soils overlying the Keuper marls and Jurassic limestones are intensively farmed. Forest land remains only on the sand-stone and limestone heights, where modern re-afforestation has replaced timber felled frequently in the past to provide charcoal for iron smelting. The iron ore is associated with the Jurassic limestone of the Osnabrück region and it is worked today as the basis of heavy industry on the coalfield at Ibbenbüren.

The Teutoburger Forest

This finger-like ridge, rising in a crescentic sweep to the east of the Münster ' bay ', extends for over 60 miles through Bielefeld and Tecklenburg towards the Ems valley, the ridge varying in width from 5 to 10 miles. The landscapes of the Teutoburgerwald offer the closest parallel to the scarplands of the English Plain to be found in northern Germany. There are two main ridges, the Teutoburgerwald proper, developed on Cretaceous and Jurassic limestones, and the Wiehen-Gebirge, trending west–east, an area of eroded Triassic rocks fringed by Cretaceous. This scarp and vale country divides the Ems from the Weser drainage. There are several dry wind gaps as well as the water gap of the Porta West-falica at Minden, and they provide sites for local route centres and small industrial towns such as Herford and Bielefeld, with its light engineering works. The Teutoburgerwald marked the effective limit of Roman conquest in Germany and it was not effectively settled until the later Middle Ages, though the *Hellweg* road of Charlemagne passed to the south of it through Soest and Paderborn. The half-timbered houses of such medieval settlements as Tecklenburg reflect the forest environment and much primeval beechwood remains, with firs on the sandy outcrops. In the Lippe valley, oak wood prevails on the Keuper marls. Salt and gypsum are worked near Bad Pyrmont, at the foot of the Pyrmont Berg (820 ft.).

The Harz and Kyffhäuser Ridge

The massif of the Harz is one of the most clearly defined physical regions in Germany, though today it is cut by the boundary be-tween West and East Germany. It forms an elliptical block, trending north-west to south-east, between the valleys of the Leine and the Saale. The hill country of Brunswick lies to the north; the *Goldene Aue* and the Kyffhäuser ridge dividing it from the Thuringian basin to the south. It has a maximum extent of 50

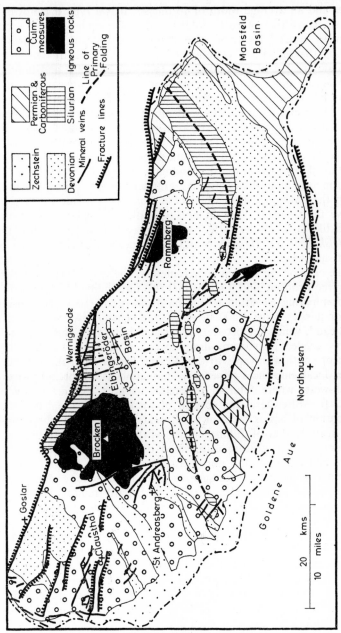

FIG. 111. The structure of the Harz mountains.

miles and an average width of 16 miles.   It is a typical Hercynian massif, consisting of rocks folded and metamorphosed in Carbo-Permian times.   Its trend also shows the influence of Jurassic folding (Saxonian), in common with the Weser hills.   The post-Jurassic erosion of the massif was followed by uplift and faulting in Miocene times, so that the block presents the appearance of a true 'horst' with a steep, faulted northern edge; while other lines of faults trend from east to west along the southern margin, and they also occur in the north-west, north–south faults traversing the centre of the block.   The relief is, however, generally subdued; the sky line exhibiting broad, rounded outlines, the product of long-continued erosion.   Even the landmark of the Brocken (3,745 ft.) is a smooth, hump-like mass; the grandeur of the scenery resulting from the sweeping views obtainable from the summit which rises above the tree-line (here under 3,000 ft.).   The blocks of granite piled like tors on the surface of the massif have been called the *Teufelskanzel* and *Hexenalter* and they appear to be the product of frost shattering.

The core of the Harz is represented by the igneous rocks under-lying the Brocken, and it seems that this upstanding block may owe its dominating elevation to the hardness of the rocks composing it, for it rises some 1,500 ft. above the general level of the Harz 'plateau', which lies between 2,000 and 1,500 ft.   This surface is deeply eroded by streams draining either north-eastwards to the Elbe or south-westwards to the Weser.   Apart from the Brocken, other local eminences appear as 'monadnocks', especially to the south-west, where Silurian quartzites underlie *Auf der Acker* at 2,822 ft.   Elsewhere, the erosion of weaker rocks has led to the formation of basins between the Brocken and the Raumberg mas-sifs, such as that of Elbinggeröder where the Culm measures are preserved.   This feature is repeated on the southern side of the Harz and again in the north-east.   Across these basins, streams meander in incised valleys such as that of the Bode, opening east-wards to the Mansfeld basin.   The northward-trending valleys are deep and narrow, while those leading southwards are broader but still incised.

The Harz may be divided into four sub-regions: the upper Harz, between St. Andreasberg and Goslar, in the north-west; the Brocken massif; the eastern Harz; and the southern Harz.   The upper Harz mountains are developed on Devonian and Carboniferous rocks, strongly folded and fractured.   These high, well-dissected ridges rise steeply from the northern foreland.   Within this region is the Clausthal mining district in the Culm belt.   Contact metamorphism around the margins of the Brocken igneous massif is related to the occurrence of a variety of non-ferrous metals worked since medieval times, notably copper, silver-lead and zinc ores. Exploitation of these mineral veins led to extensive deforestation in the production of charcoal for smelting, but today interest lies mainly on the working of radio-active ores. To the east of the mineralized region, the Harz Mountains exhibit generally lower relief, except for the isolated massif of the Raumberg. Here are a number of fractures marking the broken descent to the northern plain around Quedlinburg. Silurian and Devonian rocks predominate in this eastern zone, where the Hercynian folding of the rocks gives rise to a marked east–west ridge and valley feature, especially where the Selke basin is divided by the Homburger saddle from the Mansfeld basin with its potash deposits. In the southern Harz, there are traces of Caledonian folding along a north-east–south-west axis, but the main trend is Hercynian. In the south, the high points are the Sonneberg (2,801 ft.) and the Rehberg (2,933 ft.), where quartzites form resistant ridges rising above the Culm Measures.

Although much of the forest has been cleared in the past during the course of settlement, mining and quarrying, many of the steep slopes of the range remain clothed in fir forest. This may extend to the crest of the range, except on the Brocken which exceeds the tree limit by over 300 ft., so that wind-swept moorland covers the summit. There is much peat in the valleys and, on account of the short growing season, there is less land under crops than in most of the Hercynian massifs of Central Europe. Exposure to cold north-east winds in winter and heavy snowfall characterize most of the Harz, and winter temperatures are below freezing point. De Martonne has described the Harz as ' deeply humanized '. Its effect as a relief barrier is minimized by its compactness and detachment; while its mineral wealth attracted German miners to the region from the *Rodungszeit* onwards, though the settlements of Clausthal and St. Andreasberg date from the Reformation. Some industrial centres have developed, utilizing originally local ores and raw materials as well as water power, but, in place of the charcoal of former times, coal is now brought from the Ruhr for the smelting of ores. Tip heaps and hammer ponds may be seen in many of the western valleys, bearing witness to former mining and smelting industries. The flooding of the European market with cheap bullion from Spanish America and the devastating effects of the Thirty Years' War meant a serious set-back to mining in the 17th century but it revived again in the following century, the mining academy at Clausthal dating from 1775. Today the massif is divided politically, for the boundary between West and East Germany passes through the Harz. There are a number of small towns around the periphery of the massif, including Goslar, Halberstadt, Aschersleben, Mansfeld and Nordhausen. In recent years, villages of early medieval origin have developed into spas and health resorts, for example Bad Harzburg, Wernigerode, Blankenburg and Quedlinburg.

The Kyffhäuser Ridge

This outlier of the Harz lies to the south-east of the main massif, from which it is divided by the *Goldene Aue*. It presents a steep slope to the north and a gentle one to the south, rising to a general height of over 1,500 ft. It has a core of gneissic and granitic rocks, flanked by Upper Carboniferous and Permian formations, including bands of *Zechstein*, yielding salt. The highest point reaches 1,554 ft. and the ridge provides extensive views northwards over the *Goldene Aue* (Golden Meadows) towards the Harz and also southwards towards the Thuringian Forest. Beechwoods cover many of the slopes, while a local feature is the Barbarossa cave, where alabaster and gypsum occur. Mineral salts have led to the growth of the spa town of Bad Frankenhausen and there are also other health resorts such as Rossla and Sonderhausen.

THURINGIA

The upper basin of the Saale is composed of two sharply contrasted regions, the Thuringian Forest and the Thuringian basin. Both lie within ' Hercynian ' Europe, the Thüringerwald forming the divide between drainage southwards to the Main (partly by the Franconian Saale) and northwards to the Elbe (*via* the Thuringian Saale). Whereas the Thuringian Forest forms a sharp line of demarcation between Thuringia and Franconia to the south-west, the western and eastern limits of the district are less clearly defined by natural boundaries. In the west, the Meissner hill country beyond the Werra valley forms a break between the Forest and the Fulda depression, which the Werra enters at Münden north of the Meissner block. To the east, the Thuringian basin slopes to the Leipzig ' bay ', which the Saale enters below its confluence with the Unstrut at Naumburg. To the north, the Thuringian basin is divided from the Hercynian outpost of the Harz by the tectonic trough of the *Goldene Aue*, drained by the Helme tributary of the Unstrut. The Kyffhäuser ridge separates the *Goldene Aue* from the main Unstrut basin.

The medieval province of Thuringia evolved on the physical

divide between north and south Germany and also in a region where the speech of Franks, Saxons and Slavs intermingled. The Forest, in contrast with the Thuringian basin, was settled late, in spite of the importance of the Eisenach ' gate ' at the north-western end of the ridge. Much of this forest region was populated during the *Rodungszeit*, and the population increased as the traditional craft industries developed using local timber, sand for glass, clay for pottery and porcelain, and mineral ores, now including pitchblende.

The Thuringian Forest

Thrusting north-westwards from the Fichtel-Gebirge massif in bayonet fashion, the Thuringian Forest extends from the upper Saale valley at Hof to Eisenach, a distance of 65 miles. The ridge averages 3,000 ft. and attains its highest elevations in the Grosser Beerberg (3,222 ft.), the Schneekopf (3,209 ft.), and the Grosser Inselsberg (3,005 ft.). It has many features in common with the other Hercynian highlands of Central Europe. It is an excellent example of a dissected block mountain bounded by faults and its width does not exceed 10–15 miles. The Forest differs in detail from other parts of the *Mittelgebirge* in structural form and it is mainly composed of Permian sandstones and conglomerates, with large-scale porphyry intrusions forming the highest points. There are ' windows ' where the underlying granites are exposed, for example at Brotterode, Suhl and Zella-Mehlis, while mica schists underlie the Ruhla saddle. There is a sharp structural break south-east of a line from Gehren to Lichtenau, where the Permian cover has been stripped to reveal the underlying Cambrian slates. Here the broad, swelling uplands form a continuation of the Frankenwald in the Upper Palatinate.

The Thüringerwald, folded in Permo-Carboniferous times and subsequently peneplaned, underwent uplift *en bloc* and also faulting and fracturing in Miocene times. Erosion has subsequently partly destroyed this horst-like character, but from a distance the even sky line gives the impression of a uniform plateau almost to the summit. Actually, there is a series of rounded crests divided by saddles, as at Ruhla, and the Forest is dissected by a number of streams which rise below the crest. The divide is followed by an ancient trackway, known as the *Rennsteig*, and this traverses the Forest from Hörschel on the Werra to Blankenstein on the Saale, the tract providing wide views over the Forest.

The youthful character of the Thüringerwald is probably best exemplified in the north-west, where fracture lines converge on

Eisenach and here the ridge is at its steepest and narrowest. Around this town lies a down-faulted depression in which younger rocks have been preserved, notably Triassic marls and Lias. The name 'Thuringian gate' has been given to this historic passage land. On account of its mid-European location, together with its exposure to moisture-laden winds from the south-west, the Thuringian Forest experiences a severe winter climate with considerable snowfall, and generally higher annual precipitation than occurs on the surrounding lowlands and basins. Moreover, soils weathered from the Palæozoic rocks are thin and poor, and it is on account of the mineral and forest resources that population has long been attracted to the region. Iron ore has been smelted here with the aid of charcoal since the 11th century, the renowned centres of metal working (including both iron and copper ores) being Suhl and Schmalkalden. The suitability of the local sand as the basis of a glass industry led to the location of this craft at Ilmenau, north of the Forest. Kaolin, weathered from the local granite, provides the raw material for the production of porcelain at Sonneberg south of the Forest, and also at Waltershausen to the north near the Inselsberg. Many of these typical Thuringian hand industries have now been transplanted to West Germany. Within the Thuringian Forest, mineral springs frequently occur and their attraction, together with the ' green heart of Germany ', has led to the growth of a number of small spas, such as Bad Salzungen in the Werra valley and Bad Liebenstein in the shelter of the Inselsberg.

The Thuringian Basin

Inner Thuringia lies between the Thuringian and Franconian Forests to the south and the Kyffhäuser and Bottendörfer heights to the north. The lowland is drained from west to east by the Unstrut and Ilm rivers, both of which in turn join the north-flowing Saale. The basin lies between the two Hercynian uplands of the Harz and the Thuringian Forest and so has served for many centuries as a passage land, a fact reflected in the historic rôle and growth of such regional centres as Weimar, Jena and Erfurt. The structure and relief compare to a certain degree with the scarplands of Swabia and Franconia, though there is less variety. The diversified landscapes of the Thuringian basin are developed on Triassic sandstones, limestones and marls and, since Miocene tilting, the more resistant Bunter sandstones and *Muschelkalk* limestones have been eroded into steep scarp ridges. These scarps wind in festoons across the basin and they have largely retained their primeval forest cover, in contrast with the cleared and cultivated land developed on the more easily eroded Keuper marls. The *Muschelkalk* scarpland is well developed north of Gotha and Erfurt, where the Gera river cuts a narrow gorge through the ridge known as the Fahnersche Höhe, which rises to 1,345 ft. North of Weimar, the scarp is less well preserved but it reaches 1,122 ft. in the Ettersberg. To the east, the Ilm and Saale rivers pursue a winding course through scarp and vale country. These meandering streams flow in rejuvenated valleys, with well-marked Pliocene and Pleistocene river terraces. In contrast, the Unstrut drains the western basin, flowing in a broad sweep across Keuper marls. Its course appears to antedate the Miocene uplift of the Harz and Thuringian Forest, and its direction has been modified by the advance of the Saale ice, the limit of which may be traced along a line through Gotha, Erfurt and Weimar. To the north of this limit, boulder clay and other glacial drift material were laid down and loess deposits occur to the south. These loess regions form open country, with rich though relatively light soils, and they have long been free of woodland, so that they have attracted settlement from prehistoric times onwards. Steppe-heath vegetation occurs on these black earth soils but this has been mostly replaced by arable farm land, especially where the soils are enriched by downwash from *Muschelkalk* limestones giving a rich loam, with an abundant water supply derived from springs issuing at the base of the scarp. In contrast, the cold clay lands are best suited to pasture, and they, together with the rather sterile tracts found on the Bunter sandstones, carry a much lower population density than those derived from *Muschelkalk*, loess and glacial drift.

SAXONY

The Highlands of Saxony: The Erz-Gebirge and the Vogtland

The boundary between East Germany and Czechoslovakia follows the crest of the Erz-Gebirge, from the Fichtel-Gebirge in the south-west to the Dresden 'gate' in the north-east. These highlands offer a fairly simple example of Hercynian folding, presenting a rugged and abrupt slope to Bohemia and a gentle one to Saxony and the Elster-Mulde basins. The long, level sky line is broken only occasionally over a distance of 45 miles, especially where vulcanism has occurred. The basaltic eminence of the Hässberg (3,248 ft.) offers an example. On both sides of the range, Coal Measures have been preserved in synclinal basins, notably at Chemnitz (now renamed Karl-Marx-Stadt) and at Zwickau. There are also lignite beds of Tertiary age on the margins of the uplands.

The Riss-Saale ice extended into the Erz-Gebirge, so that drift lies thickly spread in many of the mountain valleys and there is some accumulation of peat resulting from poor surface drainage. The raw climate and acid soils favour thick stands of fir forest but some of this timber has been cleared, especially on the Saxony slope, for upland pasture and strip cultivation.   However, the main attraction to settlement since medieval times, as the name Ore Mountains suggests, has been the mineral wealth, especially silver, lead and copper ores.   Today, abandoned tip heaps and workings point to this formerly important activity.   There are a few small market and industrial towns such as Freiberg and Annaberg, where local raw materials, notably silver ore, as well as water power, provided the original bases of industry.   The density of population is highest on the coalfields at the foot of the uplands, where it varies from 520 to 1,550 to the square mile.

The Erz-Gebirge

Two types of country may be distinguished.   The western region resembles the Thuringian Forest in structure and land forms, with schists and slates predominating.   To the east, these rocks thin out and are replaced by gneiss which forms the core of the mountain system, accompanied by intrusions of granite and porphyry.   In the west, there are also large granitic masses weathering into rounded eminences, rising in the Auersberg to 3,333 ft.   The greatest elevations occur, however, in the centre of the range, where mica schists form narrow resistant ridges between the Cambrian slates to the west and crystalline rocks to the east.   The Keilberg (4,088 ft.) and the Fichtel Berg (3,980 ft.) are two of the highest points, drainage radiating from this region.   Towards the east, the landscape is strikingly monotonous and unbroken.   The general altitude seldom exceeds 2,900 ft., while fir forests cover great tracts of country.   This part of the Erz-Gebirge includes many of the former mineral-bearing districts, notably around Freiberg, where its once famous lead mines are now exhausted.   Veins of silver, nickel, cobalt, zinc and copper ores have also been worked here.   The fact that a medieval salt road penetrated the forest here also led to settlement.   After the flooding of the Old World by precious metal from Spanish America and the devastation of the Thirty Years' War in the first part of the 17th century, the miners of the Erz-Gebirge turned to new activities, especially the making of glass and paper, wood working, and the dyeing of textiles with cobalt. There was also some increase in the amount of cleared and improved land at the expense of the forest. Today the exploitation of radio-active ores increases the political significance of this frontier region.

The Vogtland

This distinctive region lies in the south-west of Saxony, between the Erz-Gebirge and the Thuringian Forest. It is drained north-wards by the Elster. The Vogtland was penetrated by the Slavs in early medieval times and, before the second world war, there was much admixture of German and Czech elements. Fairly easy of access compared with the neighbouring highlands, this broken hill country lies on a major route through Hof and Plauen to the industrial region around Zwickau, while another route converges on Hof from Cheb in the Ohře valley in Bohemia. The hills of the Vogtland, with their abundant mineral springs, are noted for a number of small spas and health resorts, such as Bad Brambach and Bad Elster, both with radio-active mineral springs. Plauen is, however, the chief regional centre, with important textile manufactures.

Saxon Switzerland and Ober Lausitz

To the east of the Erz-Gebirge lies the Cretaceous sandstone country which was named by Swiss artists in the 18th century ' Saxon Switzerland '. It is traversed by the Elbe gorge between Teschen and Pirna in the region of the Czech-German frontier. To the east of the Elbe or Dresden ' gate ' lies the Lausitz-Gebirge, where land forms similar to those of the Erz-Gebirge occur. The scenery found in Saxon Switzerland forms a striking contrast. The Elbe and its tributaries have eroded the Cretaceous sandstones into fantastic landscapes, which, in places, assume desert and canyon-like forms. The yellowish rocks have been weathered into arches, stacks and pinnacles, while jagged buttes rise above the plateau. Across this surface, the Elbe has cut an epigenetic gorge, reminiscent of that of the middle Rhine, and margined by sheer sandstone cliffs which rise to over 600 ft. A local viewpoint is that of the Bastei, which attains a height of 1,040 ft. and stands over 700 ft. above the Elbe river. The Elbe has been regulated in this section, so that, until the post-war paralysis of traffic between Czechoslovakia and Germany, barges made their way through the gorge to the Czech port of Ústí (Aussig).

In contrast to Saxon Switzerland, the uplands of Ober Lausitz mark the continuation of the Hercynian framework of Bohemia. Bautzen is the chief town. To the north-west, in a region of heaths and lakes, a number of Slavonic villages occur, populated by Wends.

Kaolin has long been worked in the neighbourhood, especially for the world-famous porcelain industry of which Dresden is the centre. Today, the production of works of art at Meissen, where the ' Dresden ' factories are located, have to fit into a succession of Five- and now Seven-Year plans. Much of the industry has been re-established in West Germany.

CHAPTER 16

NORTHERN GERMANY: THE NORTH GERMAN LOWLAND

THE STRIKING monotony of the north German lowland offers a sharp contrast with the varied landscapes of the *Mittelgebirge* to the south. There are few districts which rise above 1,000 ft., except in those regions which now lie in Poland, where the Turmberg and the Kernsdörfer Höhe near Danzig (Gdansk) attain over 1,025 ft. Only the extreme south is endowed with rich soils and this is the region of the Börde, described elsewhere (p. 369). Apart from this sub-Hercynian zone, the northern lowland may be regarded as a plain of recent accumulation, differentiated only according to variations in the occurrence of the Pleistocene drift deposits, for solid rocks appear hardly at all. An exception occurs on the Baltic island of Rügen, where the Chalk forms steep cliffs known as the Königstuhl. The thickness of the glacial drift is very variable but it attains its greatest depth in the regions of the Newer Drift, east of the Elbe. The lowland may be considered in four distinct regions: the North Sea coastlands; the short stretch of Baltic coast left within post-war Germany; the central lowland or *Geest*; and primeval valleys or *Urstromtäler*.

The North Sea Coastlands

West of the Elbe, in Hanover, Oldenburg and Lower Saxony, the north German lowland is mantled by the Older Drift of the Riss-Saale phase. Much of this drift has been modified, reassorted and redistributed, and the great terminal moraines found east of the Elbe have been largely destroyed here. The relief is low and monotonous and the slope from the Hanover Börde to the North Sea coast is very gradual. This is a lowland of glacial accumulation and post-glacial deposition. There are deep-seated traces of Saxonian folding (Jurassic), perhaps reflected in the trend of the drainage of the Weser and Elbe from south-east to north-west. The plain appears to have been entirely base levelled before the advance of the Pleistocene ice.

The North Sea coastlands of the German Federal Republic extend from the Dollart on the Dutch frontier, to the island of Sylt in North Frisia south of the Danish frontier, a total distance

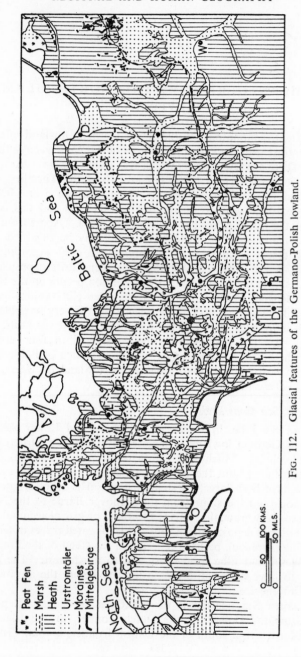

FIG. 112. Glacial features of the Germano-Polish lowland.

of 165 miles. This stretch of coast which faces the Heligoland Bight falls into two sections: a westerly one, where the East Frisian islands lie offshore, and an easterly one, where the low coast is broken by bays and great estuaries, notably Jade Bay and the tidal mouths of the Weser and the Elbe rivers.

The East Frisian coast is a continuation of that of the Low Countries both physiographically and climatically. The land slopes almost imperceptibly into the sea and there are no cliffs, while the winters are the mildest in Germany and humidity is high. As the result of the partial submergence of the coast during the post-glacial Flandrian transgression, the Frisian islands were detached from the mainland. Today wide stretches of mud-flats known as *Watten*, exposed at low tide and criss-crossed by rivulets submerged at high tide, divide the islands from the mainland. Behind the coast, with its low sand dunes, are the dyked and reclaimed polder lands, forming rich coastal marshes. These polders have been partly reclaimed by natural processes, the sea samphire aiding consolidation of the mud if left long above the reach of the tide, but the work of the Dutch engineers in building the sea dykes, especially in the 17th century, is largely responsible. Farms are situated above the limit of winter floods, often on dykes or on the inner edge of the marshes, where the sandy tracts of *Geest* begin. These are the ' golden marshes ', renowned for their Frisian cattle. The islands off the coast form a *cordon littoral* and they extend from Borkum to Wangeroog. They consist partly of sand dunes and partly of polder land; the islanders combining the life of fisher-folk with that of dairy farmers. The islands peter out off the great estuaries of the Weser and the Elbe, except for the isolated Bunter sandstone bevelled stack of Heligoland, but they reappear off the coast of Scheswig-Holstein, where prevalent westerly winds have also piled up sand dunes, especially in the North Frisian islands. Marine sand and glacial material underlie the most northerly island of Sylt, the shape of which resembles the head of a hammer. Apart from the former strategic importance of the pre-war naval base of Sylt, approached from the mainland by the Hindenburg dam, the island also became a famous seaside resort, with magnificent sand dunes rising behind the dead-straight North Sea coast.

The estuarine section of the North Sea coast is broken by the mouths of the Ems, Weser and Elbe rivers. These great funnel-shaped estuaries are subject to strong tidal scour but nevertheless they call for constant dredging to prevent silting. Only Emden is sufficiently accessible to deep water to make the development of a modern outport unnecessary. In contrast, the outports for Bremen are at Bremerhaven and Wesermunde, where deep water favours the launching of ships; while Cuxhaven serves as the passenger output for Hamburg, which is 85 miles up the Elbe estuary.

To the east of the mouth of the Elbe lies the southern part of the Jutland peninsula in Schleswig-Holstein. This isthmian region, between the North Sea and the Baltic or *Ostsee*, lies at the root of the Danish peninsula and exhibits transitional features, especially climatically, for the west coast from the Elbe estuary to Sylt is fully exposed to mild, maritime westerly influences, with high humidity, autumn fogs and mists. Soils are frequently badly drained and peat tends to encroach on beech woods. In contrast, the eastern side of the peninsula experiences a more continental type of climate, where ice accumulates in winter, notably in Kiel Bay. Between these two types of coast is the backbone of the peninsula, formed by the terminal morainic ridges which swing round from Jutland through Schleswig-Holstein into Mecklenburg and which mark the terminal phase of the Würm-Vistula ice.

The west coast of Schleswig-Holstein is a continuation of that of Frisia. Great stretches of mud-flats or *Watten* are revealed by the retreating tide and they are then criss-crossed by a maze of winding channels. Behind the coastal dunes are reclaimed marsh polders, protected by sea dykes from inroads from the North Sea. These pasture lands again give way to sandy *Geest* country, marking the Pleistocene shore line. Here sandy tracts alternate with heath and marsh so that the scenery resembles the Lüneberg Heath, while extensive pine forests occur in the vicinity of the health resort of Bad Bramstedt. This rather forlorn region is estimated to be 9 per cent under peat, 47 per cent under heath and only 23 per cent under cultivation. Settlement is of the ' dry point ' type and is mainly to be found on the higher ground of the terminal moraines. On the Baltic slope of the peninsula, the relief is more accentuated. Here the *Förde* coast is the product of partial submergence during the Yoldia stage of the glacial retreat and again during the Littorina phase which de Geer put at 7,000 years ago. Post-glacial ravines lead down to these inlets and this region has been named Holstein Switzerland. Behind the coast, hills rise to over 300 ft. and lakes lie in the depressions between the ridges. On the Danish frontier stands the town of Flensburg, on the largest of the *Förde*, the inlet penetrating 25 miles inland. Today it has a population of 93,000, compared with 67,000 prior to 1939, but its size, like that of other towns and villages in Schleswig-Holstein, has been greatly increased in post-war years by the influx of refugees from East Germany (p. 266). The increase in population density between 1939 and

1946 was estimated to be over 70 per cent for the province as a whole, but since then there has been a wholesale migration into West Germany, especially into the Ruhr and the Rhineland, where the refugees from Schleswig-Holstein have often formed strong minority groups.[1]

The pre-war naval base of Kiel lies on Kiel Bay, at the Baltic entrance to the North-Sea–Baltic or Kiel ship canal. This canal extends for 62 miles from Kiel harbour, near Holtenau, to Brunsbüttel on the North Sea coast. The canal is spanned at a height of 138 ft. by five bridges, the most remarkable of which is the high-level railway bridge near Rendsburg. It carries the main line from Hamburg to Copenhagen, approaching the bridge by means of long spiral ramps. The *Autobahn* from Hamburg to Copenhagen also crosses the canal at Rendsburg.

The Baltic Coast of Mecklenburg

In contrast to the North Sea coast, that of the Baltic or *Ostsee* is remarkably smooth and regular. It is the product of post-Pleistocene changes and the evolution of the shore line may be traced from the Yoldia Sea phase, through the Ancylus lake and the final Littorina phases. There is a marked absence of tides along the coast and the broad rivers which enter the Baltic cannot clear their estuaries. Consequently, under the influence of longshore drift, material is swept along the coast from the west and piled up in the form of fringing bars and spits which partly enclose broad, shallow bays. Das Haff, now divided by the East German-Polish boundary, provides a striking example.

The western Baltic coast may be considered in two sections: the *Förden* coast, extending from the Danish frontier at Flensburg to the Wagrien peninsula between Kiel and Lübeck, already described, and the *Bodden* coast from Lübeck to Das Haff. The latter type of coast is the result of post-glacial partial submergence of an irregular, glaciated land surface and the coast is characterized by offshore islands, spits and shingle bars which link the islands to each other as well as to the mainland, as *tomboli*. The dune ridges which have been progressively built up and added to the land are divided by narrow troughs, known as *Dünentäler*. East of Warnemünde, the feature known as Darsser-Ort provides a notable example of this process of shore accumulation, the peninsula almost completely cutting off three *Bodden* or salt-water lagoons from the Baltic Sea. Other examples occur on the island of Rügen, which has a remarkably fretted and broken coastline. Off the mouth of

[1] P. George and J. Tricart: *L'Europe Centrale*, Vol. 2, 1954, p. 337.

the Oder, two large islands, Usedom and Wollin, close the gap between the river at Stettin (Szczescin), so that the middle channel between the islands, known as the Swine, forms the main channel to Swinemünde (Swinoujscie); while there are two minor channels to the Baltic, one to the west of Usedom leading to Peenemünde and the other east of Wollin. Formerly, the Oder provided an outlet for the industrial region of Upper Silesia, but the creation of the post-war Polish-German boundary along the Oder-Neisse has virtually paralysed traffic.

The Central Lowland of ' Geest ' and ' Urstromtäler '

The low but diversified landscape of the north German lowland, apart from the coastal features already described, is developed on the Riss-Saale drift west of the Elbe-Saale line and on the Vistula-Würm features to the east. Apart from the widespread stretches of marsh and peat bog as well as broad alluvial valleys such as occur along the Weser and Elbe rivers, the most striking feature of western Germany is the *Geest*. This feature underlies the Lüneburger Heide, the Fläming and the heaths of Nieder Lausitz. Beyond the Elbe, the effects of the various stages of the Vistula glaciation may be traced in the great melt-water channels which wind across the plain and the long terminal moraines which stretch from Schleswig-Holstein across Mecklenburg and so into modern Poland, where they form the Baltic Heights or *Landrücken*.

The Regions of the ' Geest '

The *Geest* consists of fluvioglacial outwash material and it forms low hills or plateaux, seldom rising above 150 ft., though rarely it reaches 550 ft. In these regions, the water-table is deep seated on account of the pervious nature of the sands underlying the heaths and there is a conspicuous absence of surface water. In the Lüneburger Heide drainage is thrown off underground to the Elbe and the Weser respectively. Soils are light in texture and colour, leached and acid in reaction, and, in consequence, support a natural vegetation of heather moor, with here and there groups of birches, juniper, poplars and pines. Patches of sphagnum mark the boggy areas, where drainage is held up by the formation of hardpan or *Ortstein* below the surface sand. Thus a distinction may be made between the ' high moor ', with its dry heath landscape (the *Heide* or *Sandgeest*) lying above 100 ft., and the waterlogged tracts with frequent peat bogs (the *Moorgeest*) lying between 40 and 50 ft. There was a general attempt to reclaim the sandy *Geest* in the 19th century by first burning the heather and peat and sowing buckwheat in the ashes. The proximity of the *Geest* regions to the potash salts of Stassfurt proved an advantage in reclaiming the ' sand box ' of Prussia and in making the soils tractable, but the *Geest* has been modified mainly by extensive afforestation by pinewoods, both in the Lüneburger Heide and the Fläming. The heath regions remain as grazing land, especially for sheep, and honey is a local product. In the Fläming much reclamation has been done in the past by the Flemings, as the name suggests, through the cutting of drainage ditches and channels through the peat. Many of these scantily populated regions were the scene of ' colonization ' during the time of Frederick the Great, and of such ' planted ' settlements as Papenburg, in Hanover.

The Regions of the Baltic Heights and ' Urstromtäler '

East of the diagonal line of the Elbe, the north German lowland saw the advance of the Vistula-Würm ice sheet and here the impress of the ice is so recent that erosion has not yet modified the pattern of the drift as it has to the west. Consequently it is the major element responsible for the character of the relief, drainage, soils and land use. The drift attains a thickness of 1,000 ft. in some regions, notably in the Baltic Heights where the Pomeranian stage is represented. To the south of these hills lies the drift of the Frankfurt phase and, south of that, the Brandenburg phase is represented in the central plain, notably in the Spree-Havel region around Berlin. Between the main morainic ridges lie a number of badly drained depressions, frequently partly filled with peat and often containing small and irregular lakes, notably in the Mecklenburg lake plateau. Along the Baltic coast, ground moraine covers wide stretches and, behind it, there are drumlin ridges. Where the frontal moraines have been destroyed, accumulations of erratics and stony stretches form elongated ridges and some-times ' push ' moraines occur. Where sandy outwash lies in front of the moraines, heath and pinewoods occur. These districts are known as *Sander* and are usually afforested or left to pasture, for the soils are too poor for cultivation. Before the war, these coastal regions of the Baltic were the home of the *Junkers* and their large estates supported a small total population. Since 1945, under Communism, these estates have been broken up and the land divided amongst the peasants, as part of a series of ' plans ' applied to the economy of the German Democratic Republic.

To the south of the main morainic ridges are the great melt-water channels, eroded along the edges of the retreating ice sheet. West of the Elbe, these features are shallow and of minor importance, though they may be traced, for example, behind Bremen. Between the Elbe and the Oder, on the other hand, they are wider and more extensive and they break up the *Geest* into a series of detached regions. The *Urstromtäler* trend mainly west to east across the centre of the plain and they are followed in part by existing water courses. In the south is the channel which extends from the middle Oder to Magdeburg on the Elbe, and it appears to continue along the line of the Aller towards the Weser behind Bremen. Another may be traced from Glogau along the Oder and then to Kottbus and Baruth, thus to the Elbe north of Magdeburg. A third is followed by the Oder-Spree canal to Berlin, where its course is utilized westwards by the Spree-Havel canal and then by the Havel. The Warthe tributary of the Vistula also lies in such a channel and, west of the Oder, it continues north of Berlin to the lower Elbe.

HUMAN GEOGRAPHY

The rôle of the north German lowland as an historic passage land between eastern Europe and the lower Rhineland is a recurrent feature from prehistoric times to the chequered present, when the boundary between West and East Germany severs the North Sea lowlands from those draining to the Baltic east of Lübeck. Prior to the Roman conquest of Lower Germany, the Börde zone at the foot of the *Mitteldeutschen Gebirgsschwelle* had favoured the spread of the Bronze Age culture from the Danubian lands across Central Europe to the West. It is claimed that these loess lands were continuously occupied through the four centuries of Romanization of the Rhinelands and Western Germany[1] but they were subsequently to see the advance of the Slavonic tribes westwards in the wake of the Frisians, Saxons and Burgundians, during the *Völkerwanderungszeit*. It was Charlemagne who defined the boundary between the lands of the Germans and the Slavs in 900 as the *limes Sorabicus*. This historic and ' ethnic ' line extended from the south-west corner of the Baltic coast to the middle Elbe and thence along the Saale to the *Mittelgebirge*. To the east lay the *Sorbenwall*, the eastern limit of the Germanic tribes, and this later became the region of the *Grenzmark*, where a mixture of Low Germanic and Slavonic languages was spoken. In the Baltic coastlands were the Mark of the Billungs (modern Mecklenburg) and the Nordmark (later Brandenburg). The Ostmark (Lausitz or Lusatia) and the Mark of Thuringia extended northwards from the *Mittelgebirge*. Here forest clearing

[1] A. Dopsch: *Wirtschaftliche u. soziale Grundlagen der europäischen Kulturentwicklung*, 1924.

villages or *Waldhufendörfer* were established by the Slavonic Markomanni tribes, as in the Czech lands of Bohemia and Moravia. These became tributary to Germany in 950 but the independent kingdom of Bohemia was established in 1088.

West of the so-called Elbe-Saale line, settlement by Saxon and Thuringian tribes proceeded on the feudal Germanic pattern. The open-field system of cultivation spread at the time of Charlemagne and became associated with agglomerated village settlement. Along the southern margin of the plain of Westphalia, especially along the *Hellweg* route through the Haarstrang, walled towns developed, notably Dortmund, Soest and Paderborn; centres of a rich agricultural zone coinciding with loess soils. Along the lower Rhine, the Roman foundations of Cleves, Xanten and Kalcar played a minor rôle compared with the great medieval cathedral cities of Cologne and Münster; while, along the North Sea coast, Bremen and Hamburg originated as trading communities at the head of great tidal estuaries. Much of the marshland fringing the North Sea coast and lying on the Frisian islands behind the outer dunes remained unreclaimed until the arrival of the Flemings from the Low Countries in the 12th century. Similarly, the great river valley channels, with their water meadows liable to winter flooding, and the sterile heathlands of the *Geest* remained unreclaimed except for the Fläming, where afforestation was attempted by the Flemings and settlements made, not always successfully, as a number of ' deserted villages ' show. In the Teutoburgerwald and in the Weser Hill country, some forest clearance took place and settlements were founded such as Minden, in the ' Porta Westfalica ' gap, and Tecklenburg, a village with half-timbered houses in the Teutoburger Forest. Today, much of the settlement in the plain of Westphalia is dispersed, but this represents a late phase of secondary dispersal. Near the Dutch frontier, there are some fortified sites which survive as moated villages, notably Burgsteinfurt.

To the east of the Elbe was the realm of Ostelbien speech, where there were islands of Low German set in a sea of Slavonic speech and heathendom. Here arose the Mark of Brandenburg, dating from the creation of the bishopric of Brandenburg in 949. West of the Elbe lay the *Altmark*, with its early Germanic settlements such as Stendal, many of which originated as strong points established by the kings of Saxony for the defence of the eastern frontier against the Slavs. Of these fortress towns, Magdeburg, founded by Otto the Great, was one of the most important. Between the Elbe and the Oder lay the *Mittelmark*, which became the Margravate of Brandenburg in 1157, with its capital at Tangermünde; while, to

the south, lay the Marks of Thuringia and Meissen. By the end of
the 14th century, the *Neumark* became established east of the Oder
against the heathen Slavs of Pomerania and the lower Vistula
basin, and here Frankfurt-a.-d.-Oder later became a strong point
and base for further Germanic conquests, especially by the Teutonic
Knights against the heathen Letts and Lithuanians who, together
with the Poles, defeated the Germans at Tannenberg in 1410. As
part of this campaign of subjugation, Germanic outposts became
established at such key sites as Danzig at the mouth of the Vistula,
Königsberg and Memel on the south-east Baltic coast, and also
at Bromberg and Thorn in the Vistula valley. Brandenburg had,
in the meanwhile, become an electorate of the German Empire in
1351, although encircled by Slav-ruled territory in which such cities
as Leipzig, Dresden, Meissen, Berlin and Lübeck had their pre-
German origin. In 1411, the head of the House of Hohenzollern
became the Elector of Brandenburg; while Berlin replaced the city
of Brandenburg as the capital.

The territory of the *Mittelmark*, the nucleus of modern Prussia,
lay between the Elbe and the Oder, the heaths of the Fläming to the
south and the coastlands of the southern Baltic to the north. From
strong points such as Magdeburg on the middle Elbe, colonization
spread into the marshy valleys of the *Havelland* to the Spree crossing
at Berlin and so across the Barnim *Geest* to the Oder. This line
of advance is marked by the sites of Brandenburg, Potsdam, Berlin,
Frankfurt-a.-d.-Oder and Küstrin, at the confluence of the Netze and
Oder. To the south of Brandenburg lay the *Rundling* and *Waldhufendorf* types of villages associated with settlement by Slavonic tribes.
These regions were also penetrated by Cistercian monks who
founded some abbeys, especially in the poor regions of the *Sander*
soils, as well as on the desolate Baltic coast, notably at Eldena
near the university town of Greifswald; the abbey being destroyed
by the Swedes during the Thirty Years' War in 1638. To the
north and north-east of the *Havelland*, ' colonial ' settlements were
founded in the *Geest* zones of Barnim and Lebus, while Flemings were encouraged to occupy the district between Magdeburg
and Ober Lausitz. Much late-medieval reclamation of this sterile
heath and forest region took place on the northern margin of the
rich loess lands of the Magdeburg Börde. Elsewhere the Frisians
drained and reclaimed many of the North Sea coastal polders, thus
bringing additional land under pasture and cultivation, and so enabling these regions to support a higher density of rural settlement.
Here *Marshhufendörfer* arose, in which the farm buildings have roofs
of reed thatch and walls of brick and half timber. At the same

(a) Air view of the *Altstadt* of Bremen, showing the medieval core of the Hanseatic town, now restored and partly reconstructed. The Lutheran cathedral, with its twin spires, dominates the central square with its Renaissance Exchange, Customs House and Town Hall. Part of the tree-lined boulevard which marks the site of the medieval encircling walls, may be seen in the foreground.

27. MEDIEVAL AND MODERN URBAN DEVELOPMENT

(b) The Bundeshaus at Bonn, seat of the Government of the Federal German Republic.

(a) The city of Bremen on the Weser.

28. TWO GERMAN HANSEATIC NORTH SEA PORTS

(b) Hamburg and the Alster lakes.

time, the North Sea ports of Bremen and Hamburg grew to prosperity as members of the Hanseatic League, but they were surpassed by the Free City of Lübeck, founded by Henry the Lion in 1189, in place of an earlier Slavonic settlement at Bardowick. This city, which became the leading member of the Hanseatic League, with a thriving trade in salted Baltic herrings, arose on an island at the mouth of the Trave river. Like Greifswald opposite the island of Rügen, it is remarkable for its public buildings in bluish-red brick, many of which have survived the last war, notably the unique *Rathaus*, the *Holstentor* on the site of the town walls, and the great *Marienkirche*. In the 14th century, the thriving community of Lübeck built the Stechnitz canal to facilitate the cheap movement of salt from the Lüneburg Heath to the Baltic, in connection with the fish trade. After 1500, when the fishing industry of the Baltic declined and the mouth of the Trave began to silt, a second canal was built to the Elbe at Hamburg, to avoid German Baltic shipping paying tolls for the use of the Sound between Copenhagen and Malmö, for at this date both shores were Danish territory. Today Lübeck, in spite of its artificial sea cut to Travemunde, suffers from its proximity to East Germany and it lies in an economic backwater, a picturesque city encircled by the Trave, retaining much of its late medieval character, with a population of a quarter of a million.[1]

The patterns of both rural and urban settlement west and east of the Elbe-Saale line reflect historic contrasts, for the Romanization of the region west of the Teutoburgerwald resulted in the early growth of towns, related to routes across north-west Europe as well as to defensive needs and ecclesiastic significance. East of the Elbe lies a region of planned ' colonial ' settlement, partly the outcome of late German conquests from the Slavs but more especially in consequence of the consolidation of these gains under the Great Elector of Brandenburg in the 18th century. Large estates were then laid out, especially along the Baltic coastlands of Mecklenburg, Pomerania and East Prussia, following the decline of Swedish power in the lower Vistula basin after the Thirty Years' War (1618–48). These were the Junker estates, owned by the Prussian nobility and often cultivated by Slav peasants as serfs, descendants of the original Billungs. As the result of this political and economic transformation, a number of ' deserted villages ' (*Wüstungsdörfer*) were created, especially in the regions formerly occupied by Slavs. Only south of Berlin, in the wooded and marshy country of the *Spreewald*, were the Wends able to maintain their traditional mode of life

[1] *Atlas von Schleswig-Holstein*, 1960, p. 114.

and dress until recent times, moving about the local waterways in flat-bottomed punts.[1] Some German rural settlements were also established, often of the *Angerdorf* or village green type, with the main street bifurcating round the green, as at Heiligensee on the Havel near Berlin. Others were of the ' fen colony ' type, an example of which is the village of Gosen in the Spree valley near Berlin. This settlement was founded in 1754–6 by the Great Elector and occupied by farmers from the Rhenish Palatinate.[2] Here the two streets cross at right angles and the regular blocks of arable fields extend behind the farmhouses which are aligned along these two roads. Some ' colonial ' town plans were deliberately geometrical, being laid out in the form of a grid, like Neu Brandenburg, with a place for an open market and Lutheran church; while others, like Neustrelitz in Mecklenburg, had a radial street pattern and a central market place.

Berlin

The city which was to epitomize the military might of Prussia and to assume after 1866 the rôle of Vienna in Central European affairs, arose in the midst of the sterile heath or ' *Streusandbüchse* ' of the central Brandenburg *Geest*. The significance of this unpromising site, where a fishing village arose amidst the maze of waterways represented by the Havel-Spree drainage system, was first recognized by Frederick II of Hohenzollern when he built a royal castle in Berlin in 1448. By 1486, Berlin had become the permanent seat of the Prussian court.[3] Its nodal significance depended on the intersection of long-distance routes from Breslau to Hamburg and from thriving commercial cities, such as Erfurt in Thuringia, to the Baltic port of Stettin. The complex pattern of streams, lakes and marshes facilitated defence and, in 1668, the Spree was linked by canal with the Oder, followed by the Elbe-Havel canal in 1745 and the Bromberg canal in 1774. After the Treaty of Westphalia in 1648, East Pomerania fell to Brandenburg and West Pomerania to Sweden, but the acquisition of Stettin and the two Baltic islands of Usedom and Wollin off the mouth of the Oder in 1720 by Frederick William of Prussia provided direct access to the Baltic. Berlin was fortified in French style in the late 17th century, when the three settlements of Berlin, Kölln and Friedrichswerder were enclosed within the same *enceinte*. Dorotheenstadt and Friedrichstadt were added

---

[1] E. von Seydlitz: *Geographie: Deutschland*, 1925, plate 147, p. 141.
[2] B. Brandt: ' Der Nordosten ', *Landeskunde von Deutschland*, Vol. 2, 1931.
[3] Vaughan Cornish: *Great Capitals*, 1923, Chap. V. pp. 148–59.

subsequently to the then rapidly expanding city of Berlin.[1] The 18th century saw the building of the baroque cathedral with its domed roof overlooking the banks of the Spree; while the palace of Sans Souci, with its Italian garden, appeared at Potsdam, on the model of Versailles. In 1737, a Customs Wall, the *Zollmauer*, was erected and, although replaced by a ring road in 1850, it served to define the subsequent business and commercial core of 19th-century Berlin, to become the imperial capital of the German Empire after 1871. To the south-west, arose the residential districts beyond

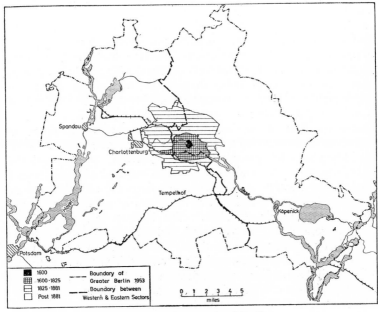

FIG. 113. The growth of Berlin.

the open space of the Tiergarten, and, to the west, Charlotten-burg, to become world renowned for its Technical High School. To the north lay the industrial district of Moabit. The 'core' area of the Kurfürstenstadt, inside the 19th-century *Ringbahn*, formed the pre-war 'city area', with a multiplicity of business houses, retail shops, offices, warehouses and wholesale markets. Beyond the *Ringbahn* are the suburbs or *Vorstädte*, outside the site of the 17th-century fortifications. Here the famous Dorotheenstadt was laid

[1] G. W. S. Robinson: 'West Berlin: The Geography of an Exclave', *Geog. Review*, Vol. 43, 1953, pp. 540–57.

out on a grid plan in 1673, based on the Unter den Linden, lined by ' linden ' or lime trees.   Berlin retained its attractiveness until the Nazi régime, when steel and concrete administrative blocks began to make their appearance, as in the Wilhelmstrasse, with its government buildings now succeeded by the grim blocks of the Eastern sector beyond the Brandenburger Tor.   Today, beyond the garishness of the Kurfürstendamm, the Berlin Wall, completed in 1961, marks inexorably the division between the Western and Eastern sectors of the former capital of the German *Reich*.   The pre-war contrast between the inner industrial zone within the *Ringbahn*, with its small-scale workshop industries, and the large industrial sites on the outskirts of the city, has been maintained. Here are the great A.E.G. and Siemens works, as well as firms concerned with the making of precision and optical instruments, machine tools, and clothing. Since the fortification of Spandau during the Thirty Years' War as part of the defences of Berlin, the town has become associated with the tradition of firearms manufacture.   Much suburban development took place between the wars, as at Grünewald and Potsdam. During the *Blitz*, at least a third of Berlin's houses were destroyed and most areas were reduced to heaps of dust and rubble.   Most rebuilding has taken place in the Western sector, especially with the aid of foreign capital, and the standard of living here is vastly higher than in the Eastern sector, especially since the establishment of differential currencies in 1948 and in spite of its isolation within the German Democratic Republic.[1]   The Eastern sector lacks coal (except from Polish Silesia), steel and machinery, though oil is brought by pipeline from the Soviet Union.   It has suffered from the migration of refugees, including many skilled workers, to the West until 1961.   Here new industries are ' planned ', especially based on the use of lignite for the generation of thermal electricity. There is much daily movement to and from each sector, and the pre-war pattern of movement of workers out from the congested core to employment beyond the *Ringbahn* is still maintained by hundreds of daily *Arbeitspendler*.   It is estimated that the total population of Berlin is now 3·27 million, 2·2 million living in the Western sector and 1·07 million in the Eastern sector, the latter figure decreasing yearly.[2]   For a detailed survey of post-war planning and reconstruction in Berlin, reference may be made to the collection of maps in the *Atlas von Berlin* now in progress.[3]

[1] Peter Hall: *The World Cities*, 1966, p. 136.

[2] T. H. Elkins: ' The Economic Background to Berlin ', *Geography*, Vol. 47, 1962.

[3] *Deutscher Planungsatlas—Atlas von Berlin*, Band 9, 1957.

The North Sea Ports

Hamburg. The Free City of Hamburg, with a present population equal to that of 1939, namely 1·8 million in 1963 compared with 1·4 million in 1946, is rapidly regaining its former importance as a major North Sea port, especially as the chief German outlet for the German Federal Republic and the main alternative to Rotterdam at the mouth of the Dutch Rhine. The pre-war enterpôt trade has gone, as has the trade *via* the Elbe with Czechoslovakia; while the exclave of West Berlin lies isolated 110 miles within the German Democratic Republic. The past twenty years have seen the phenomenal rebuilding of wharves, warehouses and port equipment, as well as of the city itself; while the reconstructed *Autobahn* serving the town facilitates road connection with Bremen, the Ruhr and the Netherlands. The pre-war industries of the port are now prospering, the Blohm and Voss shipyards are especially active, notably in connection with the construction and repair of oil tankers and the conversion of ships purchased abroad for the Hamburg-Atlantic line service, for example the passenger liner *Hanseatic*. The trade of the port is partly in general merchandise and partly in passengers, the latter docking at Cuxhaven. In bulk and value, the commerce of the port greatly exceeds that of the more specialized port of Bremen, its historic competitor. The port industries, apart from ship building and repairing, closely reflect its overseas trade, especially with the U.S.A., the Middle East, and the tropical world. They include a large Esso oil refinery at Harburg; the manufacture of tobacco, chocolate, cocoa and flour milling, mainly on the north bank of the Elbe at Altona; and the manufacture of margarine at Harburg and also at Altona.

Settlement on the site of Hamburg dates from the time of Charlemagne, and this outpost of Christianity, the seat of the bishop of Nordelbien, served as a base for the conversion of the nearby heathen Slavs and Scandinavians, leading to the foundation of a bishopric at Lund and Uppsala in Sweden, as well as at Trondheim in central Norway, where the partly Romanesque cathedral dates from the 11th century. The medieval town of Hamburg grew up on the firm building site provided by the *Geest* above the marshy valley of the Alster to the north and west and that of the Bille to the south. However, the river crossing long remained upstream at Lauenburg-Bardowick, a settlement superseded by Lübeck in 1189. Hamburg remained a minor port until the end of the 12th century. The Neo-Gothic church of St. Michael, the ornate spire of which dominates the re-built port area of the town; while the church spire of St. Nicholas overlooks the Nicolai *Fleet* or waterway; the nucleus around which merchants and traders congregated. In 1228, this settlement merged with Hamburg, and henceforward the combined city monopolized the trade and navigation of the lower Elbe. By the end of the 12th century, the drainage and dyking of the marshes above the town was begun, notably in the district of the *Vierlande*. Today, these are some of the main sources of market garden and horticultural produce serving the city of Hamburg. The medieval port traded with the lands around the Baltic and North Sea, especially in salt, grain, linen and beer. Although outclassed by Lübeck, the headquarters of the Hansa merchants, the city became, like Bremen and Cologne which also had their Staple Houses, a thriving member of this league of independent traders, and so set about suppressing piracy in the North Sea. In consequence of the developing fish trade, a German merchant colony became established in Bergen; the timbered houses of which still line the waterfront known as the Bryggen. In the later Middle Ages, many brick and half-timbered houses were constructed in the *Altstadt* of Hamburg, notably in the district known as the *Gänge-Viertel*, the cobbled lanes and courtyards of which survived until the 1939–45 War. By 1600, the Free City was estimated to have had a population of over 10,000, centred on the *Rathaus*, rebuilt in Renaissance style in the 19th century.

The rapid expansion of Hamburg was delayed until the latter part of the 19th century. During the Thirty Years' War (1618–48), the *Altstadt* was fortified against the Scandinavian invaders of North Germany. By this time the Alster waterway had begun to silt up, so the stream was dammed to provide power for driving grist mills. In consequence, the Alster became a freshwater lake known as the Binner-Alster and the Ausser-Alster, today divided into two by the Lombardo bridge in ornate Italian style and also by the Kennedy bridge. The harbour which had developed at the mouth of the Bille stream on the site of the Binnenhafen was moved downstream to the Niederhafen. In the 17th century, a single channel was dredged and the flow and scouring power of the Elbe thereby increased. Hamburg benefited from a growing trade with the West Indies, especially in sugar, rum and molasses. The Bank of Hamburg was founded in 1619 and an export trade in textiles began with the New World, based on wool and linen from Westphalia and Upper Silesia. Interest in the whaling industry off Greenland led to the growth of soap manufacture based on whale oil. After the 17th century, the *Neustadt* developed outside the medieval walls but the city declined during the Napoleonic Wars on account of the Continental Blockade. Overseas trade subsequently grew rapidly, especially with the U.S.A., in cotton and tobacco, copper and grain; with Brazil and Central America, the main sources of coffee and tropical hardwoods; with Chile, as the source of nitrates or saltpetre; as well as with German East Africa, which supplied sisal hemp, and West Africa, whence came oilseeds, cocoa and tropical hardwoods. The first steamship on the Elbe appeared in 1816, only five years after the *Comet* was launched on the Clyde, and the need for improved harbour facilities to accommodate the larger steamships was soon apparent. The tidal range in the Elbe estuary is at least 6 ft. and much transhipment of cargoes to lighters and barges is involved.

In 1847 the *Hapag* shipping company was founded and the overseas connections of the port expanded rapidly with the development of regular oceanic steamship services. The population of Hamburg increased from 260,000 in 1866 to 570,000 in 1890. In 1881, Hamburg entered the German Customs Union or *Zollverein*, except for the Free Harbour. The need for new quays led to the construction of the Baakenhafen to the east of the city and to the transformation of the south bank at Harburg, a city hitherto politically part of Hanover. With the unification of Germany after 1871, it became possible to bridge the Elbe and the great steel spiral road bridge was completed in 1872. This bridge and also the railway bridge stopped the upstream expansion of the port. In consequence, the further development of port facilities has taken place at Altona, with its multiplicity of wharves and quays, and also at Cuxhaven, a former fishing port at the western point of the estuary, where the Hamburg-Amerika liners disembark passengers to avoid the 80-mile passage up the estuary with its navigation hazards and shallowing water. This outport also provided a connection with the German naval base of Heligoland (the ' Holy Land '), a sandstone platform ending in precipitous cliffs but which offered an impregnable anchorage for warships which Britain exchanged for Zanzibar and 'a ransom of cloves ' off German East Africa (later Tanganyika) in 1890.

The 20th-century city of Hamburg developed around the ' core ' of the *Altstadt*, partly encircled by a ' green belt ' to the north-west and north, on the site of the former walls, and by the main railway line from Bremen to Kiel to the east. Beyond the *Neustadt* are the rebuilt outer suburbs extending to Altona and Wandsbek. The inner ' bishop's city ' is dominated by the late-medieval Hanseatic churches of St. Nicholas, St. Peter, St. Jacob and St. Katherine; while the 19th-century Neo-Gothic church of St. Michael crowns the *Neustadt* and St. Pauli the *Reeperbahn* sailors' quarter between the Holstenwall boulevard and Altona. In 1842, a disastrous fire destroyed many of the old wooden houses, and new buildings arose sometimes revolutionary in design and using a new material, bluish-red ' clinker brick '. A modern example is known as the Chile House, with the outline form of the prow of a ship and occupying a ' flat-iron ' site at the convergence of two main thoroughfares. This extraordinary building has survived the *Blitz*. Modern Hamburg is separated from Harburg by two great expanses of river frontage, the Norder and Süder-Elbe, with docks and quays aligned along both arms of the river.

The tendency of citizens to move out from the congested central core to the outer suburbs, begun in the early 20th century, has been reinforced by the post-war housing shortage. There is today a large-scale daily movement of *Arbeitspendler*, of business men and office workers in and out of the resurrected *Hansastadt* Hamburg, second city of West Germany and the great west–east arterial road parallel to the Elbe carries much of this.[1]

Bremen. The Free City of Bremen has a very similar site to Hamburg. It lies 50 miles up the Weser estuary and above the outport of Bremerhaven, where the river flows over a wide flood-plain fringed by the dry heaths of the *Geest*, which end abruptly against the marshes of the *Urstromtal* in which Bremen lies. Today the river is regulated and the marshes drained and dyked. The modern port is more important as a passenger port than Hamburg and its hinterland is largely served by road and railway, in addition to its canal connection *via* the Ems-Weser-Elbe system with the Nord-Rhein-Westfalen industrial region.[2] It imports cotton and wool, as well as foodstuffs, especially grain, coffee and tropical oilseeds, together with tobacco and various metals. The export trade is mainly in iron and steel manufactures from the Ruhr. In the last few years, the shipbuilding and repairing industry has been revived at the Norddeutscher Lloyd docks, and industries such as oil refining, the processing of coffee, chocolate and tobacco, the milling of flour, and the refining of sugar, as well as the brewing industry, have been revived. A new development is an iron and steel plant, with an ultimate capacity of 3–4 million tons, using low-grade iron ore from the Weser hills. In 1963, Bremen had a population of 580,956, compared with 342,113 in 1939, a figure which partly reflects the influx of refugees from beyond the ' Iron Curtain '.

The original settlement of Bremen arose around the bishopric founded on the Weser marshes in 787. The site marked the crossing

[1] *Atlas von Schleswig-Holstein*, 1960, p. 113.

[2] F. W. Morgan: ' The Pre-War Hinterlands of the German North Sea Ports ', *Trans. Inst. Br. Geographers*, Vol. 14, 1948, pp. 43–55.

of the lower Weser by the route from the Rhineland leading to the
Elbe crossing at Bardowick and thence to the Baltic. Routes also
converged from Oldenburg to the west and from Osnabrück, north
of the Teutoburgerwald, to the south-west. This function as an
early bridge point offers a striking contrast with Hamburg, where
the Elbe was so long a barrier between the Free City and the Hano-
verian settlement of Harburg. By 950, the bishop of Bremen was
reaping tolls from merchants using the crossing, and traders and
craftsmen began to gather round the cathedral nucleus of the *Altstadt*
and also in the *Stefansviertel*. In the 14th century, Bremen became
a walled town and a member of the Hanseatic League (1358),
trading with the Baltic in salted fish, timber and flax. The ' core '
of this medieval town survived until the 1939–45 War and was clearly
defined by the line of walls and outer moat, incorporated in an
ornamental park in the 19th century between the main railway station
and the *Altstadt*. The nucleus of the *Altstadt* pivots on the cathedral
with its twin towers, the *Rathaus*, the *Börse* or Exchange, and the
Schütting or Guildhall, all of which lie around the open market
square dominated by the giant statue of Roland, of Charlemagne
association. Along the Langenstrasse, parallel to the Weser, there
arose a number of gabled warehouses, several stories high, which
survived until the 1939–45 War. In the 17th century, the Free
City expanded into the *Neustadt* across the Weser, where a number
of single-storied houses were constructed, and this part of the town,
together with the *Altstadt*, was fortified in 1625, during the Thirty
Years' War. The Swedes recognized Bremen as a ' Free City ' in
1731 and then came a further period of expansion beyond the walls
in directions parallel to the north-west–south-east trend of the
Weser. Nevertheless, during the Napoleonic Wars and the Continental Blockade, the city had reached a population total of only
35,000, compared with Hamburg's 100,000.
  During the 19th century, Bremen suffered from poor waterway
connections with the hinterland of the port, the Weser being of
negligible importance compared with the great Elbe waterway,
navigable for small barges as far as Aussig (Ústí) in Bohemia. The
estuary of the Weser was also shallow and liable to silt, vessels of
only 8,000 tons being able to dock at Bremen, so that outports were
developed at Vegesack, 10 miles downstream, and also at Bremerhaven, after 1827. The Norddeutscher Lloyd shipping company
was founded in 1857 and it specialized in North American traffic,
its ships carrying a large number of German and other Central and
East European emigrants to the New World. After 1871, the
Prussian State offered favourable railway freight rates on traffic

using either Bremen or Hamburg, including cargoes originating in the Baltic and passing through the Kiel canal. This was a political and economic device to detract merchandise from the Rhine waterway and the Dutch port of Rotterdam. In the 1880's, the Weser channel was deepened to facilitate upstream navigation from Bremerhaven, but new docks became essential, the Freihafen I being opened in 1888, Freihafen II in 1891 and Freihafen III in 1906. Bremen became a member of the German *Zollverein* in 1884, although retaining her traditional status as a Free City. After the opening of the new docks early in the 20th century, the port developed rapidly, though ocean-going vessels were no longer able to use the town docks. Vegesack, Nordenham (Lloyds) and Brake became small ports; while Bremerhaven and the fishing port of Wesermünde formed one urban area, as outports for Bremen, with Geestemunde as another fishing port. Today, drilling for oil proceeds at Bremerhaven.

Emden. This most westerly German North Sea port is largely the political creation of Prussia. It lies close to the Dutch frontier, which partly follows the Ems river, and its immediate hinterland has hitherto been unproductive industrially, for it consists of reclaimed *polders*, marshland and *Geest*. The port was developed in the late 19th century, to provide an all-German outlet for the industrial products of the Ruhr, at the terminus of the Dortmund-Ems canal completed between 1890 and 1899, and also as a port specializing in the import of Swedish iron ore. In future, the Ems will also be connected with the Weser by means of the *Hansa* canal, which will benefit both Emden and Bremen in relation to the Ruhr. Shipbuilding is now an important port industry.

REFERENCES

Only major and readily accessible references are quoted here. The pre-war texts which still contain much material of value are those of G. Braun: *Deutschland* (2nd ed. 1936) and E. von Seydlitz: *Deutschland* (1925). Regional studies in the Landeskunde von Deutschland series have been made by N. Krebs: *Der Südwesten* (1931), H. Schrepfer: *Der Nordwesten* (1935), and B. Brandt: *Der Nordosten* (1931); while R. Gradmann: *Süddeutschland*, 2 vols., 1931, is still invaluable. For non-German reading, E. de Martonne: *Europe Centrale* (1930), and P. George and J. Tricart: *L'Europe Centrale* (1954) are the standard French references. The fullest studies in English are by R. E. Dickinson. *The Regions of Germany* (1945) and *Germany* (1964), while there is also a useful chapter on Central Europe in G. W. Hoffman: *Geography of Europe* (1961). H. J. Mackinder: *The Rhine* (1908) is still interesting as a piece of early regional description. T. H. Elkine: *Germany*, 1960, and K. A. Sinnhuber: *Germany, Its Geography and Growth*, 1961, are recent publications.

A most authoritative reference atlas was being produced before the war by N. Krebs, entitled *Atlas des Deutschen Lebensraumes in Mitteleuropa* (1937–), but it remains incomplete. There is also the *Deutscher Landwirtschaftsatlas* (1934). Germany produced a number of regional atlases before the war, including both the *Heimatatlas der Südwestmark Baden* (1934), now re-published, and the *Saar-Atlas* (1934). The *Atlas-Niedersachsen* was re-issued in 1965. There is also G. Hellmann: *Klimaatlas von Deutschland* (1921). Publications on East Germany are the *Klimaatlas der Deutschen Demokratischen Republik*, 1953, the *Agraratlas über das Gebiet der Deutschen Demokratischen Republik*, 1956; while the *Statistisches Jahrbuch der Deutschen Demokratischen Republik*, 1956, has appeared since 1957. In recent years, a series of regional planning atlases have been published by the Akademie für Raumforschung und Landesplanung, including the *Atlas von Berlin*, 1957, the *Atlas von Schleswig-Holstein*, 1960, the Ruhr 1960, and the *Rheinland-Pfalz*, 1965. The compendium, *Die Bundesrepublik Deutschland in Karten* has been in progress since 1965.

The geology of Germany was originally covered by 27 sheets on a scale of 1 : 500,000 compiled in colour by R. Lepsius (1894–7), while a new series on a scale of 1 : 200,000 was partly completed between the wars, known as the *Geologische Übersichtskarte von Deutschland*, 42 sheets of which were published between 1922 and 1939. Another series is now being published on a scale of 1 : 500,000, the *Geologische Karte von Bayern* appearing in 1954. A useful small-scale reference map is that of W. Schriel: *Kleine Geologische Karte von Deutschland*, 1 : 2 million, published by the Prussian Geological Survey in 1930. Topographic maps of Germany are available on scales of 1 : 100,000; 1 : 50,000 and 1 : 25,000. The maps on the 1 : 100,000 scale were based on 19th century surveys and showed relief by hachuring, a few maps making use of colour to show woodland, water surfaces, etc., but the larger-scale maps show relief by means of brown contour lines. The modern topographic maps bear comparison with those produced by other nation states in western Europe. An industrial and communications map of the Rhine–Westphalian region on a scale of 1 : 100,000, was published in 1961–2.

CHAPTER 17

THE BENELUX LANDS: GENERAL

THE CREATION of an economic unit out of the Rhine-Maas delta lands, together with Flanders, Brabant, the Ardenne block and the scarplands of Luxembourg, is a post-war development. The economic union between Belgium and Luxembourg dates from 1922, when France refused such a union in favour of Belgium. The agreement to establish a customs union between Belgium, the Netherlands and Luxembourg (Benelux) was made in 1947 and came into force in 1948. As a result, an economic unit of over 19 million people has been formed in north-west Europe with obvious advantages in terms of reciprocal free trade and in matters of currency exchange, though Belgian francs are valid in Luxembourg but not conversely. These little states are broadly complementary in their economic interests. Whereas Belgium has a highly urbanized population, with intensive and commercial agriculture integrated with a fair range of manufacturing activity, from iron and steel through chemicals and glass to textiles, the Netherlands owe their wealth to their maritime and former colonial interests, as well as to their dairy farming, while the main economic resource of Luxembourg is iron ore. Both Belgium and the Netherlands have the Rhinelands as part of their hinterland; the modern growth of Rotterdam and to a lesser degree that of Amsterdam and Antwerp greatly benefiting from the trade which they handle originating in industrial West Germany.[1]

The formation of the European Common Market, for which Brussels is the headquarters, has strengthened still more strongly the connections between the Ruhr, with its surplus of industrial coke and raw and semi-manufactured steel, and the market in Belgium, as well as to a minor degree that in Luxembourg; for most of the ' minette ' ore from the Duchy finds its external market in the blast

[1] For a study of the pre-war trade of Rotterdam, see: F. W. Morgan: ' Rotterdam and Waterway Approaches to the Rhine ', 1948, *Econ. Geog.*, Vol. 23, pp. 1–18.

furnaces of the Sambre-Meuse coalfield. The cheap movement of
coal, coke and petroleum through this 'industrial triangle' of
north-western Europe has been facilitated by the completion of the
Albert canal in 1940, linking Antwerp with the Meuse at Liège, and

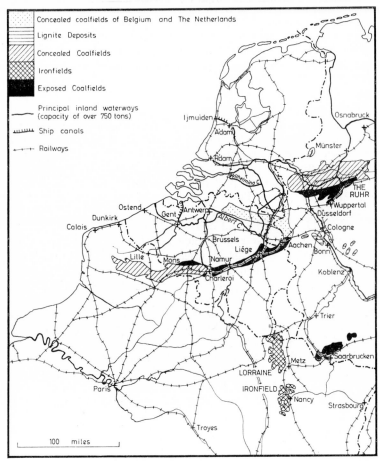

FIG. 114. The 'industrial triangle' of North-west Europe.

by the Dutch Juliana canal which enters the Maas at Maastricht. It
is now proposed to connect the Albert canal directly with the Rhine,
though this scheme is clearly contrary to Dutch interests. Another
modern development has been the canalization of the Moselle from
Koblenz to Thionville; thus cheapening the cost of Ruhr coke

destined for the Lorraine iron works based on local ' minette ' ores. The cost of transporting these ores to the Ruhr is now cheapened.[1]

GENERAL HUMAN GEOGRAPHY

It has been claimed that studies in regional geography should begin with a population distribution map and, in summarizing the modern human geography of the Benelux group, it is appropriate to review some of the demographic problems of the three small countries which form the group, for those of each are somewhat distinctive.   Both Belgium (excluding the Ardenne) and the Netherlands record the highest densities of population in the continent of Europe and this is no recent feature of the economically rich Rhine delta lands.   Rather it is a reflection of several centuries of prosperity, to which modern industrial development, intensive agriculture and commercial activity on a world-wide scale have been added.

The Netherlands have probably the highest rate of increase in population in western Europe.   It is one of the most urbanized, in spite of a high density of rural population dependent upon intensive agriculture, horticulture and dairy farming, which have all formed the basis of a lucrative export trade with the industrial markets of western Europe, particularly Great Britain.   In 1964, the total population was estimated at 12·0 million, compared with 8·6 million in 1938.   As a result, the Netherlands have a density of population now slightly higher than the British Isles and Belgium, the figure being 885 to the square mile in 1958.   In a country of such limited resources, it is no wonder that the post-war years have seen the emigration of about half a million Dutch people to Australia, New Zealand, Canada and South Africa.   The reclamation of the polders bordering the Zuider Zee, in progress since 1932, has added a tenth to the area under arable and pasture, especially valuable today in view of the heavy pressure of population on the land.   The present century has also seen the development of small but significant coalfields near the Belgian and German frontiers, and also an oilfield near Emmen as well as a major gas field in the Groningen region. In consequence there has been a resulting growth of industries notably in the Kempenland and Dutch Limburg.

The greatest rate of population increase in the past century has been in the cities of South and North Holland, especially in Rotterdam, The Hague, Amsterdam and Utrecht, and least in Friesland and Zeeland.   This growth is a reflection of the expansion of

[1] Michel: ' The Canalisation of the Moselle ', etc., *Geog. Review*, Vol. 52, 1962.

industry, commerce and transit trade since the late 19th century. Elsewhere it has been the result of the introduction or intensification of industry, as in Eindhoven, Delft and Valkenburg, and also, to some extent, through improved methods of farming. There are three towns with a population of over 700,000; Amsterdam having an estimated population of 952,197 in 1963, Rotterdam 942,803, 's Gravenhage 736,228. These towns have the status of ' conurbations ', for Amsterdam expanded its boundaries in 1921 so as to incorporate neighbouring communes and villages; the seaside resort of Scheveningen was included in The Hague in 1925, while Rotterdam now includes the Hook of Holland. The post-war increase in the population of this great port reflects the speed with which it has been rebuilt after its war-time major destruction and devastation.

In response to this expansion of urban population and the growth of industry, a number of entirely new towns have been planned and built since the end of the 1939–45 war, in response to the Dutch policy of decentralizing industry. These new towns, which are models of their kind, are designed firstly to provide living accommodation, retail shops and educational facilities in growing centres of industry. Second, Emmen, in the district of Drente, is an entirely ' new town ' in a sparsely populated area of peat fen near the German frontier. The third type consists of the new towns created on the reclaimed land of the Zuider Zee polders. In the south-west, the town which is expanding rapidly is Vlaardingen on the Nieuw Maas between Rotterdam and the Hook of Holland, where the population has increased from 30,000 before the war to 65,000 today. Between Vlaardingen and Schiedam a new ' neighbourhood area ' is now being built at Westwijk, involving building on valuable market garden land. Another new town is arising at Beverwijk, north of the ship canal between Amsterdam and IJmuiden, where there are already blast furnaces and a steel works, a chemical plant and a paper mill. The present town of 24,000 is planned to expand to 150,000 by 1980. Emmen has a population of 73,008 but was planned to house 23,000. A new industrial area is being created south of the rapidly growing town, where a nylon spinning factory employs 1,600. The town also borders on the recently developed oilfield near the German frontier. Finally, two towns are being created from sites on newly reclaimed land: Emmeloord, a market centre of about 10,000 for the farmers of the north-east polder, and Lelystad, a town planned eventually to house 50,000, the centre of the recently reclaimed East Flevoland polder, to the south-east of lake IJssel.

The remarkable recovery of the Netherlands after the German occupation from 1940 to 1944 is the result of the interplay of a number of factors, not least the determination and independent spirit of the Dutch people. The war left the Netherlands with an enfeebled population, devastated harbours, flooded fields, factories

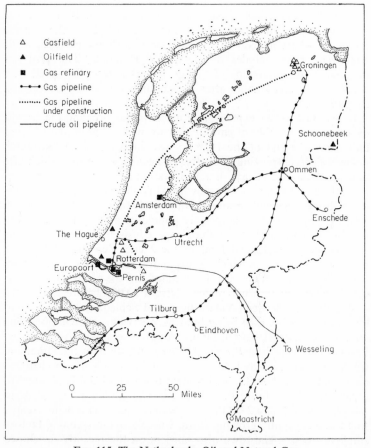

Fig. 115. The Netherlands. Oil and Natural Gas

with obsolete machinery or none at all, no transport and no raw materials, other than the soil. In 1949, a further disaster occurred when the sovereignty of the Netherlands East Indies ended and the Republic of Indonesia was set up. The winter of 1953 saw the disastrous flooding by the sea of a large part of the islands of Zeeland and South Holland, with the loss of 1,783 people. On the other hand, the creation of the Benelux Union in 1947 liberalized trade with Belgium and Luxembourg, as well as to a lesser extent with

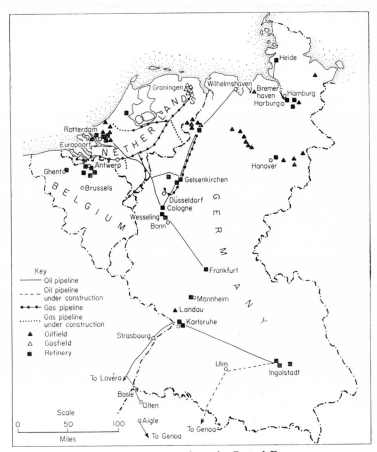

Fig. 116. Oil and natural gas in Central Europe.

other countries. Trade within the Benelux Union is now double that before the war between the three countries concerned and the existence of a common domestic market of 19 million people is a great asset. The Netherlands have also benefited greatly from membership of the European Common Market.

The rapid resuscitation of West Germany, with which the Netherlands are closely linked economically, has also aided Dutch recovery, especially of the port of Rotterdam. The Germans have, therefore, found it expedient to divert traffic from the lower Rhine by railway to Hamburg and Bremen, while the Belgians have projected a deep waterway from Antwerp to the Rhine at Duisburg-Ruhrort, which will draw away more freight from Rotterdam.[1] In 1938 traffic down the Rhine to Rotterdam amounted to 32 million tons per annum out of a total of 40 million tons passing through the port, thus accounting for over three-quarters of the total traffic. This transit trade had shrunk to 23 million metric tons in 1963. On the other hand, the great increase in traffic upstream, especially in oil, and the growth of oil refining at the port have been some compensation. Whereas before the war Rotterdam handled 3 million tons of petroleum, in 1964 the amount had increased to 30 million tons. Oil is refined at four plants in the neighbourhood of Rotterdam, the largest being at Pernis, with a capacity of 16 million metric tons. Much oil now also moves by pipeline along the Rhine Valley to the refineries at Weseling and thence to Karlsruhe and Basle. New developments are now taking place to deal with the great recent expansion of the port's trade and industries. These include the excavation of new docks at Botlek on the south bank of the New Waterway, where there are to be special facilities for handling and storing mineral and vegetable oils, coal, and Labrador iron ore. At 'Europoort', south of the Hook of Holland, new installations are under construction for oil storage and also for the erection of a blast furnace, steel mills, a coking plant and chemical factories. These heavy industries will be largely dependent on fuel and raw materials from the U.S.A., Canada and the Middle East.

Belgium, with a density of population of 785 to the square mile, is, after the Netherlands, the most densely populated country in Europe, if the Ardenne region is excluded. Apart from the high density of rural population, especially in Flanders, there is a marked concentration of population into towns, many of which have developed from a rich historic past. The distribution of urban settlement is shown in Fig. 132. The relationship between this distribution and the main centres of industry is apparent, for in Belgium modern manufacturing activity is concentrated on the Sambre-Meuse coalfield and on the concealed Kempenland coalfield developed in the present century. There are also the long-

---

[1] F. J. Monkhouse: 'Albert and Juliana: Two Great Waterways', *Scottish Geographic Magazine*, Vol. 72, 1956, pp. 163–76.

established centres of industry, where the medieval gilds monopolized the cloth industry of the Flemish towns of Ghent, Bruges
and Courtrai. The North Sea port of Antwerp has preserved its
ornate Renaissance *Hôtel de Ville* as has Brussels. After the recognition of Belgian independence in 1830, Brussels began to expand
rapidly, and, as the state capital, it became the traffic node of the
country, especially of the railway system, in this respect resembling
Paris on a smaller scale. The population of Brussels is now over a
million, including the suburbs; while Antwerp, as an entrepôt port
for the Rhine *via* the Albert canal, as well as the chief port of
Belgium, is the second city, with 878,000, including the suburbs.
Ghent (Gand), the hub of the Flemish textile industry and also a
North Sea port, totalled 155,951 in 1963 and is now the third city of
Belgium. It has surpassed Liège, which now records 154,561, a
city which is slowly declining, although it is the main centre of coal-
mining, steel production, heavy engineering and chemical industries, in the Walloon-speaking part of the country.

Belgian towns experienced relatively little physical damage during
the German occupation of 1940–4, compared with the effects of
bombardment and the deliberate flooding of the mines by the
Germans which took place in the 1914–18 War. In view of the
relatively early and speedy liberation, the subsequent recovery of
the country was rapid, though repairs to minor roads are still in
progress. The present industrial wealth of Belgium has been aided
by membership of the Benelux group and especially by the
freeing of trade barriers through the creation of the European
Coal and Steel Community and the Common Market. The main
problem of modern Belgium is the increasing dominance of the
Flemish-speaking peoples over the Walloon. When Belgium
achieved political independence from the Low Countries, French was
the language mainly spoken, whereas now French and Flemish enjoy
equal status but the Flemish population is increasing at a far greater
rate than the Walloon. The French-speaking part of the country
consists mainly of the older centres of mining and heavy industry
based on the exposed coalfield of the Sambre-Meuse valley, the
product of the industrial revolution in 19th-century Belgium, with
Liège as the ' regional capital ' of this Walloon-speaking area.
Flanders, with its prosperous intensive agriculture and its modern
centres of industry in Antwerp and the Kempenland, as well as in
the traditional ' textile towns ' of Ghent and Courtrai, is the home
of Flemish nationalism. Along the short North Sea coast, the
packet station of Ostend, as well as other former fishing ports which
have developed into flourishing seaside resorts like Blankenberge

and Knocke, attract an increasing number of visitors every year, including many from across the Narrow Seas. In this coastal region, the historic city of Bruges lives prosperously, like Venice, on its past.

Luxembourg is a small duchy which left the German *Zollverein* for a Customs Union with Belgium in 1919 and in 1948 the state was incorporated in the Benelux group. Its total population was 323,971 in 1962, compared with 301,367 in 1938, a reflection of its frontier position in relation to Germany. The average density of population is 300 to the square mile but this figure would be higher but for the section of the Ardenne included within its boundaries. The only large town is the capital city of Luxembourg, recording 74,493 inhabitants in 1962. There are some 25 settlements with more than 1,000 inhabitants, including the centres of iron ore extraction and of iron and steel production on the ironfield in the south-west of the Duchy. The political importance of the Duchy depends upon its location across vital cross-roads between Belgium, France and West Germany. In addition, the fact that it is an extension of the Lorraine ironfield of France gives the Duchy an economic importance out of all proportion to its size. The main centre of iron ore extraction and of iron and steel manufacture is Esch-sur-Alzette, with a population of 28,135 but there are a number of smaller centres of heavy industry in the south-west of the Duchy such as Differdange (17,987) and Dudelange (14,667). The population of Luxembourg is generally bilingual, for the Duchy lies on the speech divide between French- and German-speaking Europe. The dialect known as *Letzeburgesch* is also widely spoken. Most of the population, like that of Belgium, is Roman Catholic. In 1952, Luxembourg became a member of the European Coal and Steel Community and in 1957 of the Common Market, so that today her iron and steel industry is closely integrated with that of the ' industrial triangle ' of north-west Europe, and her economic prosperity is increasing. Tourism also adds to the wealth of this little Duchy, with its varied and attractive landscapes.

REFERENCES

The standard reference book on the Netherlands, Belgium and Luxembourg remains that of A. Demangeon: *Belgique, Pays Bas, Luxembourg*, Géog. Univ., Vol. 2, 1927. F. J. Monkhouse: *Western Europe*, 1964, provides extensive coverage of the Benelux lands. The volume on the Netherlands, published as part of the *International Geographical Congress Report*, Amsterdam, 1938, also contains much useful and detailed material.

H. J. Mackinder: *The Rhine*, 1908, has a useful description of the Rhine delta lands; while A. Demangeon and L. Fébvre: *Le Rhin*, 1935, deal with the relation between the Dutch ports and the Rhine hinterland. Studies of the ports of Antwerp and Rotterdam are also to be found in A. Sargent: *Seaports and Hinterlands*, 1938, and in F. W. Morgan: *Ports and Harbours*, 1952. References to the historical towns of Belgium will be found in H. Pirenne: *Medieval Cities*, 1925; while a modern study of Dutch towns by an architect is that of G. L. Burke: *The Making of Dutch Towns*, 1956. A. Lambert: ' Farm Consolidation and Improvement in the Netherlands ', *Econ. Geog.*, 37, 1961, deals with farming changes and G. Bull: ' The Netherlands Delta Plan ', *Geography*, Vol. 47, 1962, summarizes this great reclamation work now in progress in Zeeland. The monumental *Atlas National de Belgique* is in progress and is invaluable. Topographic maps for Belgium are available on various scales, the most useful being the 1 : 100,000 and the *Carte Internationale du Monde*, which covers the whole country except the extreme east (Paris, Sheet M31). For the Netherlands, maps on several topographical scales have been published, the most useful being the 1 : 200,000 and the 1 : 50,000. For the Duchy of Luxembourg, there is complete topographic and geological coverage on a scale of 1 : 25,000.

CHAPTER 18

THE NETHERLANDS: PART I. PHYSICAL AND HUMAN GEOGRAPHY

THE LOW COUNTRIES,[1] with an area of 13,120 sq. miles, two-fifths of which lie below sea-level, have been described as both 'the land added to the water' and 'the gift of the Rhine'. The Netherlands have indeed played a dual rôle, especially since freedom from Spanish rule in the late 16th century; for the North Sea frontage made possible the maritime ascendancy of the 'United Provinces' in the following century, that of 'the rise of the Dutch Republic', as Motley named it. On the other hand, the fact that the Netherlands coincide with the Rhine delta lands led to the growth of the port of Rotterdam in the 19th century as an outlet for the Rhineland and Ruhr industrial regions, as well as for much of Central Europe including Switzerland, as an alternative to Hamburg and Bremen, further from the main Atlantic shipping lanes. The importance of the Dutch waterways in relation to the Rhine also brought about a revival in the prosperity of Amsterdam, not only as a centre of commerce but also of finance and industry, although the political seat of government, together with the International Court of Justice, is at The Hague.

PHYSICAL FEATURES

The Netherlands lie in the North Sea geosyncline. To the south, the folded Hercynian floor underlies Dutch Limburg, where the Coal Measures are worked at a depth of 300 ft. around Kerkrade and Heerlen, and again in the Peel region and east of Maastricht, where the shafts are sunk to depths which vary from 2,000 to 3,000 ft. Elsewhere, the Coal Measures are covered to unworkable depths by Mesozoic and Tertiary rocks. The Pliocene transgression resulted in almost the entire submergence of the Netherlands and, as this sea retreated, a great confluent delta formed, across which the Rhine

[1] 'Low Countries' or 'Netherlands' is plural in English but singular—*Nederland*—in Dutch. To avoid confusion, the name 'Holland' should not be applied to the whole country but should be confined to the provinces of North and South Holland.

flowed to join the Proto-Thames.[1]   During the advance of the Pleistocene ice sheets from northern Europe, the Netherlands lay athwart the main limit of the Riss-Saale glaciation; the southern margin of the glacial drift deposits being marked by a line through Haarlem, Utrecht and Nijmegen.   In the eastern and northern provinces of Drente and Friesland, there are much boulder clay and ground or ' push ' moraines, and here much sandy outwash or *Geest* occurs, as well as erratics of Scandinavian origin.   South of the IJssel Meer (as the erstwhile Zuider Zee has been known since the closing of the great North Sea dyke across its mouth), between Arnhem and Amersfoort in southern Veluwe, the push-moraines (*moraines de poussée*) form distinct ridges, rising in places to 250 ft. above the plain, which lies only 25 ft. above sea-level.   Beyond the limit of the Riss-Saale ice, the Rhine and Maas renewed the process of terrace building begun in Pliocene times, so that extensive sheets of river gravels mark the Pleistocene ' Middle Terrace '.   Postglacial (Holocene) times saw the advance of the North Sea.   During this Flandrian transgression which took place about 5000 B.C., the Strait of Dover was formed, and an offshore bar developed along the southern North Sea coast from Flanders to Frisia.   Breaches occurred in the bar where the Scheldt, Maas and Rhine broke through, but it continued unbroken from the Hook of Holland to Den Helder.   Sand dunes developed along this bar under the influence of prevalent westerly and south-westerly winds, while, behind the bar, lagoons formed on a bed of marine clay.   In these freshwater lagoons peat gradually accumulated, forming the soil of the modern polders including that of the Haarlemmermeer, reclaimed a century ago.   In late Roman times, another rise in the level of the North Sea occurred and the *Lacus Flevo* was formed.   It was succeeded in the 14th century by the Zuider Zee, created during a time of exceptional storminess, when salt water broke through the shallow Wadden Zee from the North Sea and destroyed the freshwater lake.   The recent drainage of a large part of the floor of the Zuider Zee to form large modern polders is described in a later section.

Climate

The Netherlands experience a climate which is broadly uniform, for no point is more than 100 miles from the sea and, apart from the paramount influence of the North Sea, there is also that of the IJssel Meer.   The winds are mainly westerlies, though towards the east the amount of summer rainfall increases and there is a slightly

[1] A. H. W. Robinson: ' The Floor of the British Seas ', *Scottish Geographic Magazine,* Vol. 68, 1952, pp. 64–79.

greater temperature range, Flushing averaging 32 days with frost and Winterswijk 79.   During the winter, high winds often occur, favoured by the monotonous relief and by the paucity of trees to serve as windbreaks.   In summer, the depressions associated with south-westerly air streams are less frequent and the weather is often fine and calm.   The high winds of the winter greatly favoured the operation of windmills essential to the draining of the polders in former times.   The mean annual precipitation varies from 22 to 32 in., the wettest regions lying to the west and south-west of the IJssel Meer and also in the southerly ' appendix ' of Limburg, where the increased relief results in increased precipitation.   Utrecht records 28·7 in. per annum and Maastricht 25·9 in.   The late autumn and early winter are the seasons of most rainfall and there is a spring and early summer minimum.   Winter rainfall is of a depression type but thunderstorm rain occurs in summer.   The rainfall run-off is everywhere slow, because of the low gradients, but where light sandy soils occur there is rapid percolation.

Soils and Vegetation

The soils of the Netherlands are largely derived from drift and Recent deposits, except in Limburg where Chalk outcrops, and the soil map reflects the contrasting physiographic regions.   In the coastal regions, silt is deposited by each tide, notably on the floor of the Wadden See.   These tidal flats and salt marshes have been partly reclaimed by the planting of eel grass, followed by marsh samphire. Wickerwork fences also aid reclamation.   At the last stage, sea asters and sea lavender are planted.   Where dykes divide the salt marshes from the polders, excellent grazing land is formed, whereas the polders are partly under arable.   In the polder lands, peat has accumulated over marine clay and in places the clay is exposed where the peat has been removed.   Here the water-table is permanently high, as it is in the ' hoogeveen ' region of Peel in Kempenland.   A special region within the polders is the silt region of the former Haarlemmermeer, now intensively cultivated (Plate 30(a)).   The soils derived from the river clays are not quite so rich as those of marine origin.   Water frequently percolates through the dykes and the land is mainly under grassland, with some regions of orchard fruit cultivation and horticulture.   The river banks are frequently fringed by reeds, willows and alders, and poplars have been planted, the wood being used in the match industry.   In Dutch Brabant, the Pleistocene outwash sands give rise to poor soils mainly under heather, with some conifer and birch plantations, varied by patches of peat fen.   In the Chalk country of Limburg, the soils derived from pure Chalk are often under mixed farming with sheep's fescue as the type of permanent pasture.   Where loess occurs, beech and hornbeam formerly predominated, though most of these rich loam soils are now under wheat, sugar beet, orchards and rotation grasses.   Beech plantations

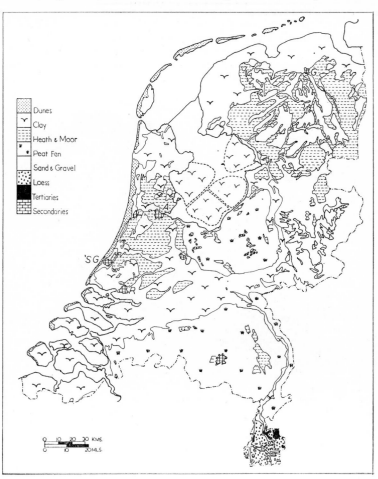

FIG. 117.   The Netherlands: drift map.

occur and roads are often lined with beech trees.   In the northeast, glacial sands and morainic deposits give rise to a region of poor soils, either under heather moor or with birch and pine plantations. As a result of land reclamation in recent years, much modification of the original soil pattern has taken place and types of farming have spread beyond soil boundaries, especially in the polder regions and the sandy tracts.

LAND UTILIZATION

In the Netherlands, over 68 per cent of the total area is improved farm land, under 8 per cent being under woodland (mostly recent plantings) and under 15 per cent wasteland (heath, dunes, bogs, etc.).

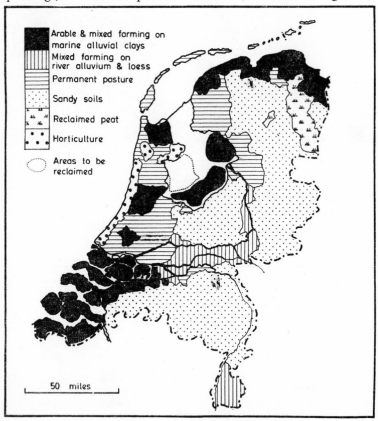

Arable & mixed farming on marine alluvial clays

Mixed farming on river alluvium & loess

Permanent pasture

Sandy soils

Reclaimed peat

Horticulture

Areas to be reclaimed

50 miles

FIG. 118. The Netherlands: chief types of land use.

The relation between pasture and arable has remained constant for a long time and the conversion of arable into permanent grassland which characterized much of the farming of the English lowland in the late 19th century was not a feature in the Netherlands.

USE OF IMPROVED FARM LAND IN 1964

Permanent grassland	1,341,759 ha.
Field crops	799,135 ha.
Market garden crops	120,857 ha.
Land for flower bulbs	12,589 ha.
Nurseries	3,274 ha.
Flower cultivation	1,818 ha.

Here the concentration has been on the improvement of the quality of the produce and on increased yields. Arable farming is associated especially with stock husbandry as in Denmark, though there is a greater proportion of land under permanent grass in the Netherlands. The polders of Holland and Wieringermeer, as well as the loamy tracts of Limburg, produce wheat, sugar beet and potatoes. Much supplementary fodder has to be imported, especially maize. Rye is grown for cattle fodder in the Kempenland and in the reclaimed heath regions of the north-east, and here, too, potatoes are cultivated for food and also for starch. Horticulture and market gardening are especially associated with the *Geestgronden* in the lee of the sand-dune belt of the west coast.

The main aim of the stock farmer is the production of liquid milk, either for sale in the towns or for conversion into factory butter, cheese, condensed milk, etc. The traditional dairy farming regions are the reclaimed peat lands of Holland and western Utrecht, where the high water-table maintains rich pasture, and the mild, moist winter climate minimizes the need for winter stall-feeding. Near the urban markets of Amsterdam, Rotterdam and Utrecht, the milk is mainly sold daily to the dairies, but in South Holland, as around Alkmaar, the chief aim is cheese production, notably at Gouda and Edam. In Friesland, where farming is on co-operative lines, much of the dairy produce is processed in the factories of Groningen. Although about two-thirds of the milk produced is taken by the home market, the rest is exported especially to Great Britain and West Germany, even Switzerland importing Dutch cream cheese and tinned milk, since its price is lower than Swiss produce. Apart from the additional land brought under pasture through the reclamation of the Zuider Zee polders, dairy farming has also increased on the sandy tracts, with the aid of imported feedstuffs and concentrates. Beef and veal are produced for the home market, and pigs and poultry are subsidiary to dairy farming. Sheep have declined in recent years, though attempts have been made to improve the breeds through the introduction of Lincoln and Wensleydale stock.

Horticulture, market garden crops, fruit and flowers, especially with a view to the export trade, have also become typical of the

Dutch farm economy. The sheltered regions of the *Geestgronden* combine soils derived from a mixture of peat and sand with sea shells and other fertilizer. Their water supply is assured from springs and they are the most favoured districts in Holland. In the Westland, between The Hague and the Hook, there is much cultivation of fruit and vegetables under glass, notably grapes, cucumbers, tomatoes and peaches. The great bulb- and flower-growing districts are also on the *Geestgronden*; Leiden and Haarlem being the marketing centres. Tulip, hyacinth, narcissus, daffodil and iris bulbs are exported all over the world and there is a considerable shipment of flowers; Dutch daffodils, for example, coming on to the Covent Garden market when the Cornish supplies are ending. Behind Rotterdam, the production of crops under glass and of bush fruit and ornamental shrubs is a special feature around Boskoop. In the Netherlands there is a marked tendency for farms to increase in number and to decline in size, the percentage of agricultural workers having decreased from 20 per cent in 1930 to 10 per cent in 1960.

THE RECLAMATION OF THE POLDERS

Two-fifths of the total area of the Netherlands is protected by sea dykes and these artificially drained lands form the historical core of the country, so that the history of reclamation and drainage is an integral part of the evolution of the Netherlands.

Two types of polder may be distinguished: those reclaimed from the sea and those associated with river flood-plains. The sea polders lie only 3 ft. above sea-level and are protected by sea dykes. They include rather higher land in the south-west where the tides are higher than in the north. The whole coast of the Netherlands, except for the western dunes and the glacial sandy areas, is in fact protected by sea dykes. Behind these dykes there are areas of low peat formed at or near sea-level and overlying beds of older marine clay (Fig. 119). There are also the areas of recently reclaimed marine clay such as the Wieringermeer polder, which lies 16 ft. below sea-level. In contrast, the polders associated with the Neder Rijn, the Lek, Maas and IJssel are above sea-level but they lie below the flood level of the rivers, so that they must be protected by massive dykes from winter flooding.

In Roman times it appears that the present polders were generally above sea-level but were liable to periodical flooding. Here peat developed up to a thickness of 16 ft., resting on old marine clay in the west and on sands in the east. However, the sea gradually gained on the land, though the most serious inundations came in the 14th century, followed by the major submergences of 1405, 1421 and 1530–2. In 1421 the *Hollandsch Diep* was formed, when the *Lacus Flevo* of Roman times was replaced by the Zuider Zee, and various changes took place in the shape of the Frisian islands. Considerable reclamation was carried out in late medieval times, especially in Zeeland and on the island of Walcheren, where dunes offered protection from North Sea storms. Here the sea dykes at Westkapelle date from the 15th century. Elsewhere, as in North Holland and in parts of western Brabant, the natural process of silting was hindered by tidal scour and sea storms. The river polders presented a different problem. The Rhine is only 33 ft. above sea-level at the German frontier and, like the Maas, it has a low velocity, both rivers tending to swing from side to side across their flood-plain. Both rivers carry a heavy load of silt in suspension

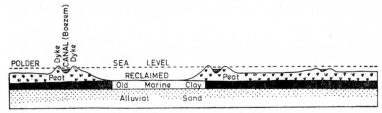

Fig. 119. Section across a reclaimed polder.

and they have built up high natural levées. In course of time, the Waal has become the dominant tributary of the Rhine and the channels of the Oude Rijn and Vecht have decayed. The danger of flooding along the Waal and the Maas has been partly overcome by the separation of the two rivers in 1883. Today, the Rhine is dyked from the German frontier to the sea, but around Arnhem morainic hills rise to the north of the river.

The windmill first appeared in the 15th century as a device for raising water from the drainage ditches, and it gradually spread all over Holland, so as to be a characteristic feature of the Dutch landscape. In the 19th century, it was gradually superseded by the steam pump and a number of these pumping stations, with their chimney stacks, remain. The present century has seen the development of the diesel pump dependent on imported oil, notably at den Oever, where there is a main pumping station for the Wieringermeer polder. In the 19th century, other major undertakings were the drainage of the Haarlemmermeer, east of Haarlem and Leiden, reclaimed in 1852, and the construction of the North Sea Ship

Canal through the centre of the polders.   This canal was cut from Amsterdam to IJmuiden between 1865 and 1872.

The polders take on several patterns.   Those reclaimed from the peat fen were formerly often small as the result of piecemeal reclamation, but the modern polders, such as those of the Wieringermeer, are large and rectangular; while those reclaimed from the tidal flats are usually long and narrow.   The dykes are only a few feet high and drainage is collected through these dykes and ditches to the point where the water can be evacuated by gravitation or pumping.   The typical polder is cut by a series of often parallel drainage ditches or *slosten*, 6 ft. deep, connected to the main ditch where the pumping station is.   At this point the water enters the *boezem* or main canal, which is often navigable for barges.

THE RECLAMATION OF THE ZUIDER ZEE

The most ambitious reclamation project so far completed is that of the Zuider Zee, dating from 1918.[1]   The first problem was to exclude the tidal salt water from a basin extending from North Holland across the island of Wieringen to the coast of Friesland. The second was the reclamation of the five large polders (Fig. 120), with the IJssel Meer in the centre.   The Zuider Zee was transformed into a freshwater lake in 1932, when the IJssel Meer dam (*Afsluitdijk*) was completed.   This 18-mile-long North Sea dyke, which carries a motor highway, shortened the road connection between North Holland and Friesland and also resulted in a considerable saving in the cost of maintaining the sea walls around the Zuider Zee, since these are no longer exposed to tidal movements. The inscription on the monument marking the completion of the dyke reads: ' A nation that lives builds for its future.'

The plan envisaged by the Dutch engineer, Dr. Lely, who has been responsible for the scheme, was to drain 546,000 acres.   Work began on the Wieringermeer polder in the north-west in 1927 and the polder was pumped dry in six months.   Here 50,000 acres lie 16 ft. below sea-level and are drained by the Lely and Leeman's pumping stations.   The canals which carry drainage water to the stations can take barges with up to 300 tons capacity.   There are minor canals for drainage purposes which can take vessels of 30 tons and there are four ship locks.   The polder is traversed by a main road from Amsterdam to Friesland.   The polder is divided into rectangular units, 2,600 ft. long and 800 ft. broad, thus covering

[1] C. H. P. Takes and A. J. Venstra: ' Zuyder Zee Reclamation Scheme, etc ', *Tijdschrift voor Economische en Sociale Geographie*, Vol. 51, 1960.

156 acres. The long sides of the rectangles are bounded by ditches with a metalled road running along the one short side and on the other a second-class canal. Farm buildings border the roadside.

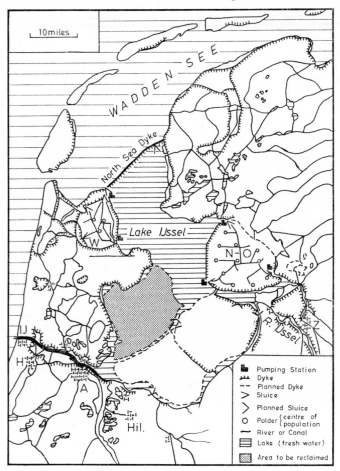

FIG. 120. Reclamation of the Zuider Zee polders.

The first stage in the utilization of the polder, once reclaimed, is the removal of salt. This is done by the action of rainwater, aided by the application of gypsum, and then the state works the land for some years. Cereals and grasses have been found to be adapted to salt in the soil and so is rape or colza, so these crops are grown before leguminous crops and potatoes. The modern farms on the Wieringermeer polder are large and highly mechanized, combine harvesters from America being in use from the beginning. The crop yields are high, wheat yielding 2½ tons per acre. After the first grain crops were harvested, peas, flax and rapeseed were sown, mainly on the soils derived from marine clay; the lighter, sandy soils being sown under pasture. Later sugar beet and potatoes could be grown. The state owns 37 farms on this polder, covering some 2,500 acres, and three villages have been built at the intersection of metalled roads and canals, namely Wieringerwerf, Middenmeer and Slootdorp, populated from all parts of the Netherlands. The monotony of the landscape is broken by trees planted as windbreaks and by a wooded park laid out in the north of the polder. The farm buildings are large and are in one piece, the dwelling house being dwarfed in comparison with the enormous tiled roof which covers the stalls for the dairy cattle. The Wieringermeer dyke was breached by the Germans in 1945 but not the North Sea dyke, so that the salt water was kept out of the polder and the dyke repaired by 1946. It is now a major area of modern mixed farming.

The Noordoost polder is based on the island of Urk, which formerly accommodated fisherfolk. Work was begun in 1936 and the dyke was closed in 1939. The polder is divided into parcels of land 1,000 ft. by 800 ft., i.e. of 60 acres, and each suffices for two farms. The process of reclamation was begun in 1941 but made slow progress during the war because of the labour shortage. After drainage, the polder was first farmed by the state but subsequently private owners have been able to lease the land. Combine harvesters have been introduced, for most of the land is under arable, though the sandy soils are kept as grassland to provide a continuous vegetation cover to prevent soil erosion. The main settlement is Emmeloord.

The southern reclamation scheme has involved three regions: East Flevoland, where 133,000 acres have been drained; Markenwaard, with 133,000 acres; and South Flevoland, with 111,000 acres; leaving 309,000 acres covered by the IJssel Meer as an inland freshwater basin. There is to be a fairway for shipping between Markenwaard and South Flevoland, *en route* to Amsterdam. In contrast with the floor of the other polders where marine clay predominates, the bed of the IJssel Meer is sandy here. Work on the East Flevoland polder was begun in 1950 and the 12-mile-long dyke was completed in 1956. The polder was pumped dry in 1957 and, by 1959, the soil was de-salted and planted with cereals. A maximum population of 150,000 is envisaged and these people will

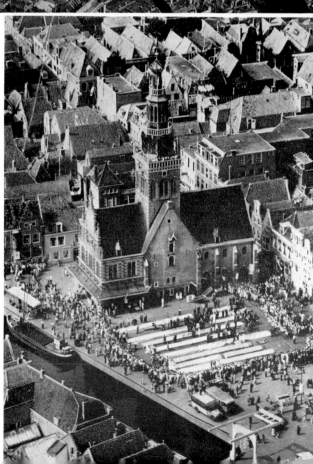

Amsterdam, city of canals (*grachten*), capital of the Netherlands and North Sea port.

TWO DUTCH TOWNS

Alkmaar, with Renaissance y hall and the open air eese market.

(a) Rectangular fields divided by drainage ditches on the Haarlemmermeer-polder

30. DUTCH POLDER LANDSCAPES—I

(b) New farms on the North-East polder at Bouderijn.

live in Lelystad, an administrative centre recently created and, likely to be incorporated in the future in the Amsterdam conurbation. The name of the town commemorates Dr. Lely, the engineer responsible for the Zuider Zee scheme The Maarkenwaard and Flevoland polders are now being reclaimed and by 1980, some

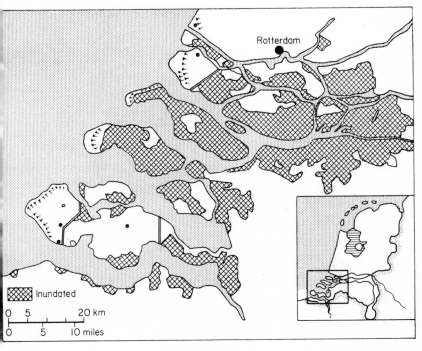

Fig. 121. The Netherlands. The areas flooded in the winter of 1953.⁻

546,000 acres of farmland will have been added to the Netherlands and the acreage increased by 10 per cent. In contrast with the original plan, which was, of course, to supplement the existing agricultural area, today the new farm land replaces former arable land used for urban expansion and new industrial sites. The 'Delta plan', which involves the construction of enclosure dams between the islands of Zeeland and the creation of freshwater reservoirs behind them is due for completion in 1980. Eventually, the West Frisian Islands may be linked to the mainland of the

C.E.—P

northern Netherlands and the mud flats known as the Wadden reclaimed.

MINING AND INDUSTRY

Although the Netherlands are considered to base their prosperity mainly on intensive agriculture, dairy farming and commerce, nearly 40 per cent of the total population is engaged in extractive

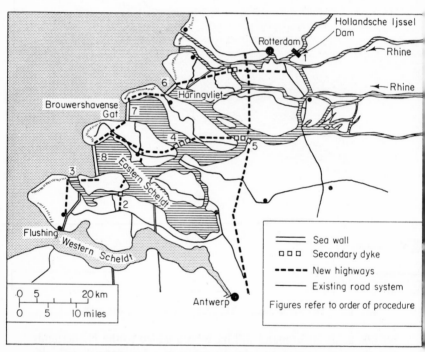

FIG. 122. The Netherlands. The Delta Plan: chief engineering works under construction. The barrages are being completed in numerical order.

industries and manufacturing, though this figure includes the processing of dairy and other farm produce. Coal-mining in the small concealed fields near the German frontier, though of minor importance compared with that of the major coalfields of western Europe, is now of considerable significance to Dutch industry. The extraction of petroleum in the eastern province of Drente, east of Emmen, and the rapid development of the Groningen-Schlochteren gasfield are major factors.   Heavy industry is only locally significant in the Netherlands, in view of the dependence upon Swedish and other imported iron ore, and the inadequacy of home supplies of coking coke, etc., though IJmuiden was developed as the ' Sparrow's Point ' of the Netherlands in 1924, at the seaward end of the North Sea ship canal, a development comparable with that at ' Europoort ' today.   New sites have also recently been established on the banks of the canal between IJmuiden and Amsterdam, as at Beverwijk.   Many branches of heavy engineering are represented, especially that of marine engineering, while the manufacture of agricultural machinery, dairying equipment, etc., is also important.   The Netherlands are noted for their highly fabricated engineering products such as diesel ships, dredgers, marine engines, cranes and diesel pumps, all of which are not suited to mass production.   Other types of industry are related to research in processing, such as margarine manufacture, radio and electrical equipment, and pharmaceutical products including quinine and insulin.   It has been said of the Netherlands that they can export only ' capital and intellect '.   Dutch industries are heavily capitalized and the costs of production are high compared with other European industrial countries. These features are the outcome of the long-established and prosperous commercial activities of Rotterdam, Amsterdam and the smaller coastal and river ports.   The high labour costs in these centres caused a number of light industries to migrate to North Brabant, Utrecht and Overijssel between the wars, especially the manufacture of textiles, boots and shoes, cigars, etc.   The industries which employ the largest numbers are those serving the home market, i.e. the building trades, clothing, food processing and tobacco manufacture; while food packaging and the production of flower bulbs, etc., are largely for the export trade.

Dutch industries have their basis in a rich historic past, for the Low Countries were renowned in the later Middle Ages for their manufacture of woollen cloth, especially in Haarlem, Leiden, Dordrecht and Rotterdam.   The expansion of the shipbuilding industry came in the 17th century with the expansion of Dutch maritime activity and colonial imperialism, especially in the East Indies and Caribbean region, as well as in South Africa.   The cutting and polishing of diamonds in Amsterdam date from the fall of Antwerp to the Spaniards in 1585; while the discovery of diamonds in Brazil in 1727, as well as in South Africa in the 1870's, provided a further stimulus to the industry.   The manufacture of porcelain at Delft reached its perfection in 1700, but after that date competition with mass-produced china and pottery from England and France caused a decline in quality but not quantity. Shipbuilding also decreased in the 18th century, after the Dutch wars with England. Holland had no supplies of iron ore and the chief 18th-century source of motive power was the windmill.   However, the influx of Protestant refugees from France after the revocation of the Edict of Nantes in 1685, as well as Flemish weavers, fostered the growth of textile industries, first wool and linen, and then cotton, while at the same time furthering the cause of Protestantism.

During the brief union with Belgium (1815–30) after the Napoleonic wars, the market in the United Provinces as well as the Dutch colonies was available to the products of Belgian manufacturing industry.   Steam power was applied to spinning in 1829 and to weaving in 1852.   In 1830 came Dutch independence and in 1867 the province of Limburg was incorporated in the Netherlands.   Shipbuilding expanded rapidly at Rotterdam with the development of the Dutch mercantile marine and the passenger and freight traffic with the U.S.A., as well as with the Dutch colonial field and South Africa.   In 1825, van Houten discovered a method of producing cocoa free from cocoa fat and the manufacture of chocolate by this firm has become world renowned.   Potato starch was made after 1840 and food processing developed rapidly with the expanding urban and industrial market in western Europe and Great Britain, especially with the manufacture of margarine after 1871 as a cheap substitute for butter.

After 1875, the Netherlands began the import of cheap steel from Belgium and Germany; while the improvement of inland waterways and the construction of new canals, such as the North Sea ship canal in 1876, greatly cheapened the cost of assembling coal and iron, as at IJmuiden.   The large shipbuilding yards of Rotterdam and Amsterdam developed especially with the increasing use of steam-powered steel ships after 1875, while smaller coastal craft, fishing trawlers and canal barges were built mainly in Groningen and Friesland.   The present century has seen the growth of industries needing much capital and applied research rather than increased quantities of raw materials, beginning with the opening of Philips electric lamp works at Eindhoven in 1895.   This factory now produces about a fifth of the world's output of electric light bulbs and is world-renowned for its radio and television equipment.   The most industrialized districts are Overijssel, Limburg and North Brabant[1]

[1] P. C. A. 't Hoen: ' Post War Industrial Development in the South of the Netherlands ', *Tijdschrift voor Econ. en Sociale Geographie*, Vol. 51, 1960.

but North and South Holland have the greatest absolute numbers engaged in industry; the percentage thus employed is reduced by the large numbers occupied in these provinces in intensive agriculture,

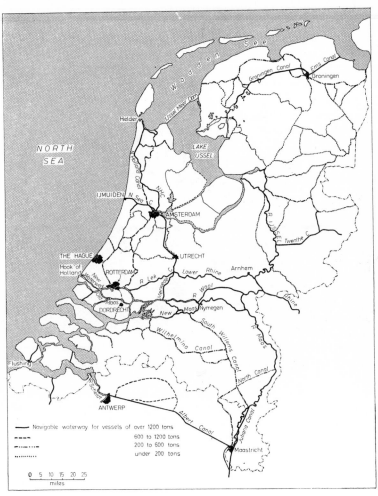

FIG. 123. Navigable waterways of the Netherlands.

horticulture, commerce and transport (Rotterdam and Amsterdam). The policy of the Dutch government today is to disperse industry and to create some new industrial sites, mentioned above. For many years, South Holland has been dominated by the great ship yards and ship-repairing industries which extend from Dordrecht, up the Maas, through Rotterdam to Schiedam. In the city of Rotterdam, there are many industries related to the varied trade of the port, notably the refining of oil at Pernis. Recent years have seen the construction of an oil pipeline between Rotterdam and the

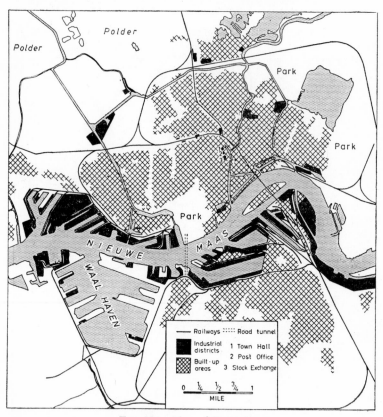

FIG. 124. Plan of Rotterdam.

modern refinery at Wesseling below Cologne. Other port industries include the processing of vegetable oils; sugar extraction from sugar cane imported from Dutch Guiana, etc.; the manufacture of chemical fertilizers, tobacco processing, distilling, especially of spirits, and the tinning of milk and milk products. Today, Rotterdam is not only the leading port of the Common Market group but also of western Europe. Dordrecht concentrates on engineering industries and chemicals; while Gouda, with its tradition of cheese production like Edam and Alkmaar, processes cheese and other dairy produce; Leiden specializing in printing and publishing; Delft in pottery, margarine and cable manufacture; while The Hague is noted for light metal working, paper, chocolate and margarine manufacture. It is also the centre of government.

The industries of North Holland are more varied than those of the province of South Holland and Amsterdam is the hub of the region.   Here are located the manufacture of chocolate, cocoa, vegetable oils, rubber goods and cigars, as well as marine engineering, shipbuilding and a large number of light industries such as food, clothing and printing.   Along the North Sea canal, industries have spread towards IJmuiden, notably those processing imported timber especially from Scandinavia, and grain, including rice.   At IJmuiden, in addition to the production of iron and steel mainly for ships plates, there are heavy chemical industries and cement works.   In North Brabant, sugar refining is carried on at Bergen-op-Zoom and at Breda, where there are also factories making matches and artificial silk.   Tilburg is a noted centre of textile manufacture including clothing, and, in addition to the Philips works at Eindhoven, this town also manufactures cigars and matches.   To the east are the coal-mining centres of Heerlen and Kerkrade; while Maastricht produces glass and pottery.   In the north and east of the Netherlands, there are numerous small-scale industries such as textiles and paper at Arnhem, textiles at Enschede and Hengelo, originally established by Protestant refugees in the 18th century; while Hengelo is also noted for its Stork marine diesel engines.   In Groningen, industries using peat as fuel have long been important, such as the manufacture of potato starch and flour, the processing of milk products and distilling.   The port also builds motor coasters.   The production of bricks, the typical Dutch building and indeed road-making material until the post-war age of steel and concrete, is very general, using river clay or Limburg loess as the raw material.   Salt is derived from borings in the Trias near Winterswijk; while petroleum is exploited near Emmen in Drente, near the German frontier.   A major discovery of natural gas was made in the Groningen region in 1959, production reaching 568 million cub. m. in 1963.

The main reserves of coal are in south Limburg where they have been worked since the beginning of the present century, and also in the Peel region and at Winterswijk.   The seams are highly folded and faulted, those at Kerkrade being nearest to the surface; while the coalfield of south Limburg is divided by a deep fault trough, in which coal lies at depths greater than 8,000 ft.   The seams vary in thickness from 2¼ to 7¾ ft. and production is of the order of 14 million tons of coal per annum.   Much of the coal produces high-quality coke and there is also some anthracite, as well as coal of domestic and industrial qualities.   The opening of the Juliana canal in 1936, parallel to the Belgian frontier, greatly facilitated the cheap transport of coal from Limburg *via* Maastricht to Rotterdam.   The Dutch output of coke is, however, insufficient for the internal market and coking coal has long been imported from the Ruhr and Britain. The integration of Dutch coal and steel production under the Common Market has had a generally favourable effect on Dutch heavy industry.   There is some small-scale working of lignite in Limburg.   The thermal stations of Rotterdam and Amsterdam depend mainly on coal moved by the elaborate inland waterway system, unless imported from Britain.   The demand for steel has been immense since the end of the war for reconstruction and also in the shipbuilding yards of Rotterdam which are today very active, after their war-time devastation.   There is also some processing of non-ferrous metals in the Netherlands, including zinc smelting at Eindhoven and tin at Arnham, while aluminium sheet rolling is carried out at Rotterdam and Utrecht.   The output of a variety of types of machinery especially for sugar refining, flour and rice milling, oil drilling, tin dredging, margarine and refrigerating plant, as well as electrical and radio equipment, is partly for the export trade.   Cables are made at Amsterdam and Delft; while Nijmegen is noted for its generators and railway equipment, and rolling stock is made at Amsterdam and Utrecht.

The light industries of the Netherlands employ over 80,000 people and they are mainly concerned with textiles including cotton and linen, though some woollen and rayon goods are produced, as well as carpets.   The pulp and paper trade, based largely on Swedish pulp, is centred in Amsterdam, Dordrecht and Rotterdam. Food-processing industries cover a wide field, ranging from sugar extraction from both beet and cane; cocoa and chocolate; the manufacture of milk products, notably factory butter, cheese, condensed and dried milk, etc.   The refining of imported vegetable oils and oil-seed for margarine and soap, etc., is largely a monopoly of Unilever, whose plant is below Rotterdam.

DUTCH TOWNS

There is a high density of population in the Netherlands, with an average of 365 per sq. km (945 per sq. mile).   There are two conurbations, Amsterdam and Rotterdam, with over 900,000 in-

habitants, out of a total population of over 12 million; while
's Gravenhage (The Hague), the third city, has over 700,000. These
large cities reflect a rich historic past, especially shown in the
prosperity of the two great seaports. Most Dutch towns have a
history rather different from that of other west European cities, for
the chief problem has been protection from inundation, either by
salt water or by river floods, in a country much of which lies below

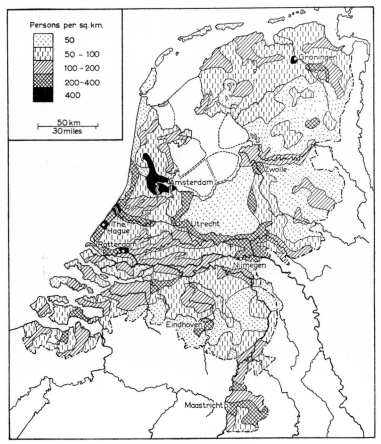

FIG. 125. The Netherlands: density of population.

sea-level. In consequence, many towns are ' planned ', being originally sited on firm ground, such as Haarlem and Alkmaar on *Geestgronden* soils; or on moraines, like Amersfoort and Utrecht; or on
low mounds of boulder clay above the peat fen, like Groningen; or

on dykes above the polders, like Leiden, Rotterdam and Amsterdam. In Holland much pile building has been necessary, notably in Amsterdam, and most building sites have had to be specially prepared. There is a marked absence of stone for building; brick and tile and today concrete and steel being the normal materials used. Few buildings survive from a period earlier than 1500, on account of destruction by fire; though sites such as Utrecht, Vechten on the Old Rhine, Nijmegen and Maastricht on the route from Cologne to Gaul, were all occupied in Roman times. In the Carolingian period, settlement focused on the *Burcht* or artificial mound, enclosed by a palisade and later a brick wall. Such towns were Middelburg and Breda. By the beginning of the 10th century, Utrecht, Dorstad (Duurstede), Haarlem, Delft, Medemblik and Groningen were commercially important, though pillaged by the Vikings. An active trade developed with the Baltic ports during the Hanseatic period in the later Middle Ages, especially in herrings, timber and naval stores. These were exchanged for river fish from the Rhine, salt from the coastal lagoons, butter and cheese from Friesland. In 1384, it was discovered that herrings could be preserved by salting in barrels and hence it came to be said that Amsterdam, the great fishing port on the Zuider Zee, was a city ' built on herring bones '.

The Renaissance period saw the rise of planned towns on defensive sites such as Naarden, a fishing port on the Zuider Zee, a small town of the ' bastide ' type, with a rectangular grid of narrow streets and two central open spaces; one including the market place and town hall, the other the church. This town was damaged by the Spaniards in 1572 and subsequently fortified by Vauban in the 17th century, with great bastions and a surrounding moat, the superstructure of which was destroyed in the 19th century, though the moat remains.[1] A distinct type of Dutch town is the *Grachtenstad* or ' water town ', sited on land reclaimed from a marshy site or lake shore. The settlement was originally encircled by a moat, to which a number of parallel drainage canals or *Grachten* were constructed. Within the moat, the land had to be raised above flood level and rendered fit for building. Pile foundations were needed for the major buildings, such as the church, the town hall, guild hall, and weigh house. Delft, on the banks of the Schie, is a classic example, the name originating in the *Delft* or ditch connecting the Vliet and the Schie rivers in the 9th century. The medieval town was enclosed by walls about 1300 and contained a church, castle, warehouses, and workshops, in addition to a number of

[1] G. L. Burke: *The Making of Dutch Towns*, 1956.

dwelling houses. Delft was a market centre for dairy produce and was also noted for its cloth weaving. The Nieuwe Kerke was begun in 1381 and dominated the market square in the same way as the Town Hall on the opposite side. A number of gabled houses arose lining the canal banks, an ' urban landscape ' immortalized by Vermeer.

Another type of early Dutch town was that of the *Geestgrond*, where the older settlement arose on the firm ground and the newer town had a planned lay-out on the ' Waterland '. Haarlem, on the edge of the Haarlemmermeer not reclaimed until a century ago, provides an example, as does Alkmaar, the name of which signifies ' all sea '. Here the contrast between the part of the town built on the *Geestgrond* and that of the *Grachtenstad* is very clear. Alkmaar became famous for its cheese gild in the later Middle Ages, on the shipping route from the Zuider Zee ports of Hoorn, Enkhuisen and Medemblik.

The later growth of Dutch towns came with the rise of Dutch commerce and large-scale trading activity. H. A. L. Fisher writes of the Dutch cities that: ' quietly, insensibly, they glided out of the medieval into the modern world '. The towns of the Netherlands are not, perhaps, so spectacular as many in western Europe, but many are remarkable for their tree-lined canals, their moats or *Singel*, crossed by narrow brick or wooden swing bridges, and for the gabled façades of the tall brick houses, with their flat windows. Amsterdam provides the supreme example of this typical Dutch architectural style and lay-out. In 1570, it became the financial and commercial centre for the Low Countries after the fall of Antwerp to the Spaniards, and also a Mecca for rich Jewish bankers and merchants, especially from Portugal. The city was built on piles; red brick and tiles being the typical building materials used in the older part of the town. Terraced housing was typical of the late 16th and early 17th century, with tall, narrow, flat-fronted façades, ' ogee ' gables and spacious windows, frequently leaded. At this time it is estimated that a third of the population of Holland lived in towns. Amsterdam was then the leading centre of commerce and banking in western Europe, the town having a population of 40,000. The nucleus of Amsterdam was the angle between the Y (IJ) and the Amstel rivers, a dam being built across the latter river to keep out the salt water of the Zuider Zee. The main town was laid out by 1610, when a series of concentric canals was planned, centring on the Y waterway. Three new canals were then built, namely the Heerengracht, Keizersgracht and Prinsengracht, and these were later extended to the Amstel. From the centre, roads were built radially over these canals by means of a number of bridges; while along the banks of the canals tall merchants' houses arose, accessible to goods moved by canal. The next landmark in the revival of Amsterdam was the building of first the North Holland canal from the Y to Den Helder between 1819 and 1824, super-

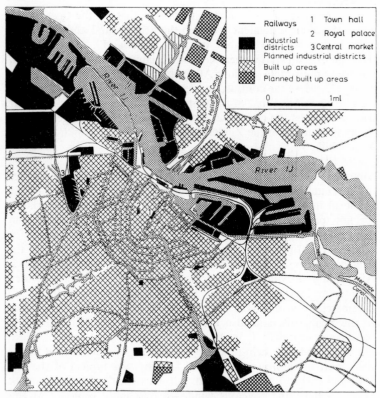

FIG. 126. Plan of Amsterdam.

seded by the North Sea canal in 1876, which enabled Amsterdam to regain some of her lost importance as a North Sea port. However, the modern growth of the port of Rotterdam, as the main outlet for the Rhine valley as well as of the Netherlands, has greatly reduced the importance of Amsterdam as a port; though as the largest city and one of the homes of the Dutch royal family, and as a centre of art and culture, it has a major rôle to play in the life of the Netherlands. After 1877, Amsterdam expanded beyond the demolished walls of the *Singel*, marked today by the willow-bordered waterway of the *Singelgracht*. In 1921, the city boundaries were enlarged to absorb a number of dormitory suburbs, so that Hilversum, Bloemendaal and Zaandvoort may now be regarded as part of the Greater Amsterdam conurbation, while modern housing developments have taken place in South Amsterdam. A vast new 'garden-city' suburb has been created to the west at Slotermeer near the Schiepol airport. Today, Amsterdam, the largest city of the Netherlands (though closely followed by Rotterdam), is also from the point of view of lay-out and historical development one of the most impressive cities of the world. Its future growth is closely linked with the concept of the *Randstad Holland*, a horseshoe-shaped conurbation opening on to the North Sea coast, which it is envisaged will extend by 1980 from Rotterdam, Eindhoven, Tilburg and Breda in the south *via* Arnhem in the east, thence to the Utrecht and Amsterdam conurbations in the north. In 1956, 4 million people or 37 per cent of the population of the Netherlands were living in this *Randstad* and by 1980 it is estimated that it will have increased to 5·5 million.[1,2]

[1] J. Winsemius: 'Urbanisation in the Western Part of the Netherlands', *Tijdschrift voor Econ. en Sociale Geographie*, Vol. 51, 1960.
[2] Peter Hall: *The World Cities:* 'Randstad Holland', pp. 95–121.

THE NETHERLANDS: PART II. REGIONAL STUDIES

THE NETHERLANDS consist almost entirely of the confluent delta of the Rhine-Maas, most of the country lying below 150 ft., while over a third is less than 3 ft. above sea-level. The general impression is that of a vast expanse of low plains lacking in conspicuous relief features, so that minor ridges, such as those formed by sand dunes and low terminal moraines, appear as quite spectacular elements in this 'straight line' landscape. The dunes average between 30 and 40 ft. in height but they attain nearly 200 ft. near Haarlem; while the moraines of the Arnhem district rise to 360 ft. in the Veluwe (the name means ' poor country'). The region of maximum relief in the Netherlands is in the ' appendix ' of Limburg, where the Cretaceous and Tertiary rocks attain over 600 ft. near the German frontier west of Aachen.

The basic physiographic regions of the Netherlands depend on contrasts in surface features, soils and drainage. They are the coastal zone of dunes and reclaimed polders; the alluvial valleys of the Rhine delta lands, known as the Betuwe; the ' plateau ' of Limburg; the region of outwash sands and peat bogs in the south; the morainic ridges of the Veluwe; and finally the glacial heath and peat bogs of the north-east.

The Coastal Zone

The 275-mile-long North Sea coast of the Netherlands consists of three sub-regions. In the south, Zeeland and the islands of South Holland form an island archipelago off the mouths of the Scheldt, Maas and Lek. These islands are low-lying, often more than 10 ft. below sea-level, except for the sand dunes which fringe their outer margin. These dunes and the great sea dykes normally protect the islands from inundation, except at times of abnormal high tide, as occurred with disastrous consequences to the islands of Walcheren, Schouwen and Overflakkee during the storm surge of January 1953.[1] The soils of these islands are derived from marine clay and they are the product of centuries of dyking and draining, so that the landscape is criss-crossed by great dykes, some of which

[1] Since 1958, work has been in progress on the 'Delta Plan', whereby the waters of the North Sea will shortly be shut off from the estuaries dividing the islands of Zeeland by a great sea wall.

438

are followed by main roads, such as that from Middelburg to
Flushing (Vlissingen).   Settlements are mainly of the ' fen colony '

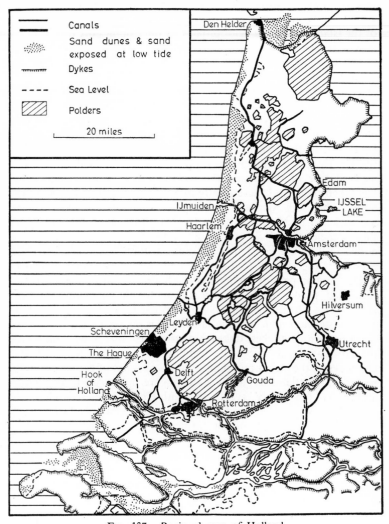

Fig. 127. Regional map of Holland.

type and extend straight along the dykes.   The small and irregular-
shaped fields are usually relics of late medieval reclamation by the
Flemings.   The medieval ' fossil town ' of Middelburg, encircled

by defensive dykes, was partly destroyed during the landings on the island of Walcheren at the end of the 1939–45 War, but the historic market town is now largely rebuilt.   It is the centre of a rich arable and market gardening region.   On the south coast of the island, on the Scheldt estuary is the fishing port of Flushing. now a packet station serving Rotterdam.   Under the Delta Plan it will eventually be linked to both Antwerp and Rotterdam by means of the Benelux Road.[1]

To the north of Zeeland, the coast of Holland extends from the Hook to the naval base of Den Helder.   It is fringed by a belt of sand dunes 2½ miles wide extending along the total length of this curved coast with its remarkable lack of indentations.   Springs break out at the foot of the dunes and provide a source of water for The Hague ('s Gravenhage) and for the city of Leiden.   On the leeward side of the dunes, the reclamation of former marshland has taken place and these *Geestgronden* form excellent horticultural land.   The soils derived from these remnants of older dunes are enriched by shell sand from the sea shore, thus making good lime deficiency; while peat, silt and farm manure are also added.   Along the coast, resorts range from Scheveningen, a train ride from the Hague, to Egmond and Bergen in North Holland.

The greater part of Holland (the ' hollow ' land) consists of the reclaimed polder lands, nearly all of which lie below sea-level (Fig. 127).   The lowest polders form a broad belt between Rotterdam and Amsterdam and here the landscape is characterized by a criss-cross pattern of ditches, dykes and straight roads, often built along the crest of the dykes; while windmills survive, together with the chimneys of the steam pumping stations, as relics of earlier drainage methods.   Settlements, as in Zeeland, are characteristically linear and of the ' fen colony ' type.   In South Holland, the river channels of the Lek, Waal, IJssel and Oude Rijn are all embanked to prevent flooding.   Here and there the former digging of peat for fuel has left pools of stagnant water but most of these have now been drained, except between Amsterdam and Utrecht.   The largest lake formed in Holocene times was that of the Haarlemmermeer in North Holland but today this reclaimed area of silt over peat forms one of the richest arable areas in the Netherlands (Plate 30) and is devoted especially to the cultivation of bulbs around Haarlem. The greater part of the polders is associated with dairy farming based on permanent pasture, but, in the vicinity of the great city markets such as Rotterdam, Amsterdam, Utrecht and The Hague,

[1] S. E. Steigenga-Kouwe: ' The Delta Plan ', *Tijdschrift voor Economische en Sociale Geographie*, Vol. 51, 1960.

horticulture and market gardening predominate, especially for the export trade. This polder region is the heart of the Netherlands and forms the basis of much of the agricultural wealth. The reclamation of the polders around the shores of the former Zuider Zee during the past thirty years will eventually add over half a million acres to the farm land of the state or a tenth of the total area of farm land in the country.

In the north of the Netherlands, the coastal zone of Groningen and Friesland, together with the line of the West Frisian islands parallel to the coast, form a distinctive region. These islands are fringed with sand dunes on the seaward margin and between the islands and the low-lying coast lies the Wadden Zee, a shallow channel which at low tide reveals tidal mud flats scored by deeper channels, similar to the English Wash. Behind the coastal belt and also on the islands are reclaimed polders, associated with the traditional rearing of black and white Frisian cattle. There is, however, some arable land along the coast, often with drainage ditches as field boundaries. Groningen is a market town and fishing port with a canal connection with the Dollart on the German frontier. The small rural settlements in this region are typical of early ' dry point ' occupation of sites above the seasonally flooded land. Such settlements originated on low artificial mounds from which the peasants descended as reclamation of the peat fen proceeded. They have various names, such as ' terpen ', ' wierden ' and ' vliedbergen ' and they extend beyond the frontier into the analogous region of reclaimed marshland found in Oldenburg, where the Friesians were also responsible for early medieval drainage and reclamation. The term ' terpen ' appears to be typical of Friesland, that of ' wierden ' being found around Groningen; while ' vliedbergen ' is associated with Zeeland rather than the fen colonies of the north-east. As these settlements became protected by massive sea dykes, some developed into market centres with the church as nucleus, such as Leeuwarden in Friesland. Here, where much secondary dispersal has taken place; isolated farms, with enormous tiled barns and with a few trees as a windbreak, are typical and the ancient mounds which formed the original settlement site have been destroyed. In Groningen, however, settlements were often rather larger and today a number of ' ring ' villages may be found, marking the progress of the original settlement from the protection of the mound to the line of the base. The rapid development of the gasfield around Slochteren east of Groningen, with its extension under the North Sea, is bringing a new element into the ' cultural landscape '.[1] A long-term project

[1] T. M. Thomas: ' Oil and Natural Gas ', *Geog.* 49, 1964.

is the eventual reclamation of the *Wadden See* and the linking of the west Frisian islands with the mainland.

The Alluvial Valleys of the Betuwe

The Rhine delta lands or the Betuwe form a distinctive element in the landscape of the southern Netherlands. In the south, the plain of the Maas and Waal divides the zone of sandy outwash in northern Brabant and Limburg from the glacial sands and moraines of the Veluwe. The alluvial clays drained by the great distributaries of the Rhine form a kind of polder landscape, across which the rivers flow between massive protective dykes high above the level of the plain which they drain. The region of the Rhine flood-plain, with its levées, forms a belt of permanent grassland 10 miles wide, with much land under grass orchards and soft fruit; focusing, for example, on the fruit market of Geldermalsen. The IJssel valley forms a similar band of green pasture land, though narrower than that of the main rivers of the Betuwe and draining northwards to the IJssel Meer. The chief settlements in this region, apart from the port of Rotterdam, are the historic bridge towns, such as Nijmegen on the south bank of the Rhine and Arnhem on the northern side, backed by the low morainic hills of the Veluwe.

The Limburg ' Plateau '

This ' appendix ' of the Netherlands extends southwards between Belgium and Germany for 25 miles. The region is developed mainly on Cretaceous rocks, deeply dissected by streams draining westwards to the Maas, and with a general elevation of 300 ft., though rising in the south-east to 1,053 ft. This rolling hill country is a natural continuation of the chalklands of Picardy and Hesbaye and the Limburg ' plateau ' is likewise partly mantled with reassorted loess or ' limon '. The resulting clay loam is highly tractable and much of the land is given to mixed farming, with the traditional wheat, sugar beet and rotation grasses of the sub-Hercynian loess regions as the main crops. Settlements are usually agglomerated, in Franconian style, and many villages are of the ' spider-web ' plan, as former centres of the open-field system of farming pivoting on the manor. This type of settlement often survives in the ' court ' or ' hof ' type of farm, in which the farm buildings are grouped around a courtyard, while a high wall fronts on to the street; a type of unit said to have been favourable to defence. In contrast to this prosperous rural landscape is the mining and industrial element, now intruding from the Kempenland. Settlements near the German frontier, such as Valkenburg, Heerlen and Kerkrade, have developed from small market towns into mining centres on the concealed coalfield of Limburg.   The regional centre of Limburg lies to the west of the province, namely Maastricht, the historic bridge town commanding the river crossing and, as such, heavily damaged during the German retreat in 1944-5, but now largely rebuilt.

The Outwash Sands and Peat Bogs of the South

South of the great sweep westwards of the Maas and its gravel terraces of Pleistocene date, lies the non-glaciated country of North Brabant and the Kempenland.   Here the fluvioglacial outwash sands and gravels, laid down in front of the Riss-Saale ice sheet, cover the Pliocene sands of the Kempenland.   Today, much of this original heath land has been reclaimed, as in Belgium, by means of afforestation.   This is the region underlain by the concealed coalfield of the Kempenland and a number of modern industrial towns have developed, notably Eindhoven, with its vast Philips electrical equipment works; while Breda and Tilburg are important centres of textile manufacture.   To the east of North Brabant lies the sparsely populated district of Peel, where much ' high moor ' or *Hoogeveen* persists.   Here the water-table is high and the soil permanently waterlogged.   In this region, as in Friesland and Zeeland, settlements originated on refuge mounds and were here known as *woerden*.

The Morainic Ridges of the Veluwe

A number of winding morainic ridges extend concentric to the former southern shore of the Zuider Zee and form the district of the Veluwe, noted for its comparatively poor sandy and gravelly soils.   The main ' push ' moraine extends from the neighbourhood of Hilversum past Utrecht towards Arnhem and Nijmegen, rising in places to over 300 ft.   The great city of this province is Utrecht, with a magnificent Gothic cathedral tower looking out over a canalized former branch of the Rhine.   A university town, Utrecht remains aloof from the commercial and industrial cities of nearby Holland, for, although it has canal connection with the IJssel Meer, it lies in a backwater as far as trade with the North Sea is concerned.

The Glacial Heaths and Peat Bogs of the North-east

In East Gelderland and Overijssel, the scenery is almost entirely dependent upon the nature of the glacial drift, apart from the areas of peat fen and strips of river alluvium.   Much of the region lies between 30 and 60 ft. above sea-level, though, towards the German frontier, in the direction of the north–south *Hondsrug* moraine, the land rises to 100 ft. To the east of this ridge lies the *Bourtanger Moor*, one of the largest remaining areas of unreclaimed *Hoogeveen* in the Netherlands. Settlement is very sparse in these regions and the average density of 250 to the square mile found here contrasts with the high-density figure of 500 per square mile found in the polder country of Holland. The typical medieval rural settlement in this area was that of the ' esch ', ' enk ' or ' eng ' ; such villages arising where a patch of well-drained and tractable soil occurred higher than the surrounding land. This usually corresponded with patches of boulder clay which could be cultivated on the medieval open-field system. This ' in-field and out-field ' method was often integrated with grazing on the common land of the heath, especially in Drente and Gelderland. Today, much of the heath has been reclaimed and secondary settlement is dispersed. Here the town of Emmen has arisen as a ' new town ' in this remote frontier region; industry and trade replacing the former digging of peat. Proximity to the recently developed oilfield on the German frontier is also modifying the economic life of this hitherto impoverished region.

REFERENCES

The standard reference book on the Netherlands remains that of A. Demangeon: *Belgique, Pays Bas, Luxembourg*, Géog. Univ., Vol. 2, 1927. *La Néerlande: Études Générales sur la Géographie des Pays-Bas*, published as part of the International Geographical Congress Report, 1938, contains much material that is still useful. The post-war years have seen the publication of the great *Handbook der Geographie van Nederland*, by G. J. A. Mulder, 1949–55. There is a study of the growth of Dutch towns in G. L. Burke: *The Making of Dutch Towns*, 1956. A. Demangeon and L. Fébvre: *Le Rhin*, 1935, include a study of traffic on the Dutch Rhine. Other sources in English, especially on the port of Rotterdam, are the writings of F. W. Morgan, especially *Ports and Harbours*, 1952. A few sheets of the *Atlas van Nederland* have been published since 1963. A soil map, *Bodenskaart van Nederland*, on a scale of 1 : 200,000, was published in 1961 and an agricultural atlas, *Landbouwatlas van Nederland*, in 1959

CHAPTER 19

BELGIUM: PART I. PHYSICAL AND HUMAN GEOGRAPHY

AT THE WESTERN end of the north European lowland, Belgium, with an area of only 11,779 sq. miles and a population in 1963 of 9·3 million people, offers a variety of interest in its physical features

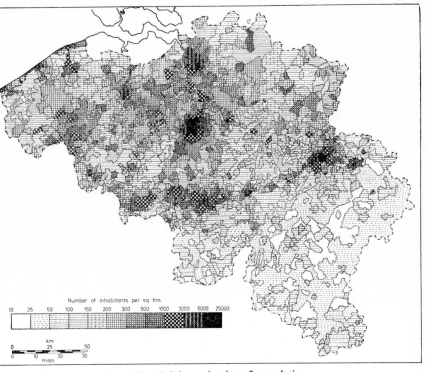

FIG. 128. Belgium: density of population.

and economic development. Transition is, perhaps, the keynote to its geography, for behind its 40 miles of Channel coastline the plain of Flanders has for centuries been a passage land between the Paris Basin and northern Germany. Its physiographic

445

features are all continued across the national frontiers, for, apart from the plain of Flanders, the Sambre-Meuse coalfield is part of a major industrial belt extending from Calais to Aachen, and the Ardenne massif is the north-western extension of the middle Rhine highlands. The Campine or Kempenland is continued into the Kempen region of the Netherlands and the district of Hesbaye into Dutch Limburg. All the major rivers of Belgium (Sambre, Meuse, Escaut and Lys) rise in France and flow generally north-eastwards to form part of the Rhine delta lands.

The population of this predominantly Roman Catholic country is bilingual and the southern limit of the Flemish-speaking population may be drawn along a line running eastwards from Ostend (Oostende) and south of Brussels to the neighbourhood of Liège. Brussels, as the capital city, is an enclave of French-speaking people and the language of the industrial region of the Sambre-Meuse valley is mainly Walloon, a French dialect. The northern part of the country, that is, the plain of Flanders including Antwerp, the Kempenland, North Brabant and Belgian Limburg, are mainly Flemish-speaking districts, but dual place-names are used officially.

PHYSICAL FEATURES

The main relief contrast is between the southern uplands, which rise to a general height of over 650 ft., increasing to between 1,500 and 2,000 ft. in the Ardenne, and the northern low plateaux and plains, descending nearly to sea-level in the coastal polders. The southern region is developed on Palæozoic rocks; Cambrian and Silurian rocks forming the core of the Ardenne as well as of the Brabant massif, though Devonian slates and sandstones dominate the greater part of the Ardenne; Tertiary sands covering the buried Brabant anticline. Carboniferous limestones also outcrop in the Ardenne, forming local hills, and a narrow belt extends from Mons *via* Namur and Liège to the German frontier. These rocks lie beneath the concealed Coal Measures of the Kempenland in the north-east, and powerful springs derived from these limestones provide an important source of water supply for Brussels. The Sambre-Meuse trough, in which the Coal Measures occur at the surface, provides a zone of division between the Palæozoic outcrops of southern Belgium and the younger rocks to the north.

In Belgium, the Triassic and Jurassic rocks are missing, except in the Belgian continuation of the scarplands of Luxembourg to the south-west of the Ardenne massif. The Mesozoic rocks are represented north of the Sambre-Meuse syncline by the Cretaceous rocks which appear north of Mons and again in the regions of Hesbaye and Herve, near Liège. The Tertiaries comprise Eocene and Oligocene sands but with clay predominating in the interior of Flanders. North of a line from St. Niklaas to Maastricht, across the Dutch frontier, Pliocene sands underlie the Kempenland, laid down on the retreating Pliocene sea-floor.

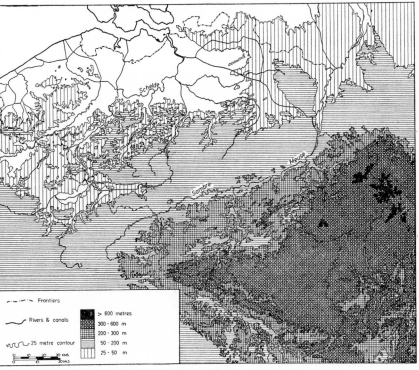

FIG. 129. Belgium: relief and drainage.

In Belgium there is no glacial drift but reassorted loess (*limon*) covers large tracts of the Chalk country of Hesbaye and Herve, as well as the Tertiaries of Brabant, Hainaut and eastern Flanders. Along the short North Sea coast, changes of sea-level have taken place since Pleistocene times comparable with those described along the Dutch coast, in sympathy with the waxing and waning of the North Sea ice. During the last great advance of the North Sea known as the Flandrian transgression, much marine mud was laid down, followed by the accumulation of peat behind the coastal dune belt. The maritime plain of Flanders has been the scene of slow reclamation, partly as the result of natural sedimentation but also through late-medieval drainage and dyking. The steady accumulation of silt along this coast is reflected in the fate of ports of significance to the ' wool ' towns of 14th-century Flanders. Bruges is a well-known example, where the natural course of the Zwyn river has ceased to be a navigable waterway and a modern artificial cut to Zeebrugge has maintained connection with the open sea. A feature of special interest, revealed for example on the morphological map in the *National Atlas of Belgium* (Plate 7) is the fan of coarse sand and gravel laid down by the Meuse (Maas) below Maastricht, during the final stage of the Würm glaciation. These gravels form a gently sloping fan which partly covers the Pliocene sands of the Kempenland.

Climate

The climatic contrasts in Belgium are between the northern plains and low plateaux and the southern uplands, and they are mainly the result of differences in relief, aspect and exposure. The plain of Flanders experiences a broadly dry and uniform climate, with maritime influences prevailing at all seasons. In the Ardenne, the rainfall is heavier and there is more cloud, while central Belgium and the Kempenland form transitional regions. During the winter, Belgium lies in the path of North Atlantic depressions, so that south-westerly winds bring steady rain, in contrast with the fine, calm conditions associated with the westward extension of the Continental ' High '. In summer, rainfall is more intense but all stations record a winter maximum and summer minimum. The lowlands average only 26 inches per annum but in the uplands the total is over 33 in., the regions of greatest mean annual precipitation being in the Hautes Fagnes and in the south-western Ardenne. Winters are generally mild, except in the Ardenne, and snow seldom lies on more than 5 to 10 days on the coast and 12 to 15 days in central Belgium, but in the Ardenne it increases to 50 to 80 days. Similarly frost is of short duration along the coast as the result of strong maritime influences, but increases rapidly inland; Brussels recording an average of 60 days with frost, the Kempenland 80 or 90 days and the Ardenne 120 days. The mean January temperature of Ostend is 37·4° F., that of July, 62° F., compared with the slightly greater range of Charleville, in the Sambre valley, where the difference is between 35° F. in January and 65° F. in July.

Vegetation and Soils

In Belgium, a country with a long tradition of intensive cultivation, very little ' natural vegetation ' remains. The coastal belt of dunes is generally devoid of vegetation except where the blown sand has been fixed by the planting of marram grass and brushwood. This is a waterless region, with poor, acid soils, where developed. Behind the maritime dunes lie the polders, a low-lying region overlying heavy marine clays. These impermeable soils support grassland rather than crops and they have been reclaimed from peat fen by ditching and draining since the 13th century. The polder landscape is generally flat and treeless and fully exposed to sea winds, except or the protection offered by the dunes.

In contrast with maritime Flanders, the interior lowland is higher and the soils vary from those derived from Eocene clays and those from Oligocene sands. The sandy soils have a clay sub-soil and so are retentive of moisture but the water-table is nowhere so high as in the coastal polders. Much of the Tertiary region of Flanders is wooded or coppice, though, with an increase in the *limon* cover to the south, the *bocage* aspect decreases. The central uplands of Brabant, Hainaut and Hesbaye have an extensive covering of *limon*, which weathers into a deep, tractable soil, though in Brabant it overlies Tertiary sands, in Hainaut mainly clay, and in Hesbaye, Chalk. The whole region forms a featureless, dissected and rolling plateau, with a general absence of woodland or coppice, except for some fine beech and sweet chestnut woods in the Forêt de Soignes south of Brussels.

The Kempenland (Campine) is one of the few regions of Belgium with some vestiges of primeval vegetation. Here the outwash gravels of the former Meuse delta overlie Pliocene sands and the resulting soils are highly permeable and heavily leached. The formation of a zone of hardpan in the sub-soil favours the formation of *landes*, where the water-table is high. The region is one of heath, juniper and birchwood, with some stretches of bare sand. The former covering of light oakwood has long vanished and the woodland today is the result of afforestation, especially with Scots pine and Norwegian spruce, for the production of pit props for the mines of the district.

The upland of the Ardenne provides a striking scenic contrast with the lowland to the north. In the foothill region of the Famenne and Condroz, there are woodlands of Scots pine, birch and oak, with hornbeam or oak coppice, but, in the Sambre-Meuse depression, the development of the coalfield, with its associated industries, has destroyed most of the original vegetation and the landscape is partly man-made, with afforested tip-heaps. In the Ardenne massif the acid soils weathered from the Devonian slates and sandstones support a great deal of woodland, except where it has been cleared for pasture and limited cultivation. On the lower slopes, beech forms magnificent stands of timber, with oak, birch and hornbeam on the higher levels; while there are regular plantings of Norwegian spruce and Scots pine. The region of the Hautes Fagnes stands apart, for here the ill-drained soils weathered from Cambrian slates have encouraged the development of peat fen. A final contrast is with Belgian Lorraine, where the Mesozoic rocks give rise to soils varying from poor sands to heavy clays, with fine loamy soils weathered from limestones. Here birch and pine occur on the light, sandy soils; beech forms woodland on the calcareous slopes; while the clays remain partly under oakwood but with much pasture.

LAND USE

The proportion of land in Belgium which is improved (60 per cent) appears rather low in relation to the importance of agricultural production in the country's economy. The figure is a reflection of the large area covered by the Ardenne, where much of the 18 per cent of the land under forest and woodland occurs. The Kempenland, very partially reclaimed, accounts for much of the 7 per cent waste land, the rest occurring largely in the coastal dune belt. It is characteristic of Belgian agriculture that much of it is highly intensive and specialized and this is a feature of long standing, resulting from the early growth of considerable urban markets in Flanders and Brabant. Of the arable land, 56 per cent is under cereals, 20 per cent under rotation grasses, 14 per cent under root and other food crops, and 8 per cent under industrial crops, especially flax, tobacco and hops. There is also a close integration of crop cultivation and stock rearing, especially dairy farming. Much farm work is still done with the aid of Flemish draft horses. In view of the high density of population and of its predominantly urban and industrial character, Belgium is a heavy importer of cereals especially wheat, maize and barley, though the country is self-supporting in beet-sugar and meat. On the other hand, there is a surplus of eggs and market garden produce, especially tomatoes and spring vegetables, as well as glasshouse crops including flowering shrubs and hot-house grapes.

Belgian farms are typically small, for 91 per cent of the holdings

are below 5 hectares.[1]   This feature is partly the result of the overcrowding of the rural areas, especially in Flanders.   It sometimes
results from the custom of industrial workers to run a part-time
agricultural holding.   In some areas the reason is highly specialized
production of either industrial crops or high-priced market garden
and horticultural crops, grown partly for the export trade.   Belgium
is characterized by a remarkably wide range of produce, in view

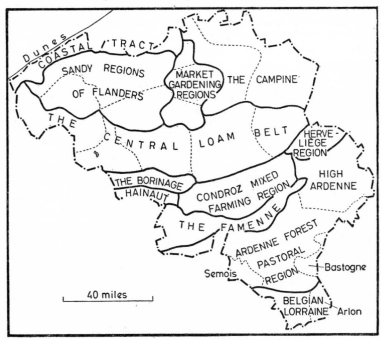

FIG. 130.   Belgium: major land use regions.

of her small total area and rather limited soil resources.   There is,
however, no lack of farm labour and in consequence mechanization
is very retarded.

The agricultural regions of Belgium may be summarized as corresponding to the main belts of terrain already outlined.   The two-
mile-wide dune belt along the coast is only significant agriculturally
where the light sandy soils have been improved by the addition of
sea shells to provide lime.   In the vicinity of Ostend and the seaside resorts, there is some market gardening, as well as the culti-

[1] S. W. E. Vince: ' The Agricultural Regions of Belgium ', Chap. 15 in *London
Essays in Geography*, 1951.

vation of potatoes and other root crops. In marked contrast are the polders, where 40 per cent of the land is under permanent grass. These regions are used for cattle fattening and dairy farming; the arable land producing mainly fodder crops and beans, in addition to wheat. This flat landscape is cut by the straight lines of the dykes and drains and is generally treeless except for the willows fringing the dykes and the poplars lining the main roads. The farms here are small, generally between 5 and 20 hectares, and the farmhouses are single-storeyed, with thatched roofs.

Inland, the sandy plain of Flanders presents a clear-cut contrast. This is a region of small-scale intensive cultivation, with minute subdivision of holdings. Up to 80 per cent of the land is under arable; of this, 25 per cent is under rye and 15 per cent under potatoes. The rest is sown to clover, sugar beet, horse beans or market garden crops. Stock farming is integrated with the production of feedstuffs and it is concerned largely with the supply of dairy produce, bacon, eggs and poultry for the Brussels and Antwerp markets. In the west, especially in the Lys valley, there is marked concentration on industrial crops, especially flax, chicory and tobacco; the flax being retted in the waters of the Lys before being dispatched to the linen mills of Ghent and Courtrai. To the south of Flanders there is an increase in grassland and fruit orchards, while hops are grown for the breweries of Brussels and Antwerp. To the north-east, the Kempenland stands apart with its small farms; producing mainly rye, oats and potatoes on the light soils reclaimed from the heath. On the outskirts of Antwerp, especially around Aarschot and also in the neighbourhood of Mechelen (Malines), market gardening is important, including the cultivation of strawberries.

In the central uplands, farming is on a much bigger scale, with large holdings and isolated farmsteads, set in a generally treeless landscape characterized by great rectangular fields of cultivation. Many farms are over 30 hectares in extent, but some exceed 200. Much mechanization of agriculture has taken place here, though horses still play a large part in farm work; in fact Hainaut is noted for its breeding of draft horses. The major crops in this *limon* country are wheat and sugar beet, with rotation grasses as a third essential feature. Towards Brussels, farming becomes much more intensive and there is a marked concentration on field peas, chicory, flowers and nursery plants; while grapes, tomatoes and cucumbers are grown under glass. There is a similar emphasis on market garden crops and fruit around Liège, as well as in the industrial Sambre valley between the Borinage and Charleroi.

The Ardenne massif is a region of extensive pastoralism, with limited crop farming. In Condroz and Entre Sambre-et-Meuse, farms are large and often worked by tenants. They are mainly pastoral, with an emphasis on dairy production for the Liège market and other industrial towns. In the Ardenne massif, peasant farmers work pastoral farms of a fair size, chiefly with a view to butter production, with pigs reared on skimmed milk. Methods in these remote valleys remain largely traditional. To the south-west of the Ardenne in Belgian Lorraine, the damp climate but fairly rewarding soils make possible the cultivation of oats rather than wheat, and also orchard fruit, though the main economy is based on grassland. Bastogne is the market town of this region.

INDUSTRIAL DEVELOPMENT

Belgium is, for its size, one of the most industrialized countries in Europe and 55 per cent of its population is employed in industry. Today, internal resources are meagre, apart from coal, zinc and flax, though there is a good network of communications by railway, road and canal, especially linking Antwerp with the Sambre-Meuse coalfield. The centuries of tradition in spinning and weaving and the abundance of skilled labour find their expression in the modern textile mills of Ghent and Courtrai, in the linen and lace industry of Ghent, the lace and carpet industry of Brussels and the lace industry of Mechelen (Malines). The types of industry show a wide range, with much local specialization, and the concerns are often small or medium-sized. Most raw materials have to be imported through Antwerp, notably iron ore, coal and coke, wool, cotton, jute, timber, wood pulp and chemicals.

The local specialization in manufacturing activity is illustrated in Fig. 131. Flanders and the Lys valley remain pre-eminently the region of textile production, including not only the traditional linen industry, but also cotton, wool, jute and synthetic fibres. The mills are concentrated along the valleys of the Lys, Escaut (Schelde) and Dendre. Brussels, with its excellent communication facilities, is a centre of light industries, ranging from furniture production (partly from tropical hardwoods), paper and printing, food processing, clothing, carpets and lace making. The city of Antwerp, in view of its function as the chief commercial port of Belgium, with a hinterland including the Ruhr and Rhineland, refines oil and has small shipbuilding yards, as well as carrying out flour milling and sugar refining. Diamond cutting, based on a long-established trade with the Union of South Africa and the Belgian Congo, remains a specialization of the port, which it shares with Amsterdam. The port had developed an important trade with the copper belt of Katanga in recent years, and it also handles radio-active ores from the former Belgian Congo. Between Antwerp and the Kempenland lies a new industrial zone, with potential industrial sites along the Albert canal. In the neighbourhood of the modern colliery town of Genk, there are several chemical works and zinc foundries, as well as establishments producing glass, pottery and cement. This modern development contrasts with the long-established zone of heavy industry in the Sambre-Meuse valley, extending from Mons to Liège. Here is the main concentration of iron and steel production and heavy engineering. Liège, Charleroi and Mons are great industrial towns; centres of coal-mining, coke and gas production, blast furnaces, steel works and zinc foundries.

The production of coal in Belgium is gradually declining, the output in 1963 being 21 million metric tons compared with 29·6 millions in 1938. In the Sambre-Meuse field, where coal-mining has long been established, conditions of working are some of the most difficult in Europe, for there is much faulting and overthrusting of the soal seams which often dip at a high angle, while the workable ceams are thin. Coal outcrops at the surface at Liège but the Coal Measures dip steeply under Cretaceous and Tertiary rocks beyond Mons and here pits are over 3,000 ft. deep. There is little mechanization of coal-working in this field. For many years, Belgium has employed much foreign labour in the pits, especially Poles and Italians. The field produces various types of coal, including semi-anthracite near Namur suitable for briquetting, semi-bituminous coal near Charleroi for the production of industrial coke, and long-flame coal for the manufacture of gas and formerly used in the iron puddling furnaces, especially at Mons. There is a general production of gas and steam coal, as well as household coal, but the resources of long-flame and coking coal are insufficient for the iron and steel industry and these are imported, mainly from the Ruhr. Belgium's membership of the European Common Market is an advantage here. Many of the older workings are becoming derelict, especially around Mons, and costs of working are everywhere high. The relative ease of mining in the concealed Kempenland coalfield around Genk has resulted in it producing an increasing proportion of Belgium's coal output, now equal to over a third of the total.

The heavy industries of Belgium are located either in relation to the coalfields including the concealed coalfield of the Kempenland or to supplies of iron ore, as in Belgian Lorraine. Traditionally, the smelting of iron ore depended on charcoal from the foothills of the Ardenne and some hæmatite was once worked near Namur. New technical processes first applied in Great Britain were intro-

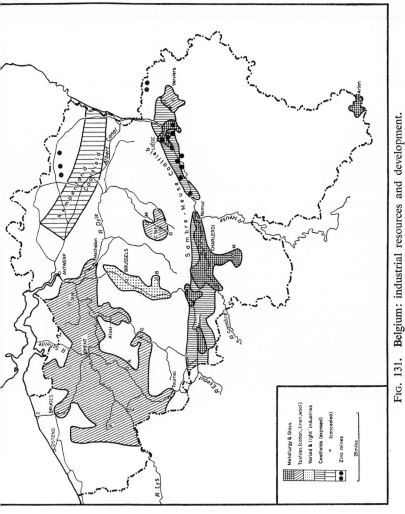

Fig. 131. Belgium: industrial resources and development.

duced at an early date in Belgium; for the first coke-burning blast furnaces were established near Liège in 1823, where an Englishman, John Cockerill, established an iron works at Seraing, in the narrow, incised valley of the Meuse. Elsewhere, charcoal smelting continued until 1851. The exhaustion of local ores was relieved by the development of the ' minette ' ores of Lorraine and Luxembourg after 1870, worked with coke imported from the Ruhr and the Saar coalfields. Today, high-grade hæmatite is imported from Sweden and Algeria, while some bog ore is worked in the Kempenland as well as in the Duchy of Luxembourg. The Belgian steel industry is monopolized by a small number of great industrial organizations, and there is marked vertical integration; the steel firms owning collieries, coke ovens and blast furnaces. Methods of production differ from those in general use in Britain and the Ruhr, on account of the need to employ the basic Bessemer or ' Thomas ' method to deal with pig-iron smelted from the phosphoric ores of Lorraine. The Siemens-Martin or open-hearth method is also in use at Liège, dependent on imported hæmatite and scrap metal. There are also electric-arc furnaces here for the production of steel alloys and for use in the machine tool industry. The main product of the Liège steel mills is, however, sheet steel and, after the war, modern semi-continuous wide strip mills were installed and much of this sheet steel is exported. A new development is the jointly owned Belgian-American steel plant at Genk, on the Albert canal, planned as the largest in the Common Market group, with an annual output of 18,000 metric tons of stainless steel.

Belgium also has non-ferrous metal industries; refining copper, lead and zinc from Katanga. The acquisition of the zinc mines at Moresnet and Eupen, near Aachen, after the 1914–18 War, proved an advantage here but zinc is also imported from Mexico, Scandinavia and elsewhere. Hoboken, outside Antwerp, is the main centre of copper refining. As well as exporting raw and semi-finished steel, together with some finished products such as nails and wire, Belgium is an important source of refined zinc. There is a wide range of engineering in Belgium, mainly concentrated on the coalfield, but also located in Antwerp, Brussels and the Kempenland. The Cockerill works at Seraing produced the first locomotive in 1835 and the building of diesel engines and rolling stock is today of major importance. Firearms have long been made at Liège. In modern times, Liège, Brussels and Antwerp have become centres of electrical engineering, including radio apparatus; while Genk, in the Kempenland, has a car assembly plant.[1] With the completion of the Albert canal in 1940, Liège was linked to Antwerp by a modern waterway, navigable for barges of up to 2,000 tons. It is mainly used for the transport of coking coal from the Campine,

[1] T. H. Elkins: ' Liège and the Problems of Southern Belgium ', *Geography*, Vol. 41, 1956, pp. 83–98.

(a) The 'water town' of Elburg in Veluwe, on the southern edge of the East Flevoland polder.

31. DUTCH POLDER LANDSCAPES—2

(b) Closing the dyke of the East Flevoland polder at Elburg, January 1957.

(a) The Moselle valley at Wellenstein, a centre of viticulture on the south-eastern margin of the *Bon Pays* or *Gutland*.

32. TWO LUXEMBOURG LANDSCAPES

(b) Esch-sur-Sûre, a medieval defensive site within the incised meander of the Sûre, in the *Oestling* region of the Ardenne.

and also of petroleum products. In future a canal may be constructed to the Rhine.

The chemical industry is found partly in the Sambre-Meuse valley, in the Kempenland, and also in Antwerp, Brussels and Ghent. While the production of heavy chemicals, such as acids and salt compounds, is found in association with the zinc industry, light industries such as the production of drugs, dyes, and photographic materials (Gevaert), are found in the large urban centres of Brussels, Ghent and Antwerp. The craft of glass making, associated with Charleroi since the arrival of Venetian glass blowers in the 14th century, survives in the production of plate and window glass, as well as the mass production of bottles and machine-cut crystal. In the Kempenland, the long-flame coal is very suitable for use in the glass furnaces and so is the local silver sand. The other necessary raw materials, including sodium salts, limestone and manganese, are brought *via* the Albert canal.

The concentration of the textile mills of Belgium into the Lys and Escaut valleys, except for the woollen industry of Verviers, is a clear example of industrial inertia. The Lys is still used to some extent for the retting of flax fibres but the local supply of flax is quite insufficient, though the acreage has recently been increased. Ghent and Courtrai produce all types of linen, from the traditional cambric, lawn and damask to coarse sail cloth and tent canvas. The cotton industry of Ghent dates from the introduction of English machinery in 1798. Jute from E. Pakistan is used for the manufacture of sacking and hessian, while silk yarn is imported for the silk mills of Ghent and Brussels. Here the introduction of the Jacquard loom in the 18th century mechanized the weaving of carpets, hitherto made on the hand loom. Today Belgium manufactures a wide range of textiles based on rayon and nylon as raw materials.

BELGIUM: PART II. REGIONAL STUDIES

THE MAIN physiographic contrast in Belgium is between 'High Belgium', comprising the Ardenne massif, Belgian Lorraine and the southern low plateaux north of the Famenne depression, and the northern lowlands of Hesbaye, Brabant, Flanders and the Kempenland. The Sambre-Meuse furrow follows a synclinal depression related to the Hercynian folding of the Palæozoic rocks of southern Belgium but it also divides two parts of a once continuous erosion surface. It appears that the Pliocene Sea advanced across Belgium to cover part of the Ardenne, and the 1,000-ft. planation surface is traceable from the northern Ardenne into the Condroz plateau, north of the Famenne (Sambre-Meuse) depression. Following the Miocene uplift of 'High Belgium', streams were rejuvenated and the deep-cut valleys of the Meuse across the western end of the Ardenne and its tributary the Semois add to the scenic variety of this Hercynian upland, especially where associated with limestone land forms, as around Dinant. Whereas much of 'High Belgium' remains wooded, the low plateaux to the north are partly loess-covered; the landscape of Hesbaye and southern Brabant being largely open, cultivated and thickly settled, thus resembling Dutch Limburg, the Börde regions of Germany and the limon-covered low plateaux of north-eastern France. The plain of Flanders offers local variety in spite of its uniformly low relief, for the intensely cultivated interior plain contrasts with the maritime plain with its coastal dunes backed by a belt of polder country. The scarplands of Belgian Lorraine and the sands and gravels of the Kempenland complete the pattern of regions.

Belgian Lorraine

As in eastern France and the south-west of the Duchy of Luxembourg, of which Belgian Lorraine forms a minor continuation, the gently dipping Jurassic rocks have been differentially eroded to form a series of scarps and vales, so that the relatively resistant sandstones and limestones form wooded ridges, while the shales and marls form the vales. Fragments of the 1,000-ft. erosion platform of the Ardenne also occur here, notably around the Roman road centre of Arlon. The Longwy limestone escarpment forms the frontier region with France. The uplands are mainly pastoral but there is also some mixed farming in the vales, the average density of population being rather higher than in the Ardenne. A small amount of ' minette ' phosphoric ore is worked at the base of the Jurassic escarpment and the ' iron and steel ' region of French Lorraine and Luxembourg is represented by the blast furnaces and steel works of Angleur-Athus.

The Ardenne

This upland barrier, which extends to the boundaries of Germany, Luxembourg and France, is a crescent-shaped continuation of the middle Rhine highlands. The highly folded and metamorphosed rocks which underlie this Hercynian massif range from the Cambrian slates of the *Hautes Fagnes* or *Hohes Fenn* and their associated quartzites forming local ridges, through Devonian slates and sandstones, to the Carboniferous limestones of the northern margin. The generally slab-like appearance of this part of ' Haut Belgique ' results from the Oligocene-Miocene uplift followed by Pliocene peneplanation. The greatest heights are towards the German frontier, where the Botrange attains 2,277 ft. and Baraque Michel, 2,215 ft. Flat-topped and also rounded heights rise locally to about 1,650 ft. and between these ridges broad depressions occur, the swampy gathering ground of much of the upland drainage. The Ardenne descend in two stages towards the Famenne depression, one summit level occurring over wide areas at about 1,300 ft. and another at 1,000 ft.

As the Celtic name of ' Ardenne ' suggests, the region was originally thickly wooded, except in tracts too exposed to support tree growth, such as the upland of the *Hautes Fagnes* which form desolate *landes*, where ill-drained peat bogs support a vegetation of mosses and lichens and there is an absence of settlement. Much of the Ardenne forms a valuable reserve of timber, with much recent afforestation. Whereas silver fir and larch prevail on the higher slopes, mixed woods of oak, beech and chestnut, intermingled with firs, cover the lower slopes and there are some forestry industries, such as lumbering and resin extraction. The raw climate, persistent cloudiness, prolonged snowfall and summer thunderstorms all handicap farming, apart from the prevalence of steep slopes and thin, acid soils. There is, however, some utilization of the upland pastures for the grazing of sheep and cattle and there is some co-operative dairy farming, mainly for butter production. The gentler slopes have been largely cleared of timber and improved for cultivation, so that there is an increasing amount of cereals, mainly rye and oats, and also potatoes grown for sale. In contrast is the subsistence agriculture of the more remote farms, where traces of the open-field system persist. There are few large settlements, apart from Dinant, commanding the bridge point over the Meuse in its limestone defile, and the resort of Spa. The Carboniferous limestone country, of which Dinant is the tourist centre, offers a variety of interest, for karst features are represented by the grottoes and caverns of Han and there are numerous instances of streams disappearing through swallow holes into the fissures of the porous limestone. The gorge of the Meuse, between Dinant and Namur, offers fine examples of limestone cliff scenery, and the river itself flows as a rushing torrent, although its gradient is virtually that of a plain. The river therefore frequently floods between Givet, on the French boundary, and its confluence with the Sambre at Namur.

The Southern Low Plateaux

These relief features cover a belt of country 20 miles wide and are drained by the northward-flowing Meuse and Ourthe. Here the Palæozoic rocks, especially the sandstones, give rise to poor soils and, since the winters are severe and the duration of frost long, the land is mainly under pasture. West of the Meuse, the local name of 'la Fagne' persists but the forest which once covered this district has now been mainly cleared. The general density of population is only 130 per square mile but it increases in the relatively prosperous valley of the Meuse, where vines and the fig appear, in addition to fodder crops, potatoes and orchard fruits, all of which flourish on the limestone soils. These districts are also noted for stock rearing on large farms, including both cattle and horses.

Four subdivisions of this physiographic region may be distinguished: along the northern edge of the Ardenne, the Famenne depression, lying at about 600 ft., is an old erosion feature, following a synclinal furrow, revived during the incision of the Meuse and Ourthe into the Upper Devonian shales, as the result of the Oligocene-Miocene uplift of the region. These 'Appalachian' features are finely illustrated in the morphological map of Belgium prepared by Mlle Lefèvre (*National Atlas of Belgium*, plate 7). In contrast, the Condroz plateau, lying between 650 and 1,050 ft., is an eroded anticline, trending from north-east to south-west, in sympathy with the Carbo-Permian fold trend. The 1,000-ft. summit level occurs on Devonian sandstones, but the streams draining the region have exposed shales and limestones in the valleys. This belted structure is also typical of the third region, known as 'Entre Sambre-et-Meuse', which covers much of the coalfield and industrial region from Mons to Liège. To the east of Liège, towards the German

frontier, Chalk covered with re-assorted *limon* underlies the Pays
de Herve, where the landscape is characterized by beechwoods intermingled with cereal and sugar-beet production, as in adjacent
Dutch Limburg.

The Northern Low Plateaux

North of the narrow outcrop of the Coal Measures, trenched by
the Sambre-Meuse, the development of which has been previously
described, a series of low plateaux form the ' High Plains ' of Belgium. They range from the Chalk country of Hesbaye to the Tertiary (Oligocene) sands which cover the buried Palæozoic anticline
of Brabant. All these gently sloping uplands have a fine covering
of re-assorted loess and the soils are rich loams which are intensively cultivated. This is a traditional passage land, for the region
appears to have been relatively open from prehistoric times, and
thus resembles the *Hellweg* at the northern foot of the Sauerland in
Westphalia. Today, clumps of trees occur around the agglomerated
villages but the landscape is that of a chequerboard of hedgeless
fields. Wheat, sugar beet and the cultivation of rotation grasses
characterize the arable farming, with market gardening and dairying
near the urban markets. The density of population varies here
from 250 to 500 to the square mile.

Within this region, the two contrasts are between the Chalk
plateau of Hesbaye and the Tertiary sands of Brabant and Hainaut.
Hesbaye extends for 40 miles from west to east and 20 miles from
north to south. There is a notable absence of surface drainage on
account of the porous nature of the underlying Chalk and broad
' solution ' hollows occur. In Brabant and Hainaut there is an
abundance of surface drainage, especially where streams are fed by
springs which break out where loess overlies clay. This is one of
the most intensely cultivated regions in Europe, for the richness of
the soils, combined with an abundance of farm labour, have made
possible the cultivation of a very wide range of crops, including
wheat, oats, sugar beet, flax, hops and chicory. There is today still
little use of farm machinery even for wheat harvesting, since the
holdings are small and hand labour is plentiful, for it can be supplemented by casual labour from Flanders for weeding the sugar-beet
fields and for lifting the beet. Local industries include brewing at
Charleroi using local barley, sugar refining and fruit preserving.
In the vicinity of Brussels, cultivation reaches its maximum intensity, with market gardening, dairy farming and the cultivation of
fruit and flowers under glass, exemplified by the table grape industry
of Wellin. Apart from the central node of the capital city, Brussels,

a number of small towns are scattered through the region such as Louvain, with its great library and fine late-Gothic architecture, and Tournai, with its wool, linen and cement industries. Greater Brussels, with a population of over a million in 1963, has grown rapidly since the creation of the Kingdom of Belgium in 1830,

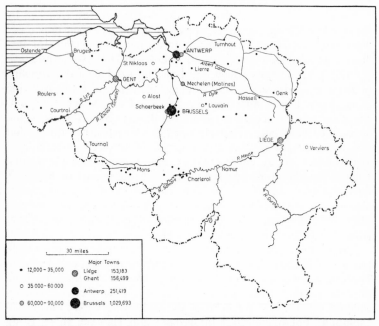

FIG. 132. Belgium: distribution of urban population. The figure for Brussels applies only to the inner city, for, including the suburbs, the conurbation now exceeds a million people; similarly the figure for the Antwerp conurbation is 878,000.

followed by the building of railways which made Brussels the centre of national communications; thus resembling in a smaller way, the nodality of Paris (Fig. 97). The city is also served by *Sabena* airlines. Local traditional industries, which depended originally on skilled hand labour and craftsmanship, include the making of lace and embroidery and the weaving of carpets.

The Northern Lowland

The plain of Flanders and the Kempenland form lowland regions sloping gently to the North Sea; their diversity of landscape and land use depending upon local variation in soils, whether derived from the Eocene and Oligocene rocks of the interior plain or the Recent deposits of maritime Flanders and the Kempenland. The Tertiary lowland of interior Flanders lies mainly less than 150 ft. above sea-level; though local heights include the Pottelbert (515 ft.), which rises between the shallow valleys of the Dendre and the Scheldt (Escaut). A low line of hills also runs from west to east as a continuation of the Mt. Cassel ridge towards Passchendaele. The plain is lightly dissected by streams which originally developed on the emerging Pliocene sea-floor and flowed northwards to a now vanished coastline. The subsequent development of a barrier to the north appears to have diverted the drainage of the Scheldt and its tributaries, the Lys, Dendre, Senne and Dyle, north-eastwards towards the Rhine delta lands. There has been some relatively recent development of independent drainage across the maritime plain directly to the North Sea, for instance by the Aa, Zwyn and Yser. The interior plain is developed on Oligocene sands and Eocene clays and the whole region is one of intensive cultivation, a feature which has characterized the plain for centuries. Wheat, oats (for draft horses), sugar beet, chicory, hops and ley grasses (including lucerne, sainfoin and clover) all form part of the rotation. The most important cash crop is, however, flax, which was introduced into the plain in the later Middle Ages, when the woollen industry, monopolized by the Gilds of Ghent, Bruges and Ypres, was challenged by the English production of fine woollen cloth. The retting, scutching, spinning and weaving of flax is typical of the Lys valley, along which numerous retting ponds occur, as well as linen mills. Ghent (Gand), with a population of 155,951 in 1963, is the hub of the linen industry, to which the spinning and weaving of cotton and other fibres have been added since the introduction of steam power. This city, with its medieval cloth hall, lies at the confluence of the Lys and the Scheldt and it is the great market town of the plain. It also serves as a port by virtue of its ship canal link with the North Sea. The production of market garden crops in the neighbourhood is an important feature and the cultivation of flowering shrubs, such as azaleas and rhododendrons which flourish on the light, sandy soils, is world renowned.

The Maritime Plain of Flanders lies below 65 ft. above sea-level and much of the polder region is as little as 15 ft. or even 6 ft. above sea-level. The peat fen which overlies the marine clay here is protected by a line of sand dunes from inundation by the North Sea, and the construction of a series of dykes and drains by the Flemings in late medieval times made possible the intensive cultivation of these polders, as in Zeeland. Like the interior plain of

Flanders, this coastal belt has long supported a high density of rural population.   The dyked lands are partly under strip arable cultivation but much of the land is also devoted to permanent pasture for

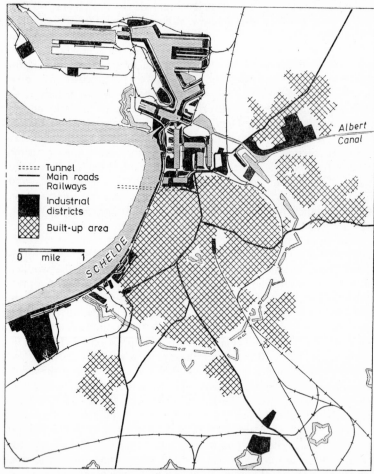

Fig. 133.   Plan of Antwerp.

the rearing of Frisian dairy cattle.   The straight line of the coast, backed by dunes in places 90 ft. high and built up by the prevalent south-westerly and westerly winds, is one of constant attack by the sea.   Damage to the sea defences during the war-time occupation by the Germans has now been repaired and at Ostend (Oostende) modern sea-walls have been built to prevent extensive flooding of the coast. Centuries of silt deposition have led to the decay of former small ports along the coast here, such as Nieuport, now some distance inland. The fate of Bruges, on the Zwyn, has already been mentioned. This town, with its late-medieval and Renaissance architecture and its maze of canals, is a town which thrives on its past, especially on account of its attraction to English tourists. Ostend, formerly a small fishing port, has become the packet station for Belgium opposite Dover and it is also a small commercial port, shipping fish, dairy produce, vegetables and fruit. The construction during the last war of an *Autobahn* from Ostend to Brussels, by-passing Ghent, has greatly speeded up communications. Many of the narrow minor roads in rural Flanders, with their stone setts, are a great hindrance to modern traffic.

Towards the mouth of the Scheldt, especially around the great city of Antwerp, the soils consist of coarser material, especially sand and gravels, laid down by the Maas and the Rhine as fluvio-glacial outwash from the Riss glaciation. Straight roads, fringed by poplars, fan out from the port across a countryside which is intensively cultivated; small fields of wheat, sugar beet, flax and chicory being ubiquitous. Sometimes high hedges serve to protect the plants from strong winds. Settlement is mainly dispersed or in small hamlets and the farm buildings are often single storeyed, with an ill-cared-for appearance, compared with the neat, clean dwellings of the Dutch polders.

Antwerp (Antwerpen) is the great commercial port for Belgium, its hinterland overlapping considerably with that of Rotterdam, for both serve the Rhineland and central Europe. In recent years, Antwerp has been connected to the Meuse at Liège by means of the Meuse-Scheldt canal, which lies parallel and close to the Dutch boundary, and also by the modern Albert canal. It is now proposed to build a canal to the Rhine, thus offering a further challenge to Rotterdam as a major outlet for Rhine traffic. The core of Antwerp is late medieval (Fig. 133) and the fine late-Gothic cathedral has survived two world wars. The growth of the port since the railway age has been the result of the increasing importance of Belgium's industrial and agricultural production in terms of world trade, and also through the use of Antwerp as an alternative port for the Ruhr industrial region and the Rhineland. Shipbuilding, oil refining, flour milling and brewing are examples of the varied industries of the port. The wealth derived from the Congo basin has also contributed to the prosperity of the port, for it handles increasing quantities of copper as well as radio-active ores from central Africa. In 1963, Antwerp recorded a population of 249,447.

The Kempenland (Campine) is the province of Belgium which has seen the greatest change in values in recent years. Here the Riss fluvioglacial sands and gravels overlie the Pliocene sands and the region was long sparsely populated and given over to stretches of heath, with some sheep rearing and rye and potato cultivation. The development of the concealed coalfield since the end of the first world war has been rapid and production has increased from 1 million metric tons in 1917 to over 8 million metric tons in 1960 (a third of the total for Belgium). The growth of this modern industrial region is fully described elsewhere.[1] Today, the sterile tracts of heather moor, with their occasional pine plantations, are varied by the sporadic occurrence of tip heaps from the collieries and by the modern villages built to accommodate the mining population. Hitherto there has been much drift of population to the port of Antwerp, especially as dock labourers. The compact, medieval town of Mechelen (Malines) is the seat of the Cardinal Archbishop of Belgium. Its Gothic cathedral has a magnificent belfry from which there are wide views over the plain. The city had a population of 64,847 in 1961 and is an important market town with a local lace industry and it serves the southern Kempenland.

REFERENCES

The standard reference on Belgium remains that of A. Demangeon: *Belgique—Pays Bas—Luxembourg*, Géog. Univ., Vol. 2, 1927. Special studies include those of F. J. Monkhouse: ' The Belgian Kempenland ', 1949, and S. W. E. Vince: ' Agricultural Regions of Belgium ', in *London Essays*, 1951. H. Pirenne: *Medieval Cities*, 1927, is a classic by a Belgian historian which deals in part with the medieval Flemish cities. In *The Changing World*, edited by W. G. East and A. E. Moodie, 1946, the latter has a chapter entitled: ' Britain, France and the Benelux Countries '. The beautifully produced *Atlas National de Belgique*, now in progress, is a splendid work of reference. Topographic maps, on a scale of 1 : 50,000, replacing the 1 : 45,000 series, have been in progress since 1951.

[1] F. J. Monkhouse: *The Belgian Kempenland*, 1949.

CHAPTER 20

LUXEMBOURG: PART I. PHYSICAL AND HUMAN GEOGRAPHY

THE GRAND DUCHY of Luxembourg lies to the south-east of Belgium; its southern boundary marches with French Lorraine and its eastern one with West Germany. It covers an area of only 998 sq. miles, with a north–south extent of 51 miles and a maximum distance from east to west of 35 miles. It had a population of 323,971 in 1962, a reduction after permanent emigration during the war. The only large town is the capital, the city of Luxembourg, with 74,493, or a quarter of the total population of the Duchy. It has an impressive site, a medieval fortress dominating the gorge of the Alzette, cut in Luxembourg sandstone. Today, this city has well-laid-out streets and fine public buildings. It is the headquarters of the Luxembourg steel industry and of *Euratom*. Luxembourg has a pivotal position between Belgium, France and West Germany. Within the Duchy is part of the ' minette ' ironfield of Lorraine which she has exploited since 1871. The Duchy was incorporated in the German Customs Union until 1919, when it passed to Belgium. Since 1948, it has been a member of the Benelux group. Apart from the modern though small centres of industry on the ironfield in the south-west of the Duchy, the Luxembourg countryside has a mainly rural aspect and methods of agriculture remain traditional, typified by the ox-drawn plough and farm cart. The fundamental physical contrast, which is reflected in the two distinctive landscape regions, is between the Luxembourg section of the forested Ardenne block, with its valleys partly cleared for subsistence agriculture, and the scarps and vales of Mesozoic rocks which form the best mixed farming land. The Primary massif of the Ardenne, with is sparse settlement and fine stands of mixed forest, is known as the *Oestling*, as distinct from the *Bon Pays* or *Gutland* to the south.

Luxembourg thus lies in a transitional belt of country where the wooded slopes of the Ardenne massif give way to the open, largely cultivated land lying to the south-east. The Devonian slates and quartzites of the Ardenne, with their Hercynian folding and metamorphism, give rise to bold and rugged scenery. Culminating viewpoints are the Burgplatz (1,847 ft.) and Napoléonsgard (1,821 ft.). Much of the Mesozoic landscape to the south-east lies

467

900 ft. above sea-level, but, along the Moselle valley to the east, it falls to 500 ft. The underlying rocks range from Bunter sandstone, which outcrops along the southern margin of the Ardenne; a narrow belt of *Muschelkalk* (shelly Triassic limestone); followed by zones of Keuper marl, succeeded to the south-west by the lower Jurassic

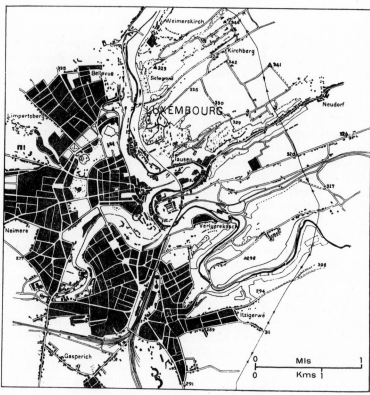

Fig. 134.   The city of Luxembourg.

series. The Triassic region is considerably faulted in the east towards the Moselle valley, notably between Echternach and Greven-macher, where sandstones, marls and dolomitic limestones are involved. The whole region is one of marked dissection, especially by the Sûre river and its tributary the Alzette, the gorge of which divides the city of Luxembourg into two distinct parts.

The lower Jurassic rocks give rise to diversified scenery. The Luxembourg sandstone forms a plateau surface in places deeply eroded, so that the scenery is quite spectacular, with sandstone cliffs, buttresses and rock pillars rising above deep-cut chasms, such as that formed by the Alzette. Another comparable region is found west of Echternach and is known as the Müllerthal or *Petite Suisse*.

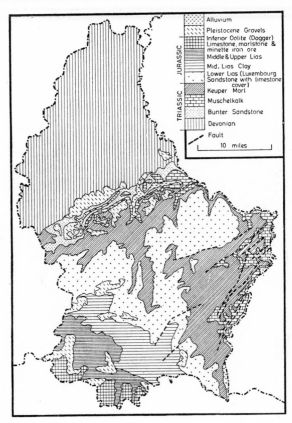

FIG. 135. Luxembourg: geology.

This Jurassic sandstone outcrop provides local building stone, its pinkish tinge being conspicuous in many of the main buildings in the city of Luxembourg. It is of a highly porous rock, so that copious springs break out at the base, notably those at Kopstal which supply the capital with pure water.

The middle and upper Lias outcrop to the south-west of the Luxembourg sandstone and consist of clays, marls and shales. This is the 'minette' zone, famed for its low-grade iron ore deposits, and it is divided by the upper Alzette valley into the Differdange basin to the west and that of the Esch to the east.   The reddish colouring of the rocks has led to the region being known as the ' Terres Rouges '.   There are few Pleistocene and Drift deposits in Luxembourg, though some Pleistocene material occurs capping the higher

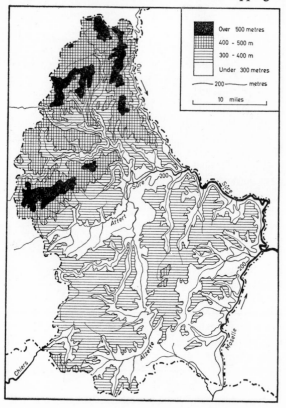

FIG. 136: Luxembourg: relief and drainage.

ground of the Ardenne.   Fluvio-glacial gravels occur in the Moselle valley at Wasserbillig and strips of alluvium fringe the course of the Sûre, Alzette and Attert rivers.   In its upper reaches the Sûre is dammed to supply hydro-electric power to the duchy.

The Duchy slopes south and east to the Moselle and so forms part of the Rhine catchment area.   Only in the south-west does the Chiers (Korn) flow to the Meuse.   The eastern frontier of Luxembourg is formed by a line of rivers, the Our flowing south to join the Sûre, which then forms the frontier as far as its confluence with the Moselle at Wasserbillig. For over 25 miles the Moselle then forms the boundary between West Germany and Luxembourg to the point where the river leaves French Lorraine. The drainage assumes a somewhat anomalous pattern, for that from the Ardenne is met by that from the *Bon Pays* in central Luxembourg and the combined systems unite at Ettelbruck, continuing as the lower Sûre to Echternach and the German frontier. The rejuvenated valleys of the south-eastern slope of the Ardenne, exemplified by the upper Sûre and Our rivers flowing south-eastwards, contrast with those of the *Bon Pays*, across which the Alzette follows a south to north course before it joins the Attert above its confluence with the Sûre, a course in part parallel with the Moselle. Above the medieval fortress of Vianden, overlooking the Moselle, is the recently completed Vianden multi-purpose power station, supplying electrical current to West Germany.

Climatically the Duchy of Luxembourg lies in a transitional position between the equable maritime type of north-western Europe and the more extreme, semi-continental régime of central Europe. The whole region is affected by prevailing west winds, associated with mild winters, high humidity and abundant precipitation. Cold spells are the result of north-easterly air streams, derived from the continental high pressure area, and these are quite frequent in winter and spring. The monthly mean temperature range for the city of Luxembourg is from 32° F. January to 63° F. July. Local factors modify this general picture, especially in the Ardenne where winters are prolonged and severe with considerable snowfall, while summers are mild rather than hot, when compared with the sheltered valleys of the *Bon Pays*. Whereas frost may occur on 100 days in the Ardenne, its average incidence is only 45 days in the Moselle valley, but here early autumn frosts may severely damage the grape harvest. The total mean annual precipitation shows the influence of relief, the ' minette ' escarpment in the south-east receiving 38 in. of rain per annum, but the valley of the Moselle, in a ' rainshadow ' area, records only 28 in.

LUXEMBOURG: PART II. REGIONAL STUDIES

THE Duchy of Luxembourg has already been described as falling into two sharply contrasted regions: the south-eastern section of the Ardenne and the *Bon Pays*. The Ardenne form a western continuation of the Eifel block of the middle Rhine highlands but the general elevation is lower than in Belgium (Fig. 136). Local eminences, flat-topped and separated by wide, shallow depressions, form inconspicuous summits. They include the Burgplats (1,847 ft.), the Botrange (2,277 ft.) and Baraque Michel (2,215 ft.). There is a sharp descent south-eastwards to the *Bon Pays* and the Devonian slates which underlie the block are deeply dissected; the tributaries of the main rivers, such as the Sûre and the Our, flowing as rushing torrents. The relief is 'inverted', as the result of the Oligocene-Miocene uplift of the region, and the lower ends of the valleys are narrow and V-shaped, with rocky and steep slopes, often wooded, and of considerable scenic attractiveness. Although the flat-topped heights form desolate open moorland, the greater part of the Ardenne is wooded, with spruce at higher levels but mainly beech and oakwood on the lower slopes. Whereas the general level of the plateau lies at 1,500 ft., there is also another erosion level at about 1,300 ft.; while isolated monadnocks rise to over 1,800 ft. (Napoléonsgard, 1,821 ft.).

In contrast, the *Bon Pays* or *Gutland* forms an upland lying between 1,300 and 800 ft. and known generally as the Luxembourg ' bay '. It is continued into the scarplands of French Lorraine and also into the Arlon district of Belgium. The Mesozoic rocks which underlie the region experienced Miocene tilting, so that, as the result of differential erosion, the relatively resistant Jurassic limestones and sandstones form escarpments, whereas the clays, marls and shales form intermediate vales. It is possible to differentiate three sub-regions: the northern or sub-Ardenne depression, the central plateau, and the valley of the Moselle in the eastern frontier region.

The break between the Ardenne and the *Gutland* or *Bon Pays* is sharp and coincides with a depression trending from south-west to north-east. It is partly drained by the Attert, Wark and Sûre rivers. To the south, this Bunter sandstone region is dominated by a line of heights developed on a narrow outcrop of *Muschelkalk*. These include the Goldknap (1,076 ft.), Herrenberg (1,260 ft.) and the Niederberg (1,348 ft.). This belt is succeeded by a zone of

Keuper marl, a formation which also underlies the lower Alzette valley and which occurs in the eastern part of the *Bon Pays*. The loamy soils weathered from the Keuper marl are mainly under mixed farming. In contrast, the division of the lower Lias known as the Luxembourg sandstone, which succeeds the Keuper, weathers into much less tractable soils. It is a coarse-grained sandstone containing resistant bands of siliceous material and it is strongly fissured. It weathers into a landscape of crags, bluffs, rock pillars and pinnacles; such scenery occurring both on the outskirts of the capital, where the Alzette cuts a deep gorge through this formation, and also in the district known as La Petite Suisse (Müllerthal), west of Echternach (Gorge du Loup). Much of this country is thickly wooded and carved by rushing torrents, such as the Ernz Noire. Caves and grottoes also occur, as at Hohllay. To the south-west, the relief is more subdued, although the oolitic limestone forms a bold escarpment overlooking the iron-working centres of Differdange and Esch. Along the eastern margin, the valley of the Moselle forms a third sub-region where the incised valley of the meandering Moselle is cut into Keuper marls and *Muschelkalk*, with a marked line of faults running north-east to south-west. The terraced slopes of the Moselle are under the vine.

The human geography of Luxembourg also reflects the two contrasted regions. The Ardenne is a sparsely populated region, with wide stretches of upland moor and much forest. Where the land has been cleared and reclaimed, rye, oats and potatoes are grown and stock reared on upland pasture improved by the addition of basic slag. Villages are compact and are of a Germanic type, with open arable land lying around the settlement. The *Oestling* has been a region of progressive depopulation in modern times, especially since the development of the iron and steel industry of the *Bon Pays*.

In the Luxembourg ' bay ', settlements are also compact but partly on account of dependence on spring water in the limestone districts. This is a region of mainly subsistence mixed farming, with the chief emphasis on cereals, especially wheat (which occupies between 5 and 10 per cent of the arable land here, compared with under 5 per cent in the Ardenne). Fodder crops are also important here, both roots (fodder beet) and rotation grasses being grown, the latter consisting mainly of clover and lucerne. Around Echternach, near the German border, the land is parcelled out on a pattern of strips, in the fashion of the German *Fruchtwechselwirtschaft*; fruit trees being scattered through the fields and along the country roads. Regions of specialization include the Moselle and Sûre valleys, where the terraces bordering the meandering rivers are utilized for the vine. The *Muschelkalk* scarp is also used for viti-culture, though the acreage under the vine has decreased in recent years. The rich soils developed on the Keuper marls around the city of Luxembourg are associated with the cultivation of roses and other flowers, partly grown for export. The *Bon Pays* is also noted for its herds of dairy cattle, Frisians being the usual breed. Oxen are still used for draft purposes but are on the decline. Although much of the countryside was formerly wooded, the demand for charcoal for iron smelting in the 18th and 19th centuries led to much felling of oak and beech. There are, however, some fine stands of silver fir and birch in the gorge of the Müllerthal but the most exten-sive forests are on the slopes of the Ardenne.

The iron and steel industry is the pivot of the modern economic life of the Duchy of Luxembourg. This little state has long been the fifth world producer of iron ore but it fell to sixth just before the 1939–45 War, in view of increasing production in the Soviet Union. The number of people engaged in mining and metallurgy was 23,801 in 1962 and this figure includes a large number of foreigners, notably Italians, Belgians, Germans and French. The modern iron and steel industry was originally built up within the German *Zollverein*, of which the Grand Duchy was a member until 1919. In particular, the large-scale exploitation of the ' minette ' ores which began in the 1870's led to the growth of a modern steel industry, in complete contrast with the older iron industry, which was concerned with the production of tools, agricultural implements and firearms for the French and Belgian markets.

There are two regions over which the ' minette ' ores are worked, namely in the Chiers and upper Alzette valleys. The iron ore occurs at the base of the Dogger (Oolite) division of the Jurassic rocks and is a continuation of the Lorraine field in France. The beds reach their maximum thickness near Esch-sur-Alzette, the main centre of the iron and steel industry. Other industrial sites are Differdange and Rodange in the Chiers valley and Dudelange in the upper Alzette valley. The iron is worked in quarries, from adits and by means of shafts. The iron content is low (under 30 per cent) and the ores are highly phosphoric. The output of iron ore in 1964 was 6·6 million metric tons, a figure which compares favourably with the pre-war output. Nevertheless, the Luxembourg steel industry is partly dependent on high-grade hæmatite from Sweden. Luxem-bourg has in all 28 blast-furnaces and 7 steel works, but these depend on imported coking coal from the Ruhr, the Saar and Belgium. Germany remains the main source of coke; the Saar coal, only 60 miles away, yielding inferior coke. Producer gas is used at Dudelange and Steinfort for firing the open-hearth (Siemens Martin) furnaces located there. Because of the nature of the local ore, most plants use Thomas (basic Bessemer) converters, but some use electric-arc furnaces installed before the war.

There is some working of antimony, copper and lead ores in the Ardenne; where slate, limestone and gypsum are also quarried. There are few important miscellaneous industries in the Duchy other than the making of leather and kid gloves in the capital, as well as brewing and the manufacture of agricultural machinery, tools and wine presses.

REFERENCES

J. Schmitthüsen: *Das Luxemburger Land*, 1940. K. C. Edwards: 'Historical Geography of the Luxembourg Iron and Steel Industry', *Inst. Brit. Geographers*, No. 29, 1961.

CHAPTER 21

CONCLUSION

THE LATE Field Marshal Smuts wrote during the closing years of the last war: ' The old Europe has gone. The map is being rolled up and a new map is unrolling before us. We shall have to do a great deal of fundamental thinking and scrapping of old points of view before we find our way through the new continent which now opens before us.' During the twenty-one years since these words were written, the pattern of the new Europe, much less the new central Europe, is still anything but clear. In fact, with the creation of the Federal Republic of Germany as a sovereign state on 5 May, 1955, with its new Parliament House in Bonn, the division of Germany between West and East seemed confirmed. West Germany has since been drawn increasingly into the orbit of western Europe, as a member of the Council of Europe, the West European Union, of N.A.T.O. and of the European Coal and Steel Community. More recently the creation of a Free Trade Area in association with a European Common Market has also been a matter of great advantage to West Germany.[1]

In this book an attempt has been made to analyse what appear to the writer to be the features basic to the understanding of the physical and human geography of that part of Europe which has been defined, for the convenience of description, as ' Central Europe '. Those who travel in these lands are met with a broad similarity of language and mode of life, whether in the Flemish and Dutch-speaking coastlands fringing the North Sea, in Germany and Austria, or in German-speaking Switzerland. Czechoslovakia is an exception linguistically and politically (as is the East German Republic), but the high level of agricultural and industrial organization, especially in pre-war Bohemia and, to a lesser extent in Moravia-Silesia, at least bear comparison with the present economic standards of the East German lands. It is, however, in Switzerland that the outstanding example of ' unity with diversity ' is to be found, for here a federal democracy unites, through the *Bundeshaus* in Berne, French, German, Italian and Romantsch-speaking elements, including such contrasting types as the peasant

[1] M. J. Wise: ' Britain and the Common Market, Part II. The Common Market and the Changing Geography of Europe ', *Geography*, Vol. 48, 1963.

of the Alpine valleys and the Jura, the skilled factory worker of
Geneva and St. Gallen, the *hôtelier* of the tourist resorts and the
business man of Basle and Zürich. The generally high standard of
living of this largely Alpine country reflects the notably successful
adaptation of the Swiss people to an exacting environment, to a
degree not equalled elsewhere in Europe. Siegfried claims, with
some justification, that ' the heart of Central Europe and indeed, of
Europe as a whole, is Switzerland '.[1] The survival of this little

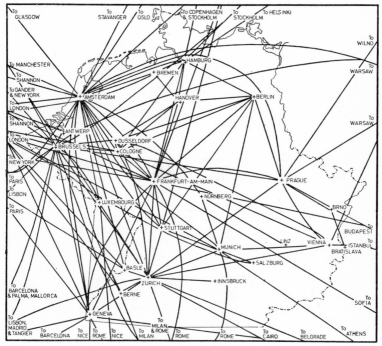

FIG. 137.   Central Europe: air services.

country amidst the storm and strife of the present century and the
rôle it has played in attempts to maintain the equilibrium of Europe
through the international conference centre of Geneva, as well as
by its political neutrality laid down in its constitution, go far to
justify this claim. The main threads of international traffic between
western and central Europe and the Mediterranean are gathered
together between Basle and the Alpine passes. The original defensive nucleus around the lake of Lucerne has become the *carrefour* of
Europe.

[1] A. Siegfried: *Switzerland*, 1950, p. 21.

INDEX

(Words are indexed under their foreign form, so that Ä, Ö, Ü, etc. appear in alphabetical order as Æ, Œ, UE, etc.)